D1590230

Children of Depressed Parents

Risk, Identification, and Intervention

Children of Depressed Parents

Risk, Identification, and Intervention

Edited by

HELEN L. MORRISON, M.D.

Director
The Evaluation Center
Chicago, Illinois

GRUNE & STRATTON
A Subsidiary of Harcourt Brace Jovanovich, Publishers
New York London
Paris San Diego San Francisco São Paulo
Sydney Tokyo Toronto

Library of Congress Cataloging in Publication Data
Main entry under title:

Children of depressed parents

Bibliography
Includes index
1. Depression, Mental—Patients—Family relationships. 2. Parent and child. 3. Adjustment (Psychology) I. Morrison, Helen L. [DNLM: 1. Depression—In adulthood. 2. Parent–child relations. 3. Adaptation, Psychological—In infancy and childhood. 4. Adaptation, Psychology—In adolescence. WM 171 C536]
RC537.C47 1983 618.92′89 82-24239
ISBN 0-8089-1545-2

Grune & Stratton, Inc.
111 Fifth Avenue
New York, New York 10003

Distributed in the United Kingdom by
Academic Press Inc. (London) Ltd.
24/28 Oval Road, London NW 1

Library of Congress Catalog Number 82-24239
International Standard Book Number 0-8089-1545-2
Printed in the United States of America

Contents

Acknowledgments

The preparation of this manuscript would not have been possible without the cooperation and interest of the contributing authors. Appreciation is also expressed to Samantha Heinz and Nancy Meade for the many hours of assistance they provided in the preparation of the final manuscript. Special thanks are given to Dr. George Dohrmann III for his support, advice, and commentary.

Preface

The goal of this volume is to present current theoretical, clinical, research, and treatment issues that promote an understanding of the effects of parental depression on the developing child. Many researchers have shown that there is a significant risk for affective illness in biological relatives, which suggests polygenetic inheritance factors. Reported research currently notes that prospective studies on children, whose parents have unipolar and/or bipolar affective disorders, display a prevalence of depression ranging from 7 to 85 percent. Although these figures have a high variability, the work presented in this volume attempts to explore the nature of and the prognostic implications for the impairments seen in many of these children. A developmental approach, which correlates the biological, genetic, psychoanalytic, and learning theory points of view, can be used to understand how genetic factors become transformed within affectively disordered families.

Chapter 1 introduces to the reader the concept of vulnerability in children. The critical developmental task presented to the child of the depressed parent is coping with the depression in the parent. To understand this crucial developmental task, the clinician must be aware of the biological principle of repetition as an ideologic mechanism for intervention. As we become increasingly sophisticated in understanding the multiplicity of variables contributing to development, we can begin to appreciate the need to understand varied approaches to the study of affective illness and its "transmission" through pedigrees. The discussion in Chapter 2 on clinical genetics, vulnerability, and psychiatric disorders clearly states that the task of the clinician (geneticist or psychiatrist) is to be understanding of human variation, whatever the cause.

In addition to biological and genetic factors, the terms "risk" and "vulnerability" are frequently used in correlation with the study of factors contributing to the later development of affective illness. The chapter on risk factors (Chapter 3) suggests that vulnerability is a better descriptive word. The genetic, perinatal, and intra-actional concepts (which can be considered mitigating factors for risk and vulnerability) provide an avenue of approach to intervention prior to the development of a serious, more overt form and expression of affective illness. Throughout this volume the reader will note that the authors uniformly caution the reader against prematurely concluding that only one variable can predict the developmental outcome as a reflection of the child's ability to adapt. The reader is also cautioned to remember that the focus on a singular affective symptom—ignoring the context of the family, social, biological, and psychological variables—renders the clinician incapable of providing the most appropriate and adequate programs of intervention. The assessment of the relationship between parental behavior and child functioning deals with this issue (Chapter 4).

Among the multiple characteristic difficulties noted in many of the offspring of depressed parents, social adjustment with peers at home and at school is one of the most prevalent (Chapter 5). Proceeding through the developmental spectrum, Chapter 6 considers the relationship between the adolescent and depressed mother.

The presentation of a child's behavior provides a clue to the manifestations of the clinical stages of the parental depression. An understanding of the interactional nature of the depressive illness and overt expressions of the parental depression in the child's behavior will provide a more effective definition of treatment planning. This planning is important not only in treating the patient but also in helping the family resume a more adaptive parental functioning. Continuing to clarify the interactional nature of depression with adolescence, the next chapter, Chapter 7, discusses the interface between adolescence and midlife transition in the context of mutually occurring developmental phases of life. The vulnerability of the adolescent and the adolescent's parents can be seen in cases where the illness adds to the potential for pathological resolution of the family conflict.

Beyond the disruptions occurring in a family in which a parent is hospitalized or requires extensive intervention is a need to understand the stress placed on the remaining members of the family system. Not only must the family cope with the illness, but also with the loss of that family member and the need to fulfill the functions of that person. Often the role of the father in maintaining a household has been neglected in many of the studies concerning depressed families. The authors of Chapter 8 report characteristic domestic and child-centered activities among the fathers whose wives have been hospitalized for psychosis or are considered to be functioning well. Continuing in the section that is devoted to intervention and treatment issues is the presentation of a model program of treatment that is based on interactions between mothers and their children. The reader is provided with an introduction to treatment and intervention in an analytic mode in the presentation of both theoretical and clinical cases. These cases follow a presentation in Chapter 9 of the difficulties and conflicts associated with the separation–individuation process in the first years of life among children of psychotically depressed mothers.

Considering multiple modes of treatment, this volume continues with discussions of cognitive behavioral treatments of depressive disorders. The authors note that this is only one of several major conceptual strategies for treatment of depression. Chapter 10 presents to the reader a systematic description of these approaches, and attempts to evaluate the efficacy of cognitive and behavioral methods as contributions toward the treatment of depression. Concluding the volume is Chapter 11 that clarifies the design and use of a training program considering the relationships among adaptation, depression, development, parenting, parental depressed parenting, and family dynamics. The responsibilities of the program include allowing the child to develop more positive self-esteem and the ability to function under more appropriate levels of stress. The outcome of the treatment is hoped to be a decrease in distortions in the development of the child related to the system of familial depression.

It is the intention of the authors of this volume that the readers be able to define a framework relevant to the needs of their patient group in the context of adapting models of intervention, or parts of these models, into their existing modes of clinical treatment. It has been noted throughout this volume that affective disorders in families provide significantly higher risk for disordered development in the child. The depressive illnesses are associated with a great deal of heterogeneity. This factor makes it impossible to predict treatment response from only one symptom or symptom pattern. Heterogeneity also interferes with attempts to understand, discover, and demand one specific etiology. Attempts to find a rational and logical treatment approach, however, must be based on the needs of the individual in the system in which they require intervention. Through the continual acquisition of knowledge and application in the clinical sphere, we hope to continue to add to the ever increasing knowledge of the effects of depressive disorders on the child and family and the devastation that frequently is exhibited throughout the life cycle and the developmental processes.

Contributors

E. James Anthony, M.D.
Blanche F. Ittleson Professor of Child Psychiatry
Director, Eliot Division of Child Psychiatry
Director, Edison Child Development Research Center
Washington University
St. Louis, Missouri

Sandra Bemesderfer, Ph.D.
Senior Psychologist
San Mateo County Medical Health and
Lecturer, Education Department
Mills College
Oakland, California

Bertram J. Cohler, Ph.D.
William Rainey Harper Professor of Social Sciences
Professor, Departments of Behavioral Science (The Committee on Human Development), Education, and Psychiatry
University of Chicago
Chicago, Illinois

Lawrence Fisher, Ph.D.
Chief, Psychology Service
Veterans Administration Center
Fresno, California, and
Associate Professor
Psychiatry and Family Medicine
University of California
San Francisco, California

Alfred P. French, M.D.
Private Practice
Sacramento, California, and
Associate Clinical Professor
Department of Child Psychiatry
University of California
Davis, California

David H. Gallant, Ph.D.
Psychologist, Health Service
Boston University
Lexington, Massachusetts

Enid Gamer, Ph.D.
West Roxbury, Massachusetts

Michael S. Greenberg, Ph.D.
Department of Psychology
Northwestern University
Evanston, Illinois

Henry U. Grunebaum, M.D.
Family Studies
The Cambridge Hospital
Cambridge, Massachusetts

Floyd S. Irvin, Ph.D.
Senior Clinical Psychologist
Michael Reese Hospital and Medical Center and
Consultant, Department of Adolescent Medicine
Cook County Hospital
Chicago, Illinois

Craig L. Johnson, Ph.D.
Director, Anorexia Nervosa Program
Michael Reese Medical Center
Psychosomatic and Psychiatric Institute
Chicago, Illinois

Carol Kaufman, Ph.D.
Brookline, Massachusetts

Ronald F. Kokes, Ph.D.
Director, Behavioral Medicine
Veterans Administration Medical Center
Fresno, California, and
Associate Professor of Psychiatry
University of California
San Francisco, California

Mark Lubinsky, M.D.
Director, Clinical Genetics Center
Children's Memorial Hospital
Omaha, Nebraska

Helen L. Morrison, M.D.
Director, The Evaluation Center
Chicago, Illinois

William H. Reid, M.D., M.P.H.
Associate Professor
Department of Psychiatry
Clinical Research Coordinator
Nebraska Psychiatric Institute
Omaha, Nebraska

Marshall L. Silverstein, Ph.D.
Illinois State Psychiatric Institute
Chicago, Illinois

Myrna M. Weissman, Ph.D.
Professor, Departments of Psychiatry and Epidemiology
Yale University School of Medicine and
Director, Depression Research Unit
Connecticut Mental Health Center
New Haven, Connecticut

Children of Depressed Parents

Risk, Identification, and Intervention

1

An Overview of the Effects of Maternal Depression on the Infant and Child

E. James Anthony

DEPRESSOGENIC EFFECTS OF BIRTH AND ITS AFTERMATH

The first 3 months following the birth of a baby is a period of high risk for psychiatric disorder in women with a fivefold increase in the general expectancy rate. The amount of risk falls off rapidly during the rest of this first year but reaches a plateau still somewhat elevated above the average rate. This risk contrasts sharply with the period of pregnancy. Then the level of risk is lower than average until the last trimester, when the risk curve begins to rise slightly.

From the evidence available—and this is by no means substantial and conclusive—it would seem that parturition constitutes, both physiologically and psychologically, a "birth trauma for the women comparable to, but greater than the psychobiological stresses of puberty and menopause." (Fathers have also been included among the "reproductive casualties," but no exact figures are available on the incidence of psychiatric disorder in fathers during the postpartum period, although a wide variety of "couvade" symptoms have been reported as occurring during pregnancy.)

The various percentages given in the literature indicate that about two-thirds of mothers have transient emotional reactions limited to the first 10 days and that about two-thirds of the psychiatric disorders that occur appear within the same highly vulnerable period, with the majority of these being affective in nature. The onset of about 16 percent of postpartum disorders is on the first day, casting doubt on the existence of the postulated latency period of 3 days prior to the hormonal decrement and supposedly offering a measure of physiological protection.

Two factors have been postulated to account for the noted higher psychiatric risks during the postpartum period. The first factor is the avalanchelike effect of hormonal changes that follow birth; these changes represent one of the most drastic endocrine shifts in the life cycle. Gonadotropin, estrogen, progesterone, adrenocortical steroid, androgen, and thyroid hormone levels all plummet during this time. This produces what amounts to a withdrawal syndrome and can be considered analogous to the withdrawal of psychoactive drugs. It is known that discontinuation of corticosteroid administration can lead to mood changes. This effect could be reinforced by the sharp rise in prolactin, a substance that has been found to influence thought and behavior in many animals after the third day. Such endocrine upheavals might certainly be responsible for some of the psychiatric vulnerability.

The second factor is parturition and the postpartum state, which also undoubtedly constitute powerful psychological stressors for some women, especially those who are psychologically unsuitable for such normative emergencies. The sudden demand made on the mothering capacity may be associated with a long-standing rejection of the mothering role to the subsequent detriment of mothering performance. To paraphrase Shakespeare, some women are born to be mothers; some achieve motherliness because of constructive experiences during adolescence and pregnancy; and some have mothering thrust on them and come—with extreme ambivalence—into the delivery room, often having unsuccessfully tried earlier to rid themselves of the undesired encumbrance. This latter group of reluctant mothers is of chief concern since these women are particularly predisposed to react with depression to the birth of the baby.

SPECTRUM AND PSYCHOLOGICAL INGREDIENTS OF MATERNAL DEPRESSION

The spectrum of maternal depression during the first 2 years of life of the infant is wide-ranging from its initial transient manifestations in the postpartum period to the more consolidated clinical depressions that run an irregular course depending on the use made of support systems, psychotherapy, and antidepressants. In our work in St. Louis on the offspring of psychotic parents, we have been able to monitor a variety of reactions of depression in women with a history of psychotic depressions that initially brought them into the research sample. In those women who have a strong proclivity to depression, birth and its aftermath are more likely to reactivate depressive disturbances than they do in women belonging to the control group. However, the numbers are too small for statistical analysis and merely indicate trends.

The following conditions have been encountered and investigated clinically:

Transient Depression

This form of depression is often popularly referred to as the "baby blues." This depression occurs in 65–75 percent of mothers and clears up in 7–10 days. The women are sad, weepy, emotionally labile, and extremely tired but unable to sleep. They are generally responsive to the comforting offered by husbands and mothers and to the presence of their babies.

Mild Persistent Depressions Extending into the First Year

These depressions appear to be largely reactive in nature, since they fluctuate synchronously with positive and negative life experiences. The mother complains of having been below par since the birth of the infant, of being generally unhappy "although at times life did not seem to be so bad," of lacking energy and interest, and of not feeling up to the task of caring for her baby at times. She characteristically reveals inexplicable bouts of crying and insomnia. There is often a history of premenstrual depressions and tensions, and subsequently there is a greater tendency to menopausal depression.

Postpartum Identity Diffusion States

These states are characterized by depressive affect, disorganization, depersonalization, disorientation for time and place, misidentification of persons, dreamy states, déjà vu (paramnesia), indecision, sudden feelings of unreality, and episodes of excitement and restlessness. Emotional contact with the baby is fluctuating. There is a marked "psychic lag" in the mother's recognition of the baby as her own. She may question whether this child has been substituted for her own and may declare that she is not prepared to mother the infant given to her until convinced of its authenticity. This acute reaction may rapidly disappear, leaving behind relatively normal attitudes and behavior on the part of the mother. Alternately, a chronic depressive state may emerge.

|| Primary Affective Disorders

These disorders can be (unipolar and bipolar) and can flare up during the postpartum period in the form of transient, mild depressions or severe psychotic depressions that are associated by a break in reality and the appearance of delusions and hallucinations that the baby is dead, deformed, monstrous, and in danger of being killed by the order of mother's "voices." The management of the baby, unless removed from the mother, is chaotic, and the chances of the baby being injured are appreciable.

|| Schizodepressive Reactions

These reactions occur during the postpartum period in schizophrenic subjects with atypical psychoses. Here again, the presence of persecutory delusions, related to the infant, is a significant hazard. The more "process" types of schizophrenic women, who show withdrawal as a primary feature, can often mother their babies under careful nursing supervision.

Beck, using a Depression Inventory, found the following characteristics occurring twice as frequently and far more intensely in psychotically depressed as compared with neurotically depressed patients: sad facies, stooped posture, slow speech, depressed mood, diurnal variation of mood, feelings of hopelessness, conscious guilt, feelings of inadequacy, somatic preoccupations, suicidal wishes, indecisiveness, loss of motivation and interest, fatigability and sleep disturbance, constipation, and loss of appetite.

He concluded that, aside from delusions, no specific signs or symptoms could distinguish psychotic from neurotic depressions. The more severe the symptoms are, the more likely the patient is to be diagnosed as psychotically depressed. One has, therefore, some justification for speaking of a depressive spectrum.

Looking at depression in terms of its potential effect on the care of the infant, I have defined four main features that are likely to disorganize or disrupt the day-to-day caring process:

1. The primary feature is helplessness and feelings of complete inadequacy. The mother does not know how to begin to look after her baby and may regard herself as equally helpless. How can the helpless help the helpless? Her own dependency is very much in evidence, as indicated by her urgent wishes to have her mother with her to look after both daughter and the new offspring. The new mother's orality and neediness can become as demanding in their urgencies as the imperatives that issue from the infant. Sometimes both mother and baby cry helplessly while the grandmother attempts to cope with both.

2. Ambivalence is always striking in these depressed mothers who may view the baby as a competitor for attention. Every now and then, the ambivalence erupts into open aggressiveness that may take the form of angry verbal attacks, and sometimes physical ones, on the baby. These attacks are often followed by a cycle of guilt, attempts to make amends, and internalization of the aggression with either a deepening of the depression or abject masochistic submission.
3. A narcissitic withdrawal is present especially from external responsibilities, such as the care of the infant, with a turning toward self and her own body, with increased self-absorption and hypochondriacal preoccupation. Sometimes anxious concerns about the baby's health may screen the mother's hypochondriasis, which, in turn, may mask substantial depressive affect. Winnicott (1958) was one of the first to point out that a large number of the mothers attending a pediatric outpatient department were depressed.
4. Associated with poor performance as a mother, there is a marked fall in self-esteem. This leads to guilt and self-reproach, feelings of inferiority, and hypersensitivity to criticism. The more the infant fails to thrive, the more incompetent the mother feels and the more hopeless and ashamed she becomes.

Each of these reactions occur in different degrees in the different depressive states. They cluster together to reduce the effectiveness of infant care and generally conduce to physical and emotional disorders in the infant.

The psychological ingredients that contribute to a manic–depressive reaction that is only rarely seen in the postpartum and early infancy periods, have been described elsewhere (Anthony, 1974a,b). Mainly one encounters the depressive component of manic–depression, whether it is unipolar or bipolar. The types of developmental environment that are generated by manic–depression have been mentioned. The main ingredients to which an infant in the first 2 years of life might be exposed if the manifestation included both mania and depression are manifest during cycles of omnipotence and impotence, of high and low self-esteem, of surplus and depleted energy, of adequate and defective reality testing, of optimism and pessimism, and above all, of surprising variations in mood. Even when the mother's condition is not severe enough to necessitate hospitalization, subclinical cycles may vary the attitudes and behavior of the mother toward her infant from day to day and from week to week. These subclinical cycles may be amplified as a result of emotional variations occurring during the menstrual cycle.

During the manic or hypomanic phase, the mother may behave like a narcissistically hungry infant, lacking the necessary external supplies and vehemently demanding them. One of our mothers in this state remarked that her baby was so gluttonous that at times she felt like eating it up and thus taking care of her own hunger and the baby's hunger at the same time. She laughed uproariously at the "joke." When the manic "festival" is over and the cycle reversed, the mother must deal with her sense of worthlessness, emptiness, impotence, and incompetence. She is pessimistic about the future and despairing about its outcome. She is unable to attend to her own personal care, let alone the care of her infant.

One of our manic–depressive mothers had a manic–depressive mother, and this is what she had to say about the effect of a biphasic disturbance:

> Dr. Anthony says it is sometimes easier for children to adjust to parents who are psychotic all the time than only part of the time. This is so true—we kids never know what to believe. Mother was so completely different when she was well. She listened, she was kind, she was generous, she was fun to be with, she never criticized Dad, and she was always at home. But the big problem was the inconsistency, hearing one thing at one period and something quite different at the next. This is what I am fretting over now with my own children: How is a mother to act? I really had no consistent model; I don't know what the image of a good mother is suppose to be. Perhaps that is why I am having problems with my own children.*

This particular mother had some difficulties in the postpartum period. She was first mildly confused, then depressed, then elated, and then depressed again. Her management of her baby was spotty. At times she functioned overzealously. At times the baby was left to cry itself to sleep while the mother turned on the music loud enough to drown out the infant's wailing.

|| MOTHERING DEMANDS IN THE FIRST YEAR OF LIFE

The postpartum environment, from the point of view of the mother, has a number of crucial functions. First, what the mother needs is a good support system. Under the limited conditions of the nuclear family, the father may be the only one to lend to both mother and baby. The women who is alone may have to run the house, attend to the needs of the older children—the "knee child" and the "yard child"—who often increase their demands when the new baby arrives, and care for the latest arrival.

---

*Reprinted with permission from Anthony, E. J. Childhood depression. In E. J. Anthony & T. Benedek (Eds.), *Depression and human existence*. Boston: Little, Brown, 1975b, p. 291.

Yet, the average mother copes with all these calls on her time and tension with an almost infinite subtlety in her management.

> It is four o'clock in the home. The baby starts to cry because it is hungry. The mother's breast begins to drip with milk as she prepares herself to suckle him. The "knee child" runs over, leans against mother's lap, pulls at the mother's skirt and pats the baby a little too fondly. The "yard child" begins to obsess around his hobbies, casting a furtive glance every now and then at the breast feeding. The adolescent storms into his room complaining bitterly about the hullaballoo and turns on his stereo at full blast. Finally, the father gets up and goes to the refrigerator and helps himself to a massive sandwich. (Paraphrased from a vignette by Brazelton, 1969.)

The first demand on the new mother is on her total attention to the needs of her baby and on her ability to construct a "perfect extrauterine milieu" for it. This primary preoccupation has been described by Winnicott (1956) as a "little illness" that lasts only a few weeks but makes all the difference to the baby. It is as if the mother recreated a psychological womb that resonated sympathetically to the baby's developing rhythms.

The next demand on the mother is in holding the infant with such a degree of molding that the dyad looks almost as if it is sculpted from the same piece of marble. This child is encompassed closely within sure arms that seem to provide a maximum of safety and security.

The handling of the baby is an art that is learned by the new mother rapidly and intuitively to cause the least discomfort and the least resistance to the free flow of the baby's movements. Handling also entails a certain sensuousness in the contact. In this context, mother and baby are referred to here as a sensuous couple.

The fourth demand is for the mother's face to provide a mirror for her baby so that when they look at each other, what the mother looks like to the baby is related to what she sees in her baby. The baby looks at the mother and sees in her face the reflection of its own feelings. Winnicott (1971) postulated the Cartesian axiom: When I look, I am seen, so I exist. I can now afford to look and see. I can now not only perceive but apperceive. And eventually, when the sense of reality is established, I take care not to see what is not there to be seen.

The next step in mutual imitation of vocalizations, movements, and expressions brings mother and child closely and playfully together.

Finally, the mother shows the world to her infant, names the objects contained in it, and fits them and uses them in her play and in teaching the infant.

The average mother (or "good enough mother") can deal with these demands sensitively, intuitively, flexibly, and attentively.

DEPRESSED MOTHER'S REACTION TO HER MOTHERING TASK

The basic fault with the depressed mother–infant relationship relates to failure in mutuality. There is no doubt that the nonverbal experiences between an infant and its mother establishes a mutuality that sets the emotional tone of interpersonal experiences and their intrapsychic concomitants throughout life. When Winnicott (1948) says that there is no such thing as a baby, he is referring to this mutuality. In the seriously depressed case, we might say that there is no such thing as a mother: there is only a self-absorbed, inwardly directed, hungry, and empty woman–infant who does not qualify to be a mother since she cannot begin to perform adequately the complete repertoire of mothering tasks. First and foremost, her preoccupation is with herself and not with her infant.

The depressed mother, holding her baby, is reminiscent of some statuesque *Madonna and Child* painting during the Middle Ages when the Holy Infant occupies his mother's lap like a throne and his mother regards Him from a distance as if no bond existed between them. The Child, in fact, is so self-supporting, that one could imagine him tumbling off were it not for His omnipotence. The depressed mother does not hold or handle the baby satisfactorily. She is sometimes jealous, sometimes casual, and sometimes rough. There is no free flow of synchronizing movement between mother and child.

With depressed mothers, the mutual imitation is missing and the playfulness is conspicuously absent. When the baby looks at the mother's face, it is in a "glass darkly." The mother reflects not the infant's expressiveness, but her depressed mood and her rigid defences. The baby, therefore, looks and does not see itself. It then looks around for other ways of getting something of itself back from the environment. Even depressed mothers, however, can respond when the baby is in trouble or being troublesome or looking ill. In such cases, what is reflected back from the mother's face is hostility or anxiety. Both of these affects make for insecurity in the baby.

Although it is not possible to predict what disorders of maternal behavior will lead to the development of transitional phenomena, the present author's experience has been that depressive withdrawal can initiate a search for comforting objects that help with difficulties in sleeping. The infant will often fall asleep with its face against the treasured object as it once did with the breast. Some depressed mothers in our sample would foster the transitional experience vigorously so as to make less trouble for themselves. But when these mothers feel better, they may resent the baby's preference for the treasured possession when it needs to be soothed or settled for sleep. In such instances, the mother does herself out of a job. When she wants to resume, she finds that the position is closed and that work is no longer available.

INFANT'S RESPONSE TO ITS MOTHER'S DEPRESSION

The infant is completely caught up in the emotional life of its mother. When she is depressed, the infant soon becomes enmeshed in her depression from which it can extricate itself only by the use of withdrawal mechanisms. It has other options open to it. In response to mother's helplessness, it can become increasingly and precociously self-sufficient. In response to her ambivalence, it can become aggressive and angry. In response to her withdrawal, overactive, demanding, attention-seeking, and aggressive behavior can develop in the infant. This response is more common in the 2-year-old who will sometimes reject the mother when she makes an effort to deal with the infant. This hostility toward the depressed mother can become dysfunctional, and a resentful rejection of her and her approaches may then occur. One of our research subjects fluctuated during the first 2 years of life, and the infant was exposed to on-and-off attention, which was very tantalizing but did not appear to induce much overt anger. The little girl was mostly listless and apathetic. At the age of 8½ years, following another depressive episode, the daughter then expressed in a series of little notes to her mother, an accumulation of anxious, angry, and depressed feelings with affirmations of continuing love in spite of what she felt had been done to her.

Bowlby (1973) was well aware of the occurrence of "psychological separation" responses in the offspring. According to him, these responses can occur under two conditions:

1. Children who are reared in an environment in which they are often threatened with abandonment or experience abandonment because of mother's unavailability develop "anxious attachments." While children with normal attachments pursue, protest, search, and are saddened by a brief separation (Ainsworth, 1973), the child with "anxious attachment" withdraws and demonstrates little responsiveness to the absence or return of the mother. Nor does the child seem capable of resorting inventively to little symbolic games that convert passivity into activity, like Freud's grandson with his cotton-reel play (Freud, 1920). In the vulnerable infants in our series, almost all of them exhibited this "anxious attachment."
2. Bowlby (1973) states that: "Yet a further difficulty rests on the fact that a mother can be physically present but 'emotionally absent.'

What this means, of course, is that although present in body, mother may be unresponsive to her child's desire for mothering. Such unresponsiveness can be due to many conditions—depression, rejection, preoccupation with other matters—but, whatever its cause, so far as her child is concerned she is no better than half present."† In our small series of depressed mothers, there is a new better way of describing her relative unresponsiveness and intense ambivalence than to describe her as "half present."

I have been able to observe the onset of depression in one mother and to record its initial impact on her 11 month-old infant. As her depression intensified and withdrawal began, a sequence of changes began to appear in the baby. At first, it looked anxious and made soft noises of distress. The sleep rhythm was obviously disordered and the bottle was refused. It lay on its side, with its limbs flexed and its head bent, occasionally sucking at its fingers. By about the third day, it appeared distraught and clinging. But after a time, the baby exhausted its resources and began to withdraw. The withdrawal gradually intensified, and a depressive layering to it was perceived. The psychic loss of the mother, as described elsewhere (Anthony, 1973), especially as a result of psychotic depressions in the parent, frequently, but not always, may follow the Bowlby (1973) sequence of events: protest–despair–detachment—compounding elements of anxiety, anger, and depression. When a surrogate takes the place of the depressed mother, the infant (say, of a period beginning in the second half of the first year) appears to become even more clinging, more possessive, and more unwilling to be left for even a minute. Such sensitized babies may not only become insatiably demanding of the substitute caretaker, but also intolerant of being left by themselves. William James (1890) recorded his view that "the great source of terror in infancy is solitude." This is particularly true of infants who have experienced actual or psychic separation. To some extent, the younger infant (below the age of 3 years) does not yet have the capacity to develop "anticipatory dread" in response to mother's predictable depressive withdrawals. The 3-year-old begins to anticipate psychological dangers that remove mother effectively from it and to react regressively even before she has become unavailable.

In the second year of life, depressive withdrawal on the part of the mother has been shown to provoke hostility, a show of anger, and disinterest in and detachment from the environment. By about the fifth day,

†Reprinted with permission from Bowlby, J. *Attachment and loss* (Vol. 2), *Separation: Anxiety and anger.* New York: Basic Books, 1973.

although there was no change in the mother (who had been put on antidepressants), the baby seemed less depressed and began again to manipulate its rattle and a soft toy. There was new response to people. By about the tenth day, the medication appeared to be working, and the mother began to attach herself again to the infant. The infant's appetite returned, its sleep was restored, and it began to respond to playful overtures. However, it still had not recovered its joie de vivre. It was much more clinging and intent on closeness. The mother responded to this by encapsulating the infant, even though she now complained that it was too demanding.

Is there in fact a folie à deux? Anna Freud (1966) noted that

> It was known in psychoanalysis long before such infant observations that depressive moods of the mother during the first two years after birth create in the child a tendency to depression (although this may not manifest itself until many years later). What happens is that such infants achieve their sense of unity and harmony with the depressed mother not by means of their developmental achievements but by producing the mother's mood in themselves.‡

Benedek sees the infant's response as more complicated than this within a three-generational framework. In a cycle of ambivalence, the maternal grandmother initially sets an affective transmission in motion (although genealogical studies, if these were possible, would undoubtedly carry the pathogenic influence further back) by frustrating the receptive needs of the mother as infant and thus establishes an ambivalence that is reactivated when demands are made of mother by her own baby. There is a reactivation also of the aggression that she once felt toward the maternal grandmother. This results in the frustration of her infant who responds by projecting aggression onto the nongratifying mother. At the same time, the infant introjects these aggressive impulses so that "bad" self and "bad" mother become equated. A core of ambivalence is then instituted in the infant and becomes the nucleus of what Benedek refers to as the "depressive constellation." One of the outcomes of this development is a depressive propensity in the infant (Benedek, 1956).

Klein's depressive position is normative and has nothing at all to do with an actually depressed mother. The depressive position, however, is the main obstacle in development, and feelings of persecution and ambivalence are always involved in it. Surmounting it involves the acceptance of responsibility for damage in the inner world of the infant (sometimes also in the outer), but if this acceptance is too painful to be borne, various

---

‡Reprinted with permission from Freud, A. *Normality and Pathology in Childhood.* London: The Hogarth Press, 1966, p. 78.

defences come into operation. The failure to resolve the depressive position predisposes toward the accounts of depression, and this failure may result from frustrating material care.

Mahler (1966) does refer to the consequences on the toddler of a deficit of emotional supplies associated with a significant lack of acceptance and emotional understanding on the part of the mother during the rapprochement subphase, compounding a traumatic failure to give that may have characterized the per verbal mother–infant interaction. This mothering deficit (typical of depressive unresponsiveness) results in an ambivalent dependency, pathological defense mechanisms, the turning of aggression against the self, feelings of helplessness, and the establishment of a specific vulnerability. Mahler's work, based on observation, would help to confirm the hunch that maternal depression, occurring before the development of object constancy, conduces to a depressive tendency, to a basic depressive moodiness, and to future clinical depressions in the child. In place of overt depression, hypochondriacal preoccupations, fostered by the mother, may be the presenting problem in the child.

The depressed mother is unable to throw her "whole self" into adapting to the needs of her infant, and this disrupts the normal process of maturation (Winnicott, 1965). But the infant in turn has its effect on the mother; thus the model is not a linear one. Nor are the effects only in the direction of depression in the infant. Some of the infants we have followed did not seem to make it easier for the depressed mother. Here one must take into consideration constitutional factors such as those Escalona (1953) has pointed out. One type of baby may be difficult for one type of mother yet not difficult for another. Overactive and overreactive infants may be disturbing for the depressed mother, who may tolerate a more passive baby. Furthermore, infants vary in cuddliness from the very start (Szurek, 1973). Noncuddly babies are somewhat hypertonic and resist being held or restrained. It is difficult to be certain that this factor is a constitutional one. Some of our noncuddlers later developed maladjustments. Their mothers had postpartum depressions. Szurek (1973) also noted this connection.

Babies also vary their smiling reactions, and a nonsmiling baby could add further disappointment to be a depressed mother. However, it is not possible again to attribute this to constitution. Some babies are slow in establishing eye contact, and this may also affect the mother's mood and intensify a depression. Cuddliness, smiliness, visual attentiveness, normal sensitivity, and normal mobility certainly would help interpersonal contact between mother and infant. On the other hand, any physical deficiency or any congenital anomaly would also influence the mother's affect negatively.

The situation is not static. In longitudinal studies of mother–infant dyads, offspring have been shown to have different meanings for their mothers at different stages of development. Mothers may find one stage more difficult than another, especially as relationships to the parent's parents are recreated (Coleman, Kris, & Provence, 1953). What Coleman and his colleagues found was that maternal depression, with its minimal interaction, was related to a developmental lag by 8 months of age. However, by 13 months, a marked improvement had often taken place in the child and in the mother–child relationship. In the intervening period, the child had spent much more time with the father and other family surrogates, and the mother received a great deal of support when she needed it.

When the child begins the process of separation–individualation (Mahler, Pine, & Bergman, 1975) the mother may experience feelings of both gain and loss (depression) and the ratio of feelings will vary with the depressive propensity of the mother. The mother may react with rejection of the baby at this time. She is most likely to become pregnant with another child to compensate for the feelings of inner emptiness, unfilled inner space, loneliness, and boredom. This is particularly evident in the case of women who feel inferior to active, extroverted husbands (Jessner et al., 1970). When the child of such a pregnancy begins to individuate, the mother goes into another depressive state. She conceives yet another child, which is the dynamic for "pregnancy as a depressive practice."

Katz (1977) has postulated the hypothesis that maternal depression occurring before the third year of life, before object constancy has been achieved, involves not only a loss of mother, but also a loss of self with the production of psychotic disturbances with a large measure of ego deviation. After the age of 3 years, neurotic reactions or anxiety states are to be expected. One problem with this study was that since it was retrospective, it was difficult to determine whether the mother had been depressed during the first 2 years of the child's life.

|| CASE VIGNETTE

|| Mother During Her Childhood

She was 1 year old and with her mother when the mother attempted suicide. A year later she was separated from her mother because of the mother's serious physical illness. She was shifted from one relative to another before being placed in an institution for a month. Here, however, she became so depressed that she had to be removed. She describes herself as a child as having been very serious, afraid of her mother, and unable to express anger.

Mother During Pregnancy

She did not know she was pregnant for the first 3 months. She was depressed, irritable, nervous, weepy, and afraid to be alone. When she discovered that she was pregnant, she became relieved and happy.

Birth and Postpartum

Birth was traumatic, and because of the mother's painful perineum, it was too painful for her to sit and hold her baby for the first 1½ months. The baby seemed so small and frail that the mother was afraid that she might hurt her. In addition, the baby had a minor defect, and she wondered about this. At about 5 months of the baby's life, she became pregnant again and described herself as depressed throughout this second pregnancy.

The Child

The baby slept days and was awake at nights and at bedtime. It would vomit "on purpose." At 13 months, the baby was sent to live with the paternal grandmother while the mother was having the second baby. When she was returned to the mother, she was regressed. At 22 months, she had an operation for the minor congenital defect and had to be confined to bed. Following this, she would not cooperate at all for the mother. At 3½ years, she was referred for evaluation because she was not talking. She had a whole cluster of additional symptoms such as temper tantrums, disobedience, refusal to separate from her mother, eating with her hands, inability to be weaned or toilet-trained, and inability to sleep by herself. She was diagnosed as suffering from symbiotic psychosis with autistic features.

The mother had apparently not worked through her own separation–individuation and was not only very dependent on her mother, but merged with her in her depression. The unavailability of the mother for the baby impeded her separation–individuation.

Our own findings would support Katz's hypothesis that maternal depression during the first 2 years of life is more likely to be followed by developmental deviations in the child, depending on factors of vulnerability that appear to be inborn. More likely deviations are followed by neurotic and depressive reactions should mother's depression have occurred after the age of 3 years. Other correlates of maternal depression are more variable, such as depression in the parents, the history of loss by death or divorce, and depression during pregnancy.

First mothers and teenage mothers with hostile dependent relationships with their mothers are especially prone to have postnatal depressions and infants that fail to thrive. Our sample included one such individual who was quite unresponsive and difficult to arouse. When the child was responsive, its face had a withdrawn and distant look. The growth rate was markedly retarded.

A SHORT FOLLOW-UP OF INFANTS CARED FOR BY DEPRESSED MOTHERS

In our sample of manic–depressive parents, the larger number were mothers. We divided them into two very distinct groups, unipolar and bipolar, based on careful diagnostic considerations. Of these, a small group had infants associated with postpartum depressions. In a 10-year outcome study, the bipolar group of mothers had more disturbed offspring than did the unipolar group. The bipolar mothers were married to more disturbed husbands, and the offspring of the bipolar mothers were considered on all measures to be more vulnerable.

CONCLUSIONS

In our work with psychotically depressed mothers, we have not been able to uncover much of the dynamics of the mother–infant situation since they seem to be unable or unwilling to introspect. Most of our conclusions about these mothers have been based on observations and inference.

With the neurotically depressed mothers, our outcome was different. Once they had established a trustful relationship with us, they were willing to share their confidences. Our understanding of them was much influenced by the pioneering book by Selma Fraiberg and her colleagues (1980). There is nothing more convincing than observing her video tapes. This is not only in watching the impact of the mother's depression on her infant, but also in observing the effects of therapy on relieving the oppressive influence and permitting the child's development to resume a more normal course. Our own dynamic findings were derived mainly from nontherapeutic encounters and are thus a pale shadow with respect to detail to her infant–parent therapies, where the infant becomes the center of treatment. Infant–parent psychotherapy represents an advance in preventive intervention. We have followed the ambivalence of the mother during the period of pregnancy to the ambivalences that dominated the postpartum period. The mothers were concerned that they did not like this baby because it was fretful and "difficult." They worried that they could not be good mothers and had to prove this by exercising skills in comforting the baby. They expressed disappointment when the baby was not developing well but were ready to blame themselves for this. When the baby refused to eat or sleep, they found themselves using stronger techniques than they felt was appropriate, and this added to their guilt. There was a inability to enjoy the baby "like other mothers" and the feeling that the baby was disappointed in them and would not love them. Their realization that much of their aggressiveness toward the baby represented an identification with the mother was a painful discovery. Finally, their acknowledgment of their helplessness as the crucial element contributing to their incompetence and of how the memories from the past stirred up feelings in the present and contributed to the difficulties and the problems of the future.

Watching these cases continuously and prospectively over the last 15 years, I am able to agree with Winnicott (1948) that the infant's depression often seems like the mother's depression. This is in reflection and a use of the mother's depression to escape from the child's own authentic depression. Later, this hampers the development of a personal capacity for restitution, since making amends does not relate to the child's own sense of guilt. This is somewhat different from Anna Freud's view that the baby makes use of the mother's depression in order to harmonize better with the mother's mood and thus gain her attention when the developmental accomplishments fail to do so. Dealing with the mother's depression thus becomes a critical developmental task for the infant and the child, and if they are successful in this, they can then begin to lead their own emotional lives. If they fail, should they later enter treatment, their task is to discover their own guilt, reach down to their own depression, and be personally responsible for what is an integral part of them. Otherwise childhood may be spent in counteracting the deadness and blackness of the mother's inner world by reacting in a lively, colorful, and dramatic manner as mother's therapist. It is far too much of a burden for the young child to have to deal therapeutically with the mother's despair and despondency.

It is clear that we still live in a world of hunches without firm correlations. The work in the field is converging toward new knowledge, and on the basis of such knowledge we should be able to institute at least tentative and groping programs of intervention. However, it is important that such programs be associated with careful and systematic follow-up studies. Only by checking on our results will we be able to advance the field of infant mental health. If our combined endeavors do advance it, it will undoubtedly prove to be a major revolution in psychiatry.

2

Clinical Genetics, Vulnerability, and Psychiatric Disorders: An Approach

Mark Lubinsky

Unfortunately, a review of hereditary factors that influence the occurrence of depression is premature. Despite convincing evidences of genetic influences (Gershon, 1979; Waters, 1979), the mechanisms are unclear. The underlying heterogeneity of depressive disorders is only beginning to be appreciated, and a synthesis of tentative and preliminary studies in the literature would not only be inappropriate, but also outdated in this publication. Instead of ending the review here, it would be more appropriate to focus on the nature of a genetic approach and its limitations and strengths in dealing with psychiatric disorders—especially depression. An attempt has been made to concentrate on general principles and philosophy applicable to both current and future efforts in research. The author's personal perspective as a clinical geneticist has been used to try to show potential benefits as well as potential problems in applying genetics to psychiatry.

Let us start by considering Mendelism, the underlying "roots." This has been a successful scientific paradigm for research in diverse areas of biology and medicine. Ironically, its successes may have resulted in inappropriate applications that hinder the use of other, more useful approaches.

Classic patterns of inheritance depend on whether one dominant or two recessive genes at a single loci are needed for a trait. Sex-linked con-

---

The work described in this chapter was done with support from the University of Wisconsin Genetics Laboratory and DHEW/USPHS Grant GM20130 from the National Institute of General Medical Sciences.

Thanks are due to Dr. Helen Morrison for her patience and suggestions and to Kathy Dougherty for her help with the manuscript. Also, most of the ideas I owe, directly or indirectly, to my teachers . . . I apologize if the lessons were garbled at any point.

ditions are accounted for with only minor modifications of this theory. Traditionally, discrete and discontinuous morphological changes, under the control of single gene loci, were studied by utilizing statistical analyses of controlled matings. More recent efforts have included investigations of the causal chain between gene and trait through biochemical studies. This is simplistically summarized as the "one gene–one enzyme hypothesis." However, Mendelism in this form is clearly an oversimplification. To start, genes are not isolated, independent entities. They operate against genetic and environmental backgrounds. Indeed, whether a gene is dominant or recessive may depend not on the gene itself, but on the effects of other genes (Fisher, R., 1958). Additionally, despite the power of Mendelian methods as a research tool, *Homo sapiens* is a singularly poor experimental subject.

There are several reasons for this. Life span is long. Pedigrees dating back any significant amount of time are unusual. Old information is often scanty and difficult to obtain. Additionally, onsets of common medical conditions are often age-dependent. It may take decades to determine the presence or absence of a disorder in a patient, and death may occur before the expected onset. Furthermore, as family size is usually small, it is probably unethical to encourage large families simply to obtain better segregation ratios for analysis; also, controlled breeding is impossible, and informative genetic crosses cannot be arranged in human populations. Often, therefore, what we know about human genetic conditions consists of approximations. For example, by definition a dominant gene has identical effects in the homozygote (two gene doses) and in the heterozygote (one gene dose). In humans, however, the term is used where one dose of the gene is clinically apparent. Since most medically significant traits are rare, the frequency of the homozygous state is, in theory, rare squared.* In practice, assortative mating and inbreeding let us see occasional examples. Frequently these homozygotes are different from the heterozygotes. For example, in achondroplasia, a common form of dwarfism, homozygotes present with a severe lethal neonatal dwarfism, rather than the milder form seen in the parents (McKusick, 1978). Another reason for the limited use of *H. sapiens* as experimental subjects in Mendelian methods is that controlled environments cannot be obtained. Human variability is largely environmental. There may be major interactions with hereditary components, which have been postulated in diverse conditions from intelligence to spina bifida. Comparison studies for isolation of individual effects are possible, but they are difficult and often imperfect. In addition, when an environmental factor may be detrimental, we obviously cannot increase exposure to such effects. Moreover, there are no "pure strains."

*Thanks are due to Dr. James F. Crow for this phrase.

Human populations are genetically heterogeneous; gene frequencies, the nature of polymorphisms, and the degree of consanguinity can vary radically from one group to another. Finally, clinical research differs from experimental. Traditional research models involve the formulation of an experiment to test a hypothesis. Medically significant disorders are "experiments of nature" presented to the clinician, who must then formulate a hypothesis to test the experiment. These factors can constitute more than just mechanical difficulties. They are potential and real limitations of our ability to analyze the genetic components of disorders.

An illustration of some of the complexities of genetic analysis can be seen in Sewall Wright's studies of polydactyly in crosses of four strains of guinea pig. Results from F_1 crosses (polydactylous × normal), F_2 crosses ($F_1 \times F_1$), and backcrosses (F_1 × parent) all supported simple dominant inheritance. However, further crosses of the segregants from one of the matings "completely exploded this hypothesis." Ultimately, Wright (1968) postulated cumulative action of multiple factors and two thresholds. Simplistic models from empirical human data may thus not only be simplistic, but also wrong.

There are other types of genetic analysis, and the same cautions and difficulties apply. In particular, there is a biometric school, even more dependent on statistical analysis. Initially this approach was considered an alternative to Mendelism. However, it ultimately became apparent that the quantitative traits studied were determined by many "Mendelian genes" acting together.

These two different analyses generally dealt with different types of conditions. (Of course, this is a generalization, but is still applicable in a surprising number of cases.) Mendelian traits are described as rare, discontinuous, and pathological. Biometric traits are described as common, continuous, and normal. Examples of the former would be phenylketonuria and Huntington's chorea; of the latter, height and intelligence. It should be noted that depression has more of the characteristics of the biometric than the Mendelian, a point to which we soon return.

Furthermore, environmental effects can easily mimic or confound genetic influences. Unfortunately, such effects have been inappropriately analyzed and have given rise to the "nature versus nurture" controversy, the translation of which has been: which is more important, environment or heredity?

Actually, that question is more semantics than substance. It can be compared to arguing whether the kidneys or the liver are more important for life. Neither environmental nor genetic influences act in isolation. Pure environment means that no living organism is involved. Genetics without environment is equally meaningless. For example, to claim that intelligence is not genetically controlled contradicts all facts. I (despite occasional assertions to the contrary) am more intelligent than an earthworm, a goldfish, or a rabbit. Indeed, some of these animals are more, and some less, intelligent than other species. It is doubtful that this variation is simply environmental. Rather, innate, genetic factors have defined these differences. Additionally, genetic influences act only in the context of an environment, which can almost always modify the hereditary blueprint. Intelligence can be affected by meningitis, lead poisoning, physical trauma to the brain, and so forth. A rather trivial modification of the environment, such as removing all oxygen from the air, will have a marked effect on intellectual potential. Admittedly, these examples are simplistic. However, they force us to modify the context of the original question of which factor is more important. Given a constant environment, genetic variations are more important. Given identical genetic backgrounds, environmental differences are more important. When both vary, their contributions depend not only on their individual characteristics, but also on their interactions.

If the above restatement is used, the task of the clinical geneticist changes from that of the traditional investigations of hereditary influences. It becomes the study of human variation, regardless of what the causes might be. The object of this approach is to first minimize all sources of variability but one. Then the investigation can proceed to study the extent of the variability that that single factor can cause. Sometimes it is possible to take the study further by varying more than one factor and observing subsequent interactions.

The redefinition of clinical genetics as the study of human variability regardless of cause has some interesting practical implications. If we talk of minimizing the sources of variation while one factor is studied, we imply that several factors can influence the same trait. Indeed, this is generally the case, and the importance of heterogeneity has been and needs to be increasingly emphasized. There are, naturally, varieties of variation. In the study of psychiatric disorders, this heterogeneity is especially important since different types imply different models and predictions.

A major question for psychiatrists has been the distinction between normal and abnormal variation. Certainly this has been largely in differentiating normal from pathological. For the geneticist, though, the question would be different. Normal variation would be polymorphic. That is, if hereditary factors are responsible for a condition, their frequency in the population would be greater than the mutation rate alone could account for. There are heated arguments as to whether or not genetic factors can be selectively neutral or whether sampling variations can affect gene frequencies in most populations. However, in the syndromes of depression that have definite morbidity and mortality, these questions are obviated because of their significant frequency.

If a genetic component is present, it should be eliminated by selective processes unless there is an accompanying advantage. The frequencies of such genes in a population should correspond to levels where the advantages and disadvantages balance. This assumes a stable situation. A change in environment might result in a decreasing or increasing frequency as a new equilibrium is reached. A model for understanding such an equilibrium is sickle-cell anemia. One gene for the variant hemoglobin confers an increased resistance to malaria. Two genes result in decreased survival because of the expression of anemia. The gene is maintained at a frequency where the two factors balance. Where malaria is not present, the gene frequency would be expected to decrease as the heterozygote advantage disappears (Vogel & Motulsky, 1979).

Unfortunately, we do not have such information about other conditions. Undoubtedly, the interactions between gene and environment are complex. We are only beginning to understand factors involved in polymorphisms as common as ABO and other blood types, or the human leukocyte, locus A (HLA) immune system. Still, depressive disorders have enough of a genetic component and are sufficiently common to strongly suggest some accompanying advantage. Biologically, therefore, depression may be a part of normal variation that gives an increased adaptability to populations.

Additional sorts of variation can be differentiated. Continuous and discontinuous or quantitative and qualitative types can be opposed. Continuous variation, (seen with traits such as height), suggests differences due to many environmental and genetic factors, each making a small contribution. Roughly speaking, the ultimate phenotype depends on the summation of these effects. Alternatively, variation may be discontinuous because of a qualitative difference. Both types can affect a single trait. For example, height can also be affected by bone dysplasias or hypothyroidism due to an enzyme deficiency. Common disorders are usually caused by continuous variation. The etiology of a pathological extreme is considered to be multifactorial, the interaction or summation of many genetic and nongenetic factors.

In considering pathological processes derived from continuous variation, the concept of a threshold effect is useful. Although multifactorially determined conditions such as cleft lip or spina bifida may appear morphologically distinct, *the underlying etiologic factors may be continuous even though the traits themselves are not.* Let us consider the example of cleft lip in understanding this concept.

Trasler and Fraser (1977) have nicely summarized the importance of time and position relationships in clefting. They state that "the critical thing is the convergence of the facial processes to permit merging or fusion. This requires that the processes appear in the right place, achieve the correct position and form, and have no obstruction to fusion." Among the possible mechanisms that might lead to cleft lip, they note (1) position and time of placode induction in relation to the brain and other adjacent structures, (2) rate of neural crest cell migration to and mitosis in the facial process, and (3) relative sizes and positions of facial processes. Variation in each of these can easily be visualized as continuous. It is only when the variation of one or more of these or other factors reaches a certain critical level that fusion is delayed beyond a certain critical time in embryologic development. If this occurs, there will be failure of the fusion process, and a cleft lip will result. Continuous variation of temporal and structural relationships can, therefore, result in discontinuous variation of morphology.

Biochemical and metabolic disorders may show similar effects. Gout most commonly reflects normal extremes of uric acid levels. However, clinical manifestations become apparent only when a certain threshold is reached. Adult diabetes mellitus may reflect in some cases normal variations of glucose tolerance. Extra loads on the system, as in pregnancy or obesity, may result in clinical findings that disappear when the stress is relieved.

Finally, variation may not always result from a traditional one-to-one cause-and-effect relationship. Sewall Wright (1968) studied an inbred guinea pig strain with a specific incidence of otocephaly, a head malformation with variable expression. In such inbred strains, all animals are genetically identical (except for the XY–XX male–female chromosomal constitution, of course). At a constant environment, a specific percentage of all newborns were affected. It was felt that a manifestation of the malformation was a threshold effect, "dependent upon the conjunction of the genetic factors with hypothetical environmental ones largely peculiar to each separate individual." Several other traits showed similar patterns (Wright, 1968).

In any case, we can see not only phenotypic variation, but also heterogeneity. The delineation of such factors has been one of the major contributions of the clinical geneticist to medicine. Conditions such as dwarfism, diabetes, and mental retardation, at one time considered single entities, are now recognized as the conglomeration of disorders that they really are and have always been.

There are two basic types of heterogeneity. First, given a single cause, there can be different effects. That is, a given event may manifest itself in several different ways. Down's syndrome has a known, verifiable, unitary cause, Trisomy 21, yet the clinical findings vary widely. Second, a given manifestation may have very different causes. The Charcot-Marie–Tooth syndrome (peroneal muscular atrophy) is a degenerative neurological disease with a hereditary basis. However, pedigree analysis shows dominant, recessive, and sex-linked forms—the same clinical picture produced by at least three different genes (McKusick, 1978)!

These factors complicate one of the major tasks of the clinical geneticist, the delineation of syndromes. Different causes may produce the same effect. The same cause may produce different effects! Both factors must be defined before we can claim to understand a condition. Ultimately, it is necessary to discover not only a first cause, but also the pathogenesis of the final clinical manifestations.

A syndrome may be defined clinically; however, an important complication is that without complete understanding, the definition may be artificial and misleading. For example, diabetes is a distinct entity with a real existence. We can define the syndrome of diabetes in many different ways. One might be blood sugar levels above 400 and 2+ or greater ketones. Using these criteria, we find common problems and clinical courses that are very different from those in patients with abnormal glucose tolerance tests only. Yet, from what we know about the pathogenesis of this disorder, our definition is totally inappropriate as a description of a disease entity.

Familial studies can be unique aids in dealing with this sort of problem. Although we may have no idea of alternate cause and pathogenesis, similar entities with a genetic basis in the same family are presumably the same "syndrome." This lets us ascertain a disorder with initially artificial (and often arbitrary) criteria and then proceed through family studies to determine the heterogeneity of effect. In turn, this permits an extension of our original definition to a more realistic delineation of the condition.

Basically, this is an attempt at defining a population with a single etiology with varying manifestations without knowing what that "first cause" really is. Heterogeneity within families can be compared with heterogeneity in the more general population. This approach can help us determine whether a particular syndrome is a single entity or several conditions. This is demonstrated in mucopolysaccharidosis Type II (Hunter syndrome), a progressive storage disorder caused by a deficiency of sulfoiduronate sulfatase. Decreased enzyme activity can be assayed and used as a confirmation of a clinical diagnosis. However, early and late onset forms of the disease are known, both with identical enzymatic errors (McKusick, 1972). This leads us to the question of whether there is a variable effect of a single gene, perhaps modified by other factors, or alleles indistinguishable in vitro but with very different in vivo effects. With the first hypothesis, intrafamilial variability should be close or equal to that of all syndrome cases. With the second, familial cases should have a much greater similarity to each other. Studies strongly favor the second possibility: pedigree analysis is more powerful than biochemistry! Similarly, the same criteria can be applied to other manifestations of the disorder. For instance, a "cobblestone" pattern of papules can be observed in some, but not all, patients. Since two brothers with this syndrome have been observed to be discordant for this finding, it could be concluded that this parameter does not delineate a variant of the disorder, but instead represents part of its natural heterogeneity.

Family studies are useful in other ways. The frequency of consanguinity can be a clue to recessive inheritance, and increased paternal age may suggest new dominant mutations. Merged data from many families may give valuable information about frequencies of a disorder in relatives of a proband, which can be useful in interpreting a polygenic model. For single gene effects, large pedigrees of a single family may be more valuable.

Unfortunately, a review of the voluminous literature on pedigree analysis that might be applicable to studies of depression is beyond the scope of this chapter. Suffice it to say that increasingly sophisticated models are being developed. These models attempt to deal with such problems as single major locus determinations of quantitative traits, threshold models, and the effects of cultural transmission and assortative mating. For a basic review of the methodology in these approaches, the reader is referred to Emery's (1976) volume. A more advanced view of the topic is provided by the collection of articles edited by Morton and Chung (1978), and many other books of varying levels of mathematical sophistication and comprehensibility are available.

Twin and adoptive studies are similarly analyzed. These approaches are primarily useful in delineating the relative importance of genetic and environmental effects. As mentioned previously, the goal of the geneticist is to minimize variability so that single influences can be studied. Although such analyses are theoretically of great value, it is difficult to obtain a suitable population, and the separations of factors are not always as "pure" as they should be. There are several critiques concentrating primarily on schizophrenia studies, which shed light on the general problem. In particular, the papers by Jackson (1960), Benjamin (1976), and Lidz (1976) make interesting reading. Worth commenting on are certain inherent difficulties of ascertainment. Unless a population is completely ascertained, including nonaffected and mildly involved cases, there will be an exaggeration of the hereditability of the disorder involved if there is a multifactorial etiology. The more severe the case, the more likely that the causative factors include heredity components. Since more severely affected probands are most likely to come to medical attention, they will be observed more frequently than mild or borderline cases. They will also have a greater chance of having affected relatives.

Sporadic cases, without known etiology, present an especially complex challenge. In dealing with these questions, clinical geneticists have developed rather sophisticated philosophies of syndrome delineation. In particular, Opitz (1977, 1979), Smith (1976), and M. Cohen (1976) have given special thought to this conundrum. Although these considerations are fairly recent, they are helping to clarify a great deal of confusion. Clinical genetics has the advantage of dealing with conditions that can often be objectively determined, even though their classification may be difficult. The thoughts and reflections of geneticists on the nature of syndromes are resources that other specialties can draw on with profit when considering similar questions.

Different types of syndromes can be defined. Opitz has characterized several possible contexts for syndromy: (1) Hippocratic—"etiologically nonspecific groupings of patients with similar manifestations"; (2) causal—etiologically defined and discrete entities; ideally, the underlying cause for the clinical picture is understood; and (3) associational—representing noncausal concurrence due to such factors as genetic linkage or predisposition to secondary complications. Finally, there is false, or coincidental, syndromy (Opitz, 1977).

A variety of techniques are being developed for sorting out "real" syndromes from the many other sorts of relationships seen with disease. The systematic application of numerical taxonomy to clinical genetics is relatively recent, although medical conditions were studied in this manner almost 60 years ago by P. Foundler and Von Seht. Basically, these are techniques for the detection of clustering of characteristics and for the separation of clusters. Several methods have been used, and their use is becoming increasingly sophisticated (Bergsma & Lowry, 1977).

To return to the syndromes of depression, however, depressive disorders are among the worst possible subjects for analysis of hereditary influences. Unfortunately, depression is common enough to be considered a normal variant. Probably the entire population is at risk to a greater or lesser degree. Certainly there is a large environmental component to vulnerability, simply in terms of life situations and stress factors. Beyond this, factors such as medications (Henning, 1979), diet (ascorbic acid deficiency) (Kinsman & Hood, 1971), and hormonal states (Warnes & Fitzpatrick, 1979) may all lead to a depressive state. This suggests biochemically mediated pathways subject to a variety of influences. Not all these influences are obvious.

Furthermore, although many factors may influence depression, the condition is still not well delineated. Arbitrary definitions are easy to come by and may be useful for separating out and categorizing the more severe subgroups. Still, physical diagnosis syndromes may represent an underlying disorder that only rarely manifests pathognomonically. Clinical depression may also represent only an occasional manifestation of an unknown primary condition. To complicate matters further, not only is there the problem of determining whether classic depression is present, but there also may be atypical presentations. Suicide, alcoholism, and drug dependence may all be manifestations of depression. Affective symptoms may be diagnosed in other conditions, such as schizophrenia. Ascertainment can be even more difficult when constructing a pedigree from second-hand information.

Undoubtedly depression is a heterogeneous group of disorders. As a syndrome, it probably best fits the Hippocratic type—an etiologically nondistinct entity. The strongly quantitative nature of the disorder involves further heterogeneity: age of onset, symptomatology, and frequency of recurrences. Therefore, it is difficult to accurately rate depressive illness in terms of severity. Is late-onset major depression worse than early-onset mild depression? Varying age of onset further confuses pedigree analysis. Some family members may be "predepressive" but not show symptoms until later in life. If the age when depression is "programmed" to appear (if such a concept is valid) is too great, the patient will be dead before any symptomatology appears. Finally, there is no animal model comparable to the multiple expressions of depression seen in humans. This makes many lines of experimentation impossible.

Despite all these difficulties, the presence of genetic factor in depressive disorders has been demonstrated. Unfortunately, its exact nature is still unclear. Most work has emphasized bipolar disorders. Pedigrees have been published suggesting dominant, recessive, and sex-linked inheritance, the latter with varying sorts of linkage (Gershon, 1979). For a geneticist, the presentation of so many contradictory models suggests either heterogeneity, with different patterns in different families, or a multifactorial etiology that may present in several ways or both.

One major question concerns the nature of the depressive process. Is it a specific abnormality, such as phenylketonuria, ultimately traceable to biochemical or enzymatic abnormalities? Is it a nonspecific response to a wide variety of causes with a final common pathway? If there is a genetic component, a frequent assumption is that a biochemical etiology follows (Kety, 1979). This is overly simplistic as can be shown by the following example. Whereas many forms of mental retardation are caused by metabolic errors, other forms have structural etiologies that are caused by morphogenic influences. These influences are very poorly understood. Similarly, seizures may have purely structural antecendents. Even the availability of chemical (i.e., drug) treatment in this disease says little about the primary abnormality. The prevention of the spread of excitability from a focus treats the pathway for a seizure. Treatment does nothing about the underlying cause!

Ultimately, as with seizures, intelligence, diabetes, and innumerable other conditions, depression will be shown to be many disorders. A search for *the* "gene for depression" would seem doomed to failure. Rather, there will undoubtedly be many such genes. Once again, even if we do define some of these in biochemical terms, it must be emphasized that these biochemical markers may actually tell us very little about the actual psychopathology. Despite the many genes that have been defined that adversely affect intelligence, we are no closer to understanding what is entailed in the normal process. Chemical analysis of a brick tells us little about the function of the watch that it has just smashed!

Depression, regretfully, is a poor paradigm for a genetic approach. The condition is sufficiently common and the literature sufficiently voluminous and confused to preclude any sort of synthesis. Rather, it would seem preferable to use infantile autism, which has a number of heuristic advantages. The condition is rare, better defined, *and lacks a strong familial component*. The last may seem an unusual point for a genetic analysis, but this characteristic emphasizes the use of a philosophy rather than a mechanical application of mathematical analyses. Additionally, the withdrawal components and the vulnerability concepts are interesting counterparts to depressive illness.

To start, there is the problem of definition. Kanner (1943) first described infantile autism and insisted on rigid criteria. Others have defined the condition far more loosely (Oritz & Ritvo, 1976). There have been debates over delineation ever since (Brubakken, Derouin, & Morrison, 1980).

As Tinbergen has pointed out, individual manifestations of autism are not necessarily abnormal. Many of these are found in the behavior of normal children. It is not a given, therefore, that there is a distinct separation of "syndrome" from "normal." Indeed, if such a separation does exist, it may still be as a discontinuity that has developed in originally what was a continuous graded scale (Tinbergen & Tinbergen, 1972).

With most syndromes, we expect variable manifestations. Extending this to autism, we would predict that some children will show all Kanner's criteria and others, only some. The number and type of findings might vary in more than one way. We might have a graduation, with more extreme findings "dropping away" in order. We might have variable clustering. Observations suggest the latter and further suggest (but do not prove) that partial clusters are necessarily different from or more severe than the "full syndrome." This implies that children lacking certain manifestations may be as refractory to treatment as those showing all components of the condition.

The above analysis also implies that autism is not defined by the presence or absence of specific symptoms. Rather, it is an overall pattern. Perhaps a functional definition is to be preferred: autistic symptomatology that consistently interferes with function. Now, such a definition says nothing about mechanism or underlying etiology; therefore, let us approach autism as a symptom complex with many potential causes rather than a unitary causal genesis syndrome. This is in opposition to much of

Table 2-1
Features of Infantile Autism with Different Intelligence Levels

Feature	"Low" IQ	"High" IQ
Autism	Always	Always
False deafness	+++	+++
Noise sensitivity	++	++
Rituals	≤1/3	About 2/3
Resistance of change and attachment to objects	+++	++
Language acquisition	Very delayed or none	Delayed
Motor delay	1/2–2/3	1/3–1/2
Late seizures	About 20%	±
Prognosis	Dependent on retardation, good for the psychosis	Variable
Sex ratio	No or only slight male bias	Strong male bias
Prevalence (estimated)	One percent of the mentally retarded population	One out of 10,000 in the general population

the psychiatric literature, where it is treated, implicitly or explicitly, as a single "disease" with specific effects on development. This approach further implies that population studies to define biological characteristics are potentially inappropriate—we may be lumping apples and oranges together. Yet, some of the only consistent findings between studies of autism seem to be population characteristics, such as male predominance and frequent mental retardation. How can this be reconciled?

The answer is obtained through definition of subgroups. As this is done, results emerge that indicate the appropriateness of heterogeneity. About two-thirds of autistic children are mentally retarded (Editorial, *The Lancet,* 1976). This has generally been considered a secondary effect, with retardation as part of a series of handicaps caused by the psychiatric disorder. Retardation can be approached alternatively as a marker of heterogeneity; in other words, children with autism, with and without retardation, represent different populations.

Comparison of these populations reveals several differences, including biological characteristics (Table 2-1) (Editorial, *The Lancet,* 1976). There is a much higher incidence of autism in the retarded population. This is calculated by using rough prevalence figures (Treffert, 1970); a two-thirds retardation rate and a frequency of retardation in the general population at 1–3 percent. The increased vulnerability of males is found only in the higher-IQ group (Goldberg & Soper, 1963; Hinton, 1963; Lotter, 1966; Schain & Yannet, 1960)! Most studies of nonautistic retarded populations show more males than females, so a certain male bias is expected even if the incidence in each sex is the same.

This analysis implies that studies of the incidences of seizures, neurological damage, birth trauma, and other disorders among autistic children are inappropriate unless the control population has a similar incidence of retardation. Certain diseases associated with autism, such as congenital rubella syndrome or tuberous sclerosis, may represent this association with retardation (and possible sensory deficits) instead (Lubinsky, 1979). Also, the use of the extent of retardation as an outcome criterion may be inappropriate if the retardation is a vulnerability factor for autism, rather than a part of the symptom complex. Since mental retardation is itself heterogeneous, further subdivision of the autistic group is possible. This leads us to a classification quite similar to that of Rutter, Lebovici, Eisenberg, et al. (1969) and suggests further observational approaches.

Autism was studied retrospectively in institutionalized retarded children (IQ below 50) at the Central Wisconsin Center for the Developmentally Disabled (CWC) who had been previously evaluated and classified into eight major groups (Opitz, 1978). Groups F (No. 15) and G (No. 47), which consisted of patients without apparent cause for their retardation, were studied. Patients in group F had been diagnosed "psychotic" at examination, but psychiatric abnormality during the first years of life had not been evaluated in either group. Charts were reviewed 3–5 years after the initial CWC study. Cases with degenerative courses, grossly apparent sensory abnormality on examination, or insufficient data were excluded, leaving 53 patients. Further investigation showed hearing loss by audiometric evoked electroencephalogram (EEG), or major EEG abnormality in 18 of these children, leaving 35 subjects (Table 2-1).

For a presumptive diagnosis of autism, four easily ascertained retrospective criteria were required:

1. Onset of abnormal behavior considered sufficiently severe to interfere with expression or evaluation of the child's potential before the age of 2 years.
2. Habitual avoidance of eye contact and lack of emotional interaction.
3. Abnormal language development, with lack of effective expressive language or abnormal usage of pronouns or echolalia.
4. Behavioral mannerisms that were management problems, including self-stimulatory activities, such as finger flicking and hand flapping, and self-abuse, such as hair pulling and face slapping.

Also, at least one of the following three "confirmatory" findings was required: (1) variable stimulus response to pain or to sound, (2) concern

Table 2-2
Loss of Autism with Increased Age

Age	Number Originally Autistic	Still Autistic
Under 11	5	3 (60%)
11–15	5	3 (60%)
16–20	8	2 (25%)
Over 20	5	0 (0%)

over environmental change expressed through either rituals or abnormal levels of anxiety, and (3) a chart diagnosis of psychosis by a trained physician.

Of 35 patients, 23 could be classified as autistic! Most likely this high frequency results from a referral bias. Institutionalization, presumably, is more likely in a child with major behavioral problems. Indeed, evidence suggested that placement improved with a change in the child's behavioral status (see the following paragraphs). In the cerebral palsy group, presumably with physical handicaps that necessitated residential placement, autism was exceptional (Durkin-Stamm, personal commmunication, 1978).

Several findings emerged. The male:female ratio was 12:11. Also, psychiatric status improved with age (Table 2-2), as did the proportion placed in community settings. Treatment consisted of a stable, supportive environment and behavior modification. In view of the generally poor outcome of institutionalized autistic children (Brubakken, Derouin, & Morrison, 1980), this may have made a real contribution to the children's improvement.

Even within this rather strictly defined group, heterogeneity emerged. After behavioral improvement, the IQ level remained below 50 *with two exceptions*. These two were the only children with a history of child neglect and/or abuse that was considered sufficient to cause removal from their home. The autism of these children also was resolved exceptionally rapidly after the children were placed at CWC. Interestingly, when put in stressful outpatient settings, they rapidly reacquired abnormal behavior. Dr. Morrison treated a child who showed a remarkable similarity to these two children: a history of severe neglect and abuse, classic autism, and rapid resolution of behavioral problems with an increase in intelligence after treatment.

The above cases suggest that several factors can increase vulnerability to autism. Rather than being a causal genesis syndrome, autism is a symptom complex that can result from many different causes. An understanding of etiologies can be obtained from isolating subgroups, rather than depending on large-scale population studies.

Similar progress in the understanding of depression may result from such a genetic approach. The study of increasingly well-defined subgroups may ultimately be of more value than classic Mendelian logic. Hopefully, the above exposition is of help in understanding some of the principles and potentialities of such an approach. Perhaps these approaches will be utilized in adding to successful primary interventions for the futures of children of depressed parents.

3

Risk Factors in Children of Depressed Parents

William H. Reid and Helen L. Morrison

The child of mentally ill parents has a greater risk of developing psychopathology than does the child of well parents (Garmezy, 1974b). This chapter addresses primarily two groups of problems to which the child of depressed parents may be vulnerable.

The first group includes childhood difficulties such as psychiatric illness, behavior problems, school problems, physical illness or battery, and—by no means least—impeded development. Important characteristics of development that may be affected in children of mentally ill parents include disturbances of affect and cognition (particularly germane to this text on depressed parents), disturbances of attention, difficulty with feelings of competence and mastery (which may decrease both ego strength and ability to deal with future major and minor crises), impeded development of ability to organize and shape styles of adaptation to new developmental tasks—"crystallized characteristics of behavior" (Bruner, 1973), and the like.

The second category addressed here involves risk for later problems as an adult. This chapter focuses on risk for children of depressed parents, especially those parents who, although not blatantly ill, provide affectual and environmental experiences for the child that are different from those of the normal family.

A few authors have spoken to the subject of the child's involvement in the parent's illness. A child who is involved in the parent's symptoms (e.g., delusions may specifically involve the child or affect parental care) is more likely to develop a psychiatric disorder. Younger children are at highest risk. Latency children show fewer adverse effects (Rutter, 1966).

Because of its much larger prevalence, the importance of the effects on the child's risk of below-potential adaptation, inadequacy, and—perhaps—adult incompetence requires greater attention. "Incompetence" refers here to the adult who is not seriously ill but for whom innate and/or environmental problems of infancy and childhood led to a developmental process in early life that was characterized by more withdrawal, fewer environmental experiences, and less motor activity than was that of peers who did not have depressed parents.

One finds in the literature some discussion about the terms "risk" and "vulnerability." Some authors feel that "risk" should be reserved for use as a statistical concept and that "vulnerability" is a better descriptive word with respect to genetic, perinatal, and interactional concepts (Cohler, 1977). Anthony, in particular, uses this term, speaking of apprehensive and constricted children who are particularly vulnerable to small departures from the predictable within the environment. Self-withdrawal from the environment was helpful for these children only provided the environment remained safe. When the barrier they were able to put up against environmental and internal stimuli was defective or "thin," the children seemed unusually sensitive and exhibited precocious ego development (Anthony, 1974a,b).

The vulnerable child's development snowballs through infancy, childhood, and adolescence, with defensive and integrating patterns being characterized by deficits that render the child at continuing risk as different critical periods are reached. This child is likely to have serious difficulties even in a relatively benign environment. Other children, because of positive innate or early environmental factors, might be seen as "invulnerable" and may be able to survive highly stressful milieus as they grow. These latter children may appear outwardly different from the average; for instance, they may appear antisocial; actually, however, they have adapted and "survived."

Anthony and others are especially interested in groups of high-risk children who do not develop problems and in low-risk children who end up being very vulnerable (Anthony, 1974a,b; Chiland, 1974; Grunebaum, 1978). They point out that certain vulnerabilities are relatively unpredictable and are a function of individual susceptibility, as in the case of a child who has few innate risk factors but is born to a family that makes little use of narrative language or linguistic play, leading to vulnerability for school failure (Bernstein, 1942). The presence of apparently vulnerable people who survive relatively unscathed and vice versa would lead one to the conclusion that the critical factor in determining vulnerability or resilience is not the risk itself, but rather the relationship between the risk and the child's psychological and biological makeup.

|| RISK FACTORS

Emotional hazards to any child include innate and environmental influences before, during, and after birth and experiences during infancy and childhood.

Innate factors that are often inseparable from environmental ones include genetic, congenital, and temperamental characteristics. Genetic loading for such diseases as phenylketonuria is well known and predictable. Genetic susceptibility to mental illness is, in some cases, well established.

Diagnosis of acute mental illness in mothers has been associated with complications of pregnancy and birth (Cohler, Gallant, Grunebaum, & Weiss, 1976). Although data have consistently indicated major differences in complications among various diagnostic categories (McNeil & Kaij, 1973; Sameroff & Zax, 1973a), most researchers would agree that delineation of predisposing factors could aid in earlier identification of the vulnerable child.

Congenital problems such as cerebral palsy, epilepsy, and the large number of other categories of ill or "defective" infants give rise to the first of the emotional stresses that the child will encounter; that is, the beginning of a skewed relationship with the parents. It is clear that a defective child is not seen in the same light, is not treated the same way, and does not elicit the same reactions from parents as does a healthy baby (Solnit & Stark, 1961).

Differences in neonatal temperament can be predictive of later behavioral disturbance. Thomas, Chess, Birch, and Hertzig (1960) found that 6-month-old infants who, by parental report, were highly irregular in sleep and eating patterns, whose behavior lacked malleability (i.e., was difficult to alter), and who were markedly nonfastidious were most susceptible to later problems. These findings may have been related to difficulty in adapting to a changing environment, brittleness, lowered threshold for stress, or other factors. On the other hand, the active, outgoing infant was reported to be likely to have developmental experiences that are outside the realm of the timid, passive, inward-looking child. These temperaments, which focus on congenital differences in infants and "primary reaction patterns" to later normal or abnormal behavior, may assist in the discrimination between normal and exceptionally vulnerable children. Thomas et al. (1960) stress, however, that neither temperament nor parental characteristics alone is extremely influential on the child's development; the two sets of factors work interdependently. In some cases the modifying influence of the parental reaction seems crucial.

Genetic risk for serious affective disorder (unipolar or bipolar affective psychosis) seems similar to that for schizophrenia, given accurate diagnosis (Rosenthal, 1970), although familial transmission has been studied less for affective disorders than for primary thought disturbance. Children of manic–depressive parents are at genetic risk for a diagnosis of schizophrenia (Cammer, 1970). More complete discussion of genetic risk for cardinal psychiatric illness is beyond the scope of this chapter.

In addition to the risk for psychosis, other significant genetically modulated characteristics are present. Some sex differences are well established; for example, the daughters of mentally ill women have been found in some studies to be more socially maladjusted as a group than are their sons (Rolf & Garmezy, 1974). This is consistent with theories of the development of identification, since socialization theory would predict same-sex effects in the transmission of social traits (Cohler, Grunebaum, Weiss et al., 1977). Sex hormones have important behavioral significance from early pregnancy. Severe childhood eczema, colic, hyperkinesis, and childhood autism are found three to four times more often in boys than in girls. This arouses curiosity about interactions between androgens and biogenic amines, as well as about the enduring effects on development of early exposure to high doses of sex hormones.

Other bridges between psychological and biological research related to risk, as discussed by Cohen at the Dakar Conference, include interactions among developmental trends involving biogenic amines, as well as concomitant alterations in such other physiological areas as the endocrine system. For example, recent research has shown that autistic and atypical children have labile serum thyroxine levels, and in normal subjects there is an inverse correlation between plasma thyroxine and the rate of production of biogenic amines in the CNS (Cohen, D. J., 1974). The latter observation is consistent with the concept that one function of thyroxine is to sensitize neurons to the effects of the biogenic amines. This is also consistent with the clinical usefulness of antidepressants, although one must be careful when theorizing in this area.

|| EARLY PARENTING

A developmental factor that is environmental, but to the all-important child's-eye view is "innate," is the makeup of the parenting to which the child is exposed early in life. Many mentally ill mothers have difficulty with the tasks of mothering. Such things as decreased maternal capacity for forming need-gratifying relationships, the mother's lack of satisfaction with her mothering activities, and her lessened feelings of adequacy as a woman are characteristic in families at risk, and all these factors are consistent with symptoms of depression in that parent.

In concert with basic mothering difficulties, subsequent problems may ensue: difficulties in exerting appropriate control over the child's aggression, in encouraging reciprocal feelings and behaviors, in establishing appropriate closeness with the child, and in experiencing feelings of competence in meeting the child's needs (Cohler, 1977). Depressed mothers' problems with sustaining attention may be important in terms of child care as well as teaching and identification (Marcus, 1972). Depression in parents may not always impair parental functioning; however, the intimate daily contact demanded by the child is subject to the detrimental effects of parental inability to meet developmental needs.

Erikson and others have commented on the quality of the maternal relationship as being considerably related to the formation of the infant's trust in his environment (Erikson, 1963). Escalona (1953) notes that "perfect mothering" includes the mother knowing just how her baby likes to be bathed, the speed at which to feed him or her, how much to put on the spoon, the position in which the baby likes to sleep, and so on. The baby is gratified by the mother's skillful ministrations, and the mother is gratified by his or her positive response. The "perfect mother" rapidly picks up and incorporates subtle cues related to the baby's needs and wishes. These skills may not be found in the depressed mother, whose symptoms of withdrawal, discomfort, self-centeredness, cognitive dissonance, and/or decreased contact with reality can separate her emotionally from her role and her infant. It should also be noted that the normal mother may be far from perfect. Recent work (Crnic, 1978) indicates the many assumptions of the parent effectiveness model may be erroneous.

It goes without saying that many of the sequelae of maternal psychopathology or deficiency apply also to disturbances in the father. Unfortunately, good studies of paternal parenting, normal or aberrant, are rare in the literature; however, inferences are often made, especially with respect to fathers' absences, their role as models for identification, and their meaningful participation in early parenting. Other chapters in this book review and discuss paternal influence on development and risk.

Among the most threatening hardships with respect to the internal sense of security in the child are the chronicity or repetitiveness of physical and mental illness in the parents (Chiland, 1974) and the unpredictability of parental mood changes (Winnicott, 1965). In such long-term disturbances, open recognition of the parental illness by everyone in the family is a protective factor for the child. The greater danger comes from living with unrecognized, or perhaps nonverbalized, chronic depressive or borderline symptoms in the parents (Lebovici, 1973). Even very young children can often come to terms with the fact of the parent's illness and protect themselves from it, if it is (1) *consistent* and/or (2) *recognized by other people who can support the child's impression that something is wrong*. Unfortunately, depression is often chronic; it may be associated with unpredictable moods, and it may go unrecognized as a "problem" or "illness."

Parental models for identification (and, in very early childhood, for incorporation) are important but often absent in the severely disturbed parent. We may again emphasize the "child's-eye view." Whether the child is incorporated in the affective psychosis of the parent (e.g., in delusions, seductions, or aggressions) or is less involved (e.g., in depression or withdrawal of the parent), the child's impression of what is going on is based on skills of evaluation, organization, and retention of the information available, and the ability to place the information into a coherent frame of reference that will aid in the realistic appraisal of the present situation and in adaptation to future ones (Anthony, 1974a,b). The presence of consistent or "healthy" figures in the family environment is important in terms of support and structure that the child may use to accomplish this (Lebovici, 1973).

Parental preoccupation with things other than the child may be a causal variable in a variety of childhood psychosomatic illnesses. For example, children of parents persecuted by the Nazis have been rated higher on conduct problems, inadequacy–immaturity, and personality problems, consistent with the literature that describes parent–survivors as in some instances more concerned with their own unending mourning and physical debilitation than with their children (Sigal, Silver, Rakoff, & Ellin, 1973). The relationship of these data to the concept of depressed parents seems clear.

Parental impact thus may occur in many ways, including contribution of genes, provision of prenatal environment, and structuring of postnatal environment including parental care, stimulation, and affection. It may be noted that in some situations, parents who themselves suffer from disturbances may, when the disturbance is not present to a severe degree, also convey some adaptive characteristics to the child. That is, a parent who has adapted relatively successfully to a biological or psychological problem may relate differently with the child and yet may convey some adaptive characteristics to the child in the process.

|| DEPRESSED PARENTS

Let us turn now to some syndromes associated more specifically with depressed parents.

Depression in the Child

A study by Welner, Welner, McCrary, and Leonard (1977) reported that 7 of 29 parents hospitalized for depression had at least one child with episodes of depression (8 out of a total of 75 children). None of the children in 41 control families with well parents had episodes of depression (152 children). "Depressive equivalents" such as hyperactivity, deviant behavior, and learning difficulty were not necessary for the authors to establish clinical depression in childhood and were not necessary to establish the correlation between depression in the children and depression in their parents. Some of the variables that appear most significant in the index cases, that is, in the children of depressed parents, included fighting, depressed mood, sad feelings, death wishes or suicidal thoughts, unexplained headaches, apathy, and crying for no apparent reason. Interestingly, children of the depressed parents showed significantly more presistence in finishing projects than did children of well parents. None of the control children had five or more depressive symptoms, a common characteristic of the index children. Five of the depressed children met diagnostic criteria for definite or probable depression as adults; that is, if adult criteria were applied to the children, they would still be seen as depressed. This study supports the theoretical status of risk for depression in children of depressed parents and does not differentiate between mothers and fathers in its implications.

Childhood Behavioral Differences

Rutter's (1974) work as well has shown that children in families with depressed parents show more behavioral deviance than do controls. He speaks of modifying factors such as existence of a good relationship with one of the parents or a change to a harmonious family setting, even in later years, as having ameliorating effects. In the child who is "vulnerable," these problems are even greater, since when parents are depressed, they may tend to "take it out on" a difficult child. The child's predisposing characteristics, innate or acquired, are thus seen to influence parental behavior. They put the child at increased risk through their influence on the child's interactions in the environment already made pathological by virtue of parental depression (Rutter, 1974).

Developmental Problems in the Child

Depression-related deficits in the parent with respect to attention, affectional behavior, and the ability to pick up subtle cues from the infant and reciprocate to fulfill its needs may be extremely deleterious, leading to ineffective development of affect, attachment, competence, and mastery (Marcus, 1972; Morrison, 1978). Such characteristics of loss (or at least effective loss) may be related to absence of parental smiling, decreased ventral (chest-to-chest) contact with the infant, and the like. Ventral contact, especially, seems to differentiate between infants who have behavioral problems and difficulty with interpersonal relationships, and normals, the former having received less ventral contact. Decreased ventral contact has also been shown to be associated with later abuse of the child, especially the premature child (Leiderman, 1974). These issues of affectual development and the absence of mothering are discussed at greater length in the accompanying chapters by Morrison and others.

|| DIVORCE

Divorce of parents is a stress that affects children at all ages and occurs in a variety of households. This particular stress may be especially applicable to the children of depressed parents. Depression in a spouse places a serious burden on the marital relationship; certainly much of this is communicated to the child, even if divorce does not actually occur (and it need not in order to precipitate symptoms in the child) (Despert, 1962).

There are many opportunities for overlap among the issues of divorce, parental depression, and the fate of the child. The stresses of marital discord and/or divorce, in addition to the more direct concomitants of depression mentioned elsewhere, can be communicated to the child in terms of chaotic family environment and structure and the sapping of the coping energies of healthier members of the family (who might otherwise have those energies available for the business of child raising).

The interactions between parents and their children are significantly altered in nonintact families. The parent—especially the father—who does not have custody of the child(ren) has been shown to generally become less available to the rest of the family over time. Divorced fathers have been found to show less attention and affection than those in intact families. Divorced parents in general make fewer "maturity demands" of their children, tend to have problems communicating with them, and tend to be less affectionate or consistent in parenting (Hetherington, Cox, & Cox, 1976).

Should the child be left in the custody of the depressed parent, as may be the case in situations of unrecognized depression, absence of psychotic symptoms, or custody systems that place arbitrary emphasis on the sex of the parent (e.g., children ordinarily staying with the mother), that child is at risk for further exposure to symptoms that are now unattenuated by the presence of the healthier spouse. In addition, the depressed parent may well become more symptomatic in response to the event of separation or divorce, causing further increase in risk. The regression and other clinical phenomena that accompany chronic depression may lead to increasing efforts by ill parents to have their own emotional needs met by the child, a supportive fantasy for the adult but an unhealthy one for a child, especially one who must cope with the loss of a parent and of a family structure.

The possible outcomes for the child in this situation include acute behavioral changes (perhaps symptomatic of depression, response to acute loss, or learned ways of obtaining needed attention and gratification); clinical symptoms of loss (related to loss of both the real object and affection and gratification), including depression and psychosomatic illness; other manifestations of regression; and subclinical setbacks in emotional maturation. The last of these may be the most significant, since such setbacks may go unnoticed and/or untreated, thus allowing vulnerable spots in the child's developmental "armor" to persist and perhaps predispose the child to coping difficulties later in life.

Anthony (1974a,b) writes that the stress on a given child from divorce is related to the child's perceptiveness, general sensitivity, age and intelligence, and level of emotional participation within the home. By latency, many children preoccupy themselves with situations and people outside the family, and many use this as a defense against closer involvement with the parents. There are many possible variations in any child's reactions to divorce; however, divorce should never be regarded as a short term "legal" event. Rather, it is an almost indefinite process, with each stage having its own psychological impact conducive to its own set of disorders.

Finally, the issue of separation and divorce is only one example of several situations of physical loss to which the child of depressed parents may be exposed more often than other children and to which that child may be more than usually vulnerable. These include hospitalization of a parent for medical or psychiatric reasons, other family and social situations that render the depressed parent even less able to function affectively and cognitively, and the broad range of instances of more symbolic emotional absences of the afflicted parent with their concomitant drains on the remaining health resources of the family.

|| STAGES OF DEVELOPMENT

Let us now briefly, and admittedly incompletely, sketch some of the characteristics related to risk and vulnerability as they are seen in children of various ages. From time to time there will be mention of the child, the parents, the family, and sociocultural risk factors. Occasionally, characteristics that reduce risk in the child are noted, although discussion of intervention is not the purpose of this chapter. Some of the pathological effects of heightened vulnerability, seen in children of various ages and in the adult, are also presented.

Neonatal characteristics are exceedingly important with respect to risk and vulnerability. Children of neurotically depressive women have been shown to have, as a group, lower Apgar scores and more fetal deaths than controls or than the children of schizophrenic mothers, although the latter difference has not been found to be statistically significant. Of course, patients with the most chronic and severe illnesses were more likely to have been on medication (Sameroff & Zax, 1973a). In the same study, children of severely mentally ill mothers were more likely to have spent long periods in the intensive-care nursery or in other institutional settings, a finding perhaps related to the fact that these mothers more often had no husband, gave the children up for adoption, or were otherwise unable to engage in basic mothering behavior immediately after the birth. In general, infants of depressive women showed more deficits at birth than did infants of schizophrenic women, and the chronicity and severity of the disturbance contributed a great deal to the infant's condition.

An important factor in physically defective infants, which begins at the neonatal stage and affects risk for emotional deficit, is that of parental acceptance and adaptation to the child's problem(s). The severely depressed parent and the accompanying family system may be less able to accept and support a damaged or premature infant, just as that infant may not be in a good position to enter a disturbed family. The presence of an underweight body or other characteristics of deviance places extra caretaking demands on new parents, further contributing to the beginning of a series of negative transactions that can easily produce lasting emotional damage, regardless of whether the infant carries genetic loading for mental illness (Sameroff, 1977). In the case of a depressed mother, other caretaking demands on new parents further contribute to the beginning of a series of negative transactions that can easily produce lasting emotional damage, whether the infant carries genetic loading for mental illness or not (Sameroff, 1977). In the case of a depressed mother or other caregiver, continuing lack of reward and reinforcement for parenting behavior contributes to withdrawal, inadequate mothering, and the like. Minkowski and Amiel-Tison (1974) give suggestions for ameliorating some of these problems, including avoidance of mother–child separations, giving the premature infant to the mother as soon and often as possible, being aware of the possibility of hospitalism, and attempting to alleviate the mother's fearfulness with respect to maternal care and to her temptation to give the baby back to the hospital's "more skillful hands."

The mother–child relationship is of paramount importance to the fate of premature children. The mother's anxiety should be mitigated by a constant supply of information, permission to visit the infant freely, and psychotherapy when needed. In addition, parents should be told as soon as possible of the prognosis for the infant and supportive measures instigated, although final testing and delineation of physical and learning deficits may not occur until early school age.

|| Infancy

Merging with neonatal risk factors and characteristics are those associated with infancy and the needs of the infant during the early months of his or her experience within the family environment. Here we begin to see both risk factors and effects characteristic of such things as the infantile "fearlike state" described by Sullivan in the 1950s, which could be induced either by trauma or by contact with an emotionally disturbed mother. The mother's anxiety was seen as inducing anxiety in the infant through "empathy" (Sullivan, 1953). This implies that maternal anxiety (and perhaps other aberrant maternal characteristics such as depression and withdrawal) is perceived by the infant as a trauma.

Continuing in the infant stage is the dynamic balance between the child's vulnerability and the family's resources and the effect of that balance on development. The equation contains as negative factors the previously mentioned congenital defects and predispositions, parental mental illness (including depression), and the added stress on the parents and family entailed in the care of a defective child. On the positive side, infants who are able to be *active* relative to the external world possess an essential component of healthy psychological development (Provence, 1974). Such activity seems both essential to and an indicator of psychic differentiation and some aspects of early ego development. Motor competence and active mastery (physical and mental), manipulation of objects, active initiation of interpersonal transactions, and so on are essential elements of healthy adaptation and learning (Provence, 1974; Rutter, 1974). These also give the infant the ability to express its emotions. Unusual *inactivity* in infancy, due to either biological or experiential factors, is a frequent characteristic of the psychologically vulnerable child (Provence, 1974), who may need even more cognitive and affective involvement from (nondepressed) parents than do the child's peers.

|| Early Childhood

As we move further into childhood, early signs of attentional deficit may be seen. The ability to sustain attention is widely understood as a predictor of (and perhaps a causative factor for) later emotional disturbance (Cohler, Gallant, Grunebaum, & Weiss, 1976; Marcus, 1972). Children of both depressed and schizophrenic parents have more attentional problems than normals. Children of depressed mothers (especially boys) have more difficulty (Grunebaum, Cohler, Kaufman & Gallant, 1978) but seem to be able to overcome this deficit with sufficient motivation, at least in certain experimental paradigms (Cohler, 1978a).

The development of object relationships, although based in infantile experience, continues to be important in early childhood. In addition, the effect of earlier aberrant mother–infant relationships begins to be seen by this time. A trust in relationships with parents, which decreases the need for the infant or child to invest large amounts of energy in either testing or defense against hurt and hostile impulses, is an important facilitating factor for psychosexual maturation. In a related fashion, the ability to fantasize and to have one's fantasies be fairly free and not constricted by threats to the ego is important in the struggle against depression in both children and adults (Lebovici & Kiatkine, 1974).

The concepts of *competence* and *mastery* have been used to signify the degree to which a person feels able to produce an effect on the environment, to reach important goals, and to elicit desired behavior from others. Mastery needs can be gratified in a number of behavioral ways; however, these can be hampered by the limitations imposed by innate defects and handicaps, as well as by a paucity of consistent, supportive, and nurturing experiences (Kagan, 1971), such as may be found in parental depression. Garmezy (1974d) notes that variations in the degree to which one works, plays, and loves "well" are closely related to vulnerability to internal and external sources of risk and may foretell one's ability to recover from (and perhaps avoid) severe mental disorder.

|| Latency

As children grow older, progressing toward latency, their activities become more visible and exposure to relationships outside the parental ones increase. This means an increased opportunity for stimulation and/or stress from other sources in the environment, further progress in a widening arena of development and maturation, and new situations in which earlier deficits and disturbances may manifest themselves as symptoms. Issues of sexual identification appear more clearly during this period than in earlier ones, and the effects of physical or emotional absences, aberrances, and inconsistencies among depressed role models (parents) become more obvious.

Teacher and peer ratings of children of mentally disturbed parents have shown that depression or schizophrenia in a parent is associated with greater measures of disturbance behaviors, impatience, and disrespect. Children studied also showed more difficulty relating to teachers and had problems with initiative and comprehension (Rolf, 1972, 1976; Weintraub, Neale, & Liebert, 1975).

|| Adolescence

Adolescent vulnerability to psychiatric symptoms is probably higher than that seen at any other stage after preschool. Biologic stresses (including hormonal ones), social changes, reemergence of early childhood conflicts, and necessary preparation for adulthood make this a particularly high-risk time, especially for vulnerable youths.

One major factor in this vulnerability is the mental health of the parents. In one study of adolescents hospitalized for medical illness without psychiatric diagnosis, a large number showed clinical depression. The presence and severity of depressive symptoms was clearly associated with parental psychiatric illness. When there was a psychiatric disorder in a parent and the adolescent's medical prognosis was poor, 50 percent of the youths showed depression. When the prognosis was poor but there was no parental psychiatric disorder, only 23 percent were seen as depressed. When there was disorder in a parent but the medical prognosis was good, 27 percent were still depressed. When both parents were mentally healthy and the prognosis was good, only 9 percent were depressed. This study involved 110 adolescents, and extensive evaluation measures were used (Hudgens, 1974). The data seem all the more impressive when one recalls that depression is the most common mental illness in the world.

|| The Adult

Excluding serious childhood psychosis, the most disruptive disorders seen in childhood are not always the most dangerous for the future (e.g., quiet depression, withdrawal, emotional unavailability, and unreadiness for maturational milestones). There seems to be little information available to support the view that clinical disturbance during childhood overlaps with the adult development of psychosis (again excluding psychoses that begin in childhood); however, there is evidence to suggest a connection between childhood disturbance and later nonpsychotic disorders, consistent with the earlier comments that implied that the most common—although perhaps the least attended to—problem is that of the eventual development of adults who are inferior to what their intellectual abilities and backgrounds might lead one to expect; that is, *"mental impoverishment" in place of mental illness* (Chiland, 1974).

An example with some relevance for our study of children of depressed parents, in terms of inconsistency of care and absence of affect and the foundations for attachment, comes from the follow-up of persons in long-term foster care. Fears of society, a masked desire to hurt society, and an excessive concern with defenses against injury to the self and hostile impulses are prominent (Murphy, 1974). As these people attain adulthood, there is a desire for marriage and home coupled with a low tolerance for the demands associated with family life. High marriage rates prevail but are accompanied by high separation and divorce rates as well. A desire for children, perhaps stemming more from a need to vicariously experience a "normal" childhood than from a desire to be a parent, is usual. When the partners in the Murphy study grew to learn how to "give," marriages lasted longer. It is important to note that none of the subjects followed up had sought formal psychiatric help or was diagnosed "psychotic."

The relationship between the quality of childhood symptoms and the diagnosis or deficit latter seen in the adult might be mentioned here. Consistent with one of the threads of this discussion, patterns of gratification, interaction, defense, and the like—presupposed by constitution, established in infancy or childhood, and reinforced in the vulnerable child throughout development—persist into adulthood and are manifest in the adult personality and behavior. Definition, discovery, and understanding of the child at risk are the first steps toward modifying that emotional outcome.

|| SUMMARY

Clinical study and review of the literature with respect to the cognitive and emotional development of children of depressed parents indicates that such children may be at higher risk than those of normal or thought-disordered parents, especially if one considers their vulnerability for "mental impoverishment"—that is, for adult social and emotional difficulty stemming from earlier delays in development, poverty of affectual experience, attachment problems, and weakened perceptions of mastery and competence—rather than for "mental illness" per se.

Early risk factors from both innate and environmental sources are seen to establish patterns of growth and interaction with the parenting figures in which the vulnerability of the child influences the impact felt from biological and environmental origins. The most prominent mitigating factors for such risks are (1) *the presence of some source of consistent parenting in the environment* and (2) *recognition of the parent's illness by other members of the family who can support the child's impression that something is wrong.*

4

Assessing the Relationship Between Parental Behavior and Child Functioning

Lawrence Fisher and Ronald F. Kokes

Understanding the influence of certain parental attributes on the behavior of their offspring is only one attempt at delving into the complex morass of research on the etiology of mental disorder. Current research has documented the necessity of regarding psychopathology as an interplay among individual, relationship, and biologic variables such that no single factor can clearly account for or explain causative factors (Engel, 1977).

If one accepts this principle of multiple determination and transactional influences (Sameroff & Zax, 1973b), the question arises as to *how* variables interact to produce a given consequence. This implies causation to some extent, a subject with which the behavioral sciences has only recently begun to wrestle. In this kind of research, one attempts not only to determine which variables correlate with others, but also which variables "cause" which outcomes. For example, many researchers are no longer interested in the fact that parental social class and value structure appear to correlate or to systematically vary with their offspring's academic performance and social role behavior. They are much more concerned with "how" parental values directly influence child behavior. It is the "how" that raises the problem because our techniques for isolating meaning from error variance, from unreliability of measurement, and from unspecified interactive components are not that well developed.

This research was supported by National Institute of Mental Health Program Project Grant MH22836, Lyman Wynne, Principal Investigator. Team leaders in this program, in addition to the authors, are Alfred Baldwin, Michael Chandler, Robert Cole, Frederick Jones, Howard Iker, Stephen Munson, Barry Ritzler, Leonard Salzman, and John Strauss.

This problem has been with us for years as various strategies for studying the etiology of mental disorder have developed, each with its assets and liabilities. The study of the effects of a specific parental attribute on child behavior, including affective variables such as depression, should be considered as only one stage in an ongoing sequence of strategies developed to counter various flaws in previous approaches. A brief review of these strategies seems warranted at present for gaining a more complete historical perspective. Such an endeavor should provide clues as to where we need to proceed in the future.

This chapter focuses on these two complex subjects: the various strategies of researching etiology of mental disorder and the particular problems inherent in what we have termed "interactional" research. In the following sections we first review the assets and liabilities of three research strategies for studying the etiology of psychopathology: retrospective, historical, and prospective. Next we describe a host of research problems in adopting an interactive approach, and finally we briefly describe a longitudinal prospective research project aimed at studying the offspring of psychiatrically disturbed parents, including those with affective disorders.

RESEARCH STRATEGIES IN PSYCHOPATHOLOGY

Despite the thousands of varied studies in the area of etiology of mental disorder, the vast majority can be categorized into three general approaches: retrospective, historical, and prospective. Each is described below along with a number of their major assets and liabilities.

Retrospective Methods

In this approach, the researcher collects data on already diagnosed patient groups. These data could be reports of past events or current performance on certain experimental tasks. The recorded differences among these patient groups are then used, in part, as evidence to support a theory of etiology, to substantiate a point of view that given premorbid circumstances or influences "caused" the disorder. This approach, then, takes currently recorded data as evidence to support a theory about past events. This inferential process obviously has many problems, but it is a widely used approach in studying hypotheses about the etiology of mental disorder. There are several types of approaches within this model, all of which share this inferential mode.

In the case history method, one gathers clinical data that are presently recorded reports of past events. There are obvious problems with memory and subject bias, but the case model provides a rich resource for the generation of hypotheses.

The same paradigm exists in family interaction, biological, and psychological research. Data on these different dependent variable domains are recorded in response to varied stimuli and differences in already diagnosed patient groups are attributed to pathogenic factors that occurred prior to onset. In each case, specific kinds of aberrant or deficit behaviors collected in the present are related to previous potential causative agents.

The primary and fundamental problem with all retrospective methods, methods that study current behavior and retrospectively infer etiology, is that it is impossible to separate cause from effect. It is never clear whether differences among patient groups are due to etiologic factors that "caused" the disorder or to the effects of the disability itself. All subjects are postonset, and we can document etiologic agents that could have initiated or influenced the process only through retrospective inference. Obviously, there are other problems as well such as memory or distortion of events in case history and the marked potential for drug or environmental influences over time in the other methods. For our purposes, however, the inability to separate cause from effect in retrospective strategies is a major drawback.

|| Historical Methods

This is the second strategy for the study of etiology of mental disorder, and it has two subheadings: what Garmezy (1974a) has called the "follow-up" and "follow-back" methods. The aim of the historical approach is to counter the main flaw of the retrospective strategy by using existing data recorded prior to or during onset of disorder.

The follow-up approach looks at the present functioning of individuals who received psychiatric diagnoses years earlier. By clocking the eventual adjustment or outcome of these former patients, one can make statements about etiology and course. For example, is it accurate to conclude that schizophrenia is a characterological disorder and that once a schizophrenic always a schizophrenic? Or, alternatively, is schizophrenia a reactive disorder or one related, in combination with other variables, to particular developmental periods? The follow-up strategy assists in resolving these issues.

A primary example of the follow-up method is Robbins's (1966) study of "Deviant Children Grown Up." In this large-scale research, Robbins obtained child guidance clinic records and sought out these referred children when they became adults. She then took several of the previously recorded variables and used them to predict eventual outcome and overall adjustment. A similar project was undertaken at the Judge Baker Child Guidance Clinic in Boston (Waring & Ricks, 1965), again using previously recorded or historical data to predict eventual outcome.

In the follow-back strategy, the reverse occurs. One identifies already diagnosed patients in the present and then seeks out records or other objective data recorded prior to onset. In this way, since the investigator cannot personally go back in time, the cause–effect dilemma is countered by obtaining historical materials that document early behavior.

An excellent example of the follow-back method is a study by Watt and his colleagues (Watt, 1972; Watt, Stolorow, Lubensky, & McClelland, 1970). These researchers identified groups of Worcester State Hospital adult patients who received their primary schooling in the state of Massachusetts. They then secured the school records of these patients, records of teachers' anecdotal comments written prior to onset of disorder. Watt and his coworkers then scored these anecdotal data into several dimensions and with appropriate controls analyzed them by age, sex of students, and other variables to predict adult status. Again, data recorded prior to onset of the disorder were utilized.

Clearly, there are several problems with this attempted remedy of the cause–effect problem. Reliance on record data is a dusty business, and missing data are rampant. A fire in a school record room or courthouse 15 years ago can wipe out an entire research project in 1983. Also, loss, misplacement, mold, and mildew can make the effective utilization of these records very difficult, if not impossible. Moreover, the reliability of the record is always open to question. How accurate is the record in reflecting the subject's behavior? Did the recorder have an adequate sample of behavior to judge the performance? Would another judge observing the same behavior report similarly? There is simply no way to check on these issues as the investigator was not present to observe the process. Furthermore, one is limited by what is in the record. We can identify at present a far greater number of potentially relevant variables than could researchers working 35 years ago. Yet only their material is on record, not ours. So the range of information available is often limited and of marginal use considering the costs involved. Also, some relevant variables are not available because the individuals collecting data years before had a different model of psychopathology and etiology; thus they observed different aspects of the symptomatic picture. Variables demonstrated to be of relevance through research since the period of initial data collection may not be available at present. Finally, access to records is often very difficult, even with appropriate permission forms, because of laws for protection of privacy. These problems are frequently insurmountable and often prevent the undertaking of many kinds of studies. Where appropriate, however, by obtaining a source of information prior to onset or at an early stage of the disorder, one can at least theoretically begin to remedy the cause and effect problem.

|| Prospective Methods

The prospective strategy for the study of etiology of mental disorder is perhaps the most complex of the three, but it has the clear advantage of separating cause from effect. Very simply, in this approach the investigator identifies an unaffected cohort, assesses relevant variables prior to onset, and then follows the cohort until a subsample manifests symptoms or the particular behaviors of interest. Next, the researcher uses initial assessment data to discriminate the affected from unaffected groups. Emphasis can be placed on factors leading to health or to illness. In this model, the researcher does not rely on records or data recorded by others as the research team is present at the beginning. Current knowledge in selecting relevant variables is also applicable, and there is little or no contamination of process with etiology.

There are two subtypes of prospective research, each of which reflects different methods for selecting the sample to begin with: the generic and the risk subtypes. In the generic approach, an entire population is utilized such as in a school district, psychiatric setting, or medical clinic. All members who come in contact with the setting are screened and then followed until the appropriate cohort is identified.

Generic prospective research is quite expensive in terms of dollars, investigator and subject time, and potential payoff. For example, if one is studying the etiology of a disorder such as schizophrenia where the rate of occurrence is roughly 0.8 percent, following a sample randomly selected from the general population would lead to the identification of a very small number of such patients. With this in mind, investigators have sought to identify cohorts whose rate of breakdown is somewhat higher than in a random or unselected sample; that is, researchers seek the identification of a cohort whose risk for occurrence of the disorder under study is higher than in the general population. In many ways, recent research on the effects of maternal depression on offspring has emerged as an outgrowth of the risk paradigm in that one crucial precursor of recurrent and severe depression in adulthood may be maternal depression when the patient was a child. Consequently, a cohort of children with depressed parents is clearly at risk for the disorder, and studies of such a cohort may provide definitive clues as to etiology.

Clearly, there are a number of assets in this research strategy: (1) etiologic hypotheses are directly testable, the data are not used to infer etiological factors on a post hoc basis, and the investigator is not restricted to working with groups of already diagnosed patients; (2) the cause–effect problem is substantially reduced but is not completely eliminated because it is possible that the seeds of the disorder were planted prior to the first assessment, as with genetic influences or in utero effects; (3) the premorbid state, course, and development of disorder are directly observable, facilitating an understanding of how other variables interact with the development of the disability and assisting in understanding the mechanisms that underlie and maintain the disorder; and (4) the strategy permits the identification of predictors of both health and disorder, which broadens the scope of the research effort and may make it generalizable to a potentially larger sample. Moreover, implications for prevention and remediation also may become apparent. So the prospective method provides a powerful addition to the armamentarium of methods for studying etiology of mental disorder. In essence, the model counters the major drawback of other approaches and permits a more systematic method for studying onset, course, and manifestation of psychopathology.

MAJOR LIABILITIES OF THE PROSPECTIVE STRATEGY

Although the prospective research strategy, including both generic and risk orientations, counters the major flaw of retrospective and historical models by separating cause from effect, a high price is paid in terms of the complexity of the enterprise. These problems, which are reviewed below, need to be well understood prior to initiation of any prospective research project and countermeasures incorporated into the overall design prior to initiation of the program. At first glance, the variety of problems presented below may appear insurmountable and may leave the impression that the strategy is not worth the effort. Our aim in undertaking this listing was not to overwhelm the reader with the pitfalls of the strategy, but to systematize these issues in a manner that will foster more effective utilization of the approach. Prospective research, at its present stage of development, requires considerable refinement in its application, and it is with these aims that its major flaws and dilemmas are presented.

The types of problem to be reviewed in this section fall into three categories: (1) those related to the strategy itself, (2) those related to the assessment of adult functioning, and (3) those related to the functioning of the child who is frequently and, for our purposes, the primary object of study. Each is reviewed in some detail in the following paragraphs from the perspective of our experience in a long-term prospective research project at the University of Rochester. The project assessed the offspring of parents hospitalized for a variety of severe psychiatric disorders, including depression and mania. The variables assessed included parental, familial, social, developmental, and psychophysiological measures. In a later section we briefly review the project as an illustration of this type of research strategy.

|| Strategic Problems

Regardless of whether one is studying the effects of parental schizophrenia or parental depression on offspring, the frequency of severe mental disorder in the general population is far too low to warrant adoption of a generic prospective model. With this in mind, some selective criteria must be established so that a relatively homogeneous sample can be defined for inclusion in a project. An immediate problem arises as to the specification of these criteria. How they are defined is directly related to the generalizability of the study's findings.

For example, the occurrence of schizophrenia in the population is less than 1 percent, leading most researchers to adopt a risk strategy within the prospective model. It is known that about 2.5–4 percent of offspring of adult schizophrenics themselves receive that diagnosis sometime during their lives and that of those who do not, many more display diagnosable behavioral disorders. Clearly, the offspring of adult schizophrenics are at increased risk for psychopathology. We also know that a majority of first-admission schizophrenics do not have parents similarly diagnosed. So if we define risk to pathology as being an offspring of an adult schizophrenic, we reduce the generalizability of our findings perhaps to those schizophrenics who carry a high genetic loading.

This illustration is applicable in the area of affective disorders as well. By limiting the development of depression as a major psychiatric disorder to those children who have depressed parents, we exclude a large number of depressed adults whose parents were themselves not depressed. In this way, the definition of risk can restrict the application of the findings within the population of patients with diagnoses of depression. It would again appear that gains effected by using a prospective paradigm are often offset by a restriction in generalizability of findings.

A second strategic problem is that although the prospective model implies a rather straightforward attempt at reducing the influence of the cause–effect problem, one can never be completely sure that antecedent conditions were not operative prior to first assessment. While genetic or in utero influences are often involved, psychological factors over the generations, early child experience, or combinations of all of these can plant the seeds of later pathology.

A third strategic problem in prospective research relates to its longitudinal character. Continuous, ongoing research over several years' duration brings with it a plethora of logistic problems not found in shorter-term, cross-sectional approaches. First, the cost of risk research is very high considering the span and breadth of measurement that is required over a period of years. The need for continuity of funding is also crucial (Fisher & Jones, 1978). Breaks in funding lead to a loss in personnel that jeopardizes maintenance of the sample itself. Also, funding follows time sequences established by granting agencies to fit fiscal needs, and these time sequences do not necessarily match critical developmental periods or milestones of the cohort. Very often risk researchers find themselves spending more time writing grant applications and progress reports than analyzing their data at time periods commensurate with important research questions.

Also, severely disturbed individuals and families often display marked occupational and residential mobility. Keeping track of the cohort for follow-up is very difficult, and one must begin a project with a sufficient sample size such that an unexpected drop-out rate at follow-up does not undermine the project. In addition, much energy and devotion need to be expressed in keeping in touch with patients and their families, energy that many researchers would rather devote toward data analysis and other academic endeavors.

Another major problem in this type of longitudinal research has to do with investigator age, burnout, and institutional support. With respect to investigator age, one senior researcher in our project estimated that he would be over 115 years of age before the youngest child completed the last period of risk for onset of schizophrenia. Investigators often display reduced energy for projects in which the final data will not be available for several years. They tend to leave institutions in search of career advances while the cohort remains at the original location. Also, young investigators need to display competencies in the academic marketplace in terms of publications and presentations. When initial data may not be available for several years, these researchers may not have the credentials to support tenure decisions. So prospective research needs to be undertaken with a high degree of institutional support and understanding that is not always possible given the current funding problems that plague most educational and research settings.

Most of these problems are common to the vast majority of longitudinal research efforts, but, for one reason or another, they seem exacerbated in the risk model. Many of them seem minor at first glance, however, our experience has been that they develop insidiously over the course of the project and can sabotage not only the continuity of the research from a logistic point of view, but can undermine the interpersonal relationships and team efforts that are the cornerstones for successful completion of the project.

This observation brings to mind one last and often neglected point with respect to strategic problems in prospective research. As is discussed in some detail below, risk research requires a range or breadth of measurement of child, adult, and family functioning. As such, risk research projects require a group of researchers with a range of skills, with some experts in one area and some in others. Consequently, these projects need to be operated from the viewpoint of a research team where investigators share a common interest and where an atmosphere of give and take is established for the good of the project. Without such a tolerant, efficient, and interpersonally positive atmosphere, such projects are doomed to failure.

Adult Assessment Problems

Risk research that defines child vulnerability to a specific disorder in terms of parental psychopathology is dependent intrinsically on the accuracy and reliability of the diagnosis and the description of the parental disorder. This diagnostic task has been aided substantially by the development of the DSM-III operational diagnostic criteria. Despite this improvement, problems persist in identifying and articulating the psychopathology of parents with affective as well as other disorders. Several variables associated with such disorders may function alone or cumulatively to regulate the degree of risk suffered by offspring. Use of DSM-III diagnoses alone as a criterion of risk without attention to these associated factors may obscure the true risk potential of specific syndromes and symptoms, such as affective disorders. The following associated factors need to be considered in this regard.

Affective disorders in particular tend to be episodic: a parent may have one, several, or many episodes. If episodic, the disorder could have been chronically intermittent, or only in response to developmentally related stressors. The episodes may have occurred recently or long ago with no residual effects. Severity of symptoms may vary across episodes and subjects. One patient might have repeated severe episodes of the disorder while another might have one severe episode preceding or interspersed among several moderate episodes.

Affective symptoms do not occur exclusively among the affective disorders. Almost all diagnostic groups exhibit significant numbers and levels of affective symptoms. Strauss, Kokes, Ritzler, Harder, and Van Ord (1978) reported depression in 93 percent of first-admission patients with diagnoses ranging across all functional categories. Depressive symptoms, elation, flight of ideas, or other affective symptoms are exhibited in schizophrenia, character disorders, and anxiety disorders. Restricting the sample to offspring of parents diagnosed according to DSM-III criteria as affectively disordered eliminates from consideration those parents who exhibit significant levels of affective symptoms but have nonaffective diagnoses. The dimensional approach to symptom measurement outlined by Strauss, Bartko, and Carpenter (1973) assesses affective symptoms independent of diagnostic categories. Selection of families at risk on the basis of high scores on parental affective dimensions, such as depression, withdrawal, and elation, regardless of diagnosis, may provide a more appropriate risk sample for the study of affective disorders. This line of reasoning is certainly applicable to other areas of research as well.

Affective symptoms appear in a variety of patterns and combinations across patients. A specific symptom may be the focal point in one patient but not in another even though both have the same diagnosis. For example, at specific times depressive symptoms may predominate in some bipolar affective patients whereas elation may prevail in others. The psychotic components, that is, delusions and hallucinations, corresponding to the manic and depressive states also reflect two completely opposite affective poles, grandiosity versus self-depreciation. Vulnerability to the development of specific types of affective disorder may be related to these opposite poles.

A child's vulnerability to the development of a disorder also may be related to the temporal relationship of parental disorder and age of the child. Many mothers develop depression during pregnancy and/or soon after the birth of a child. Are there different risk potentials for the child when the parental episode occurred long before the birth of the child, concurrently with pregnancy, birth, or neonatal stages, or those occurring during the early formative years of the child's life? The weighting of genetic and environmental influences of risk may be different for parental disorders occurring within these different time frames. Child-rearing practices and attitudes toward the child probably are altered if the episode is associated with childbirth and rearing as opposed to a situation in which the episode occurred prior to pregnancy. In the former case, cumulative risk effects are most likely enhanced, but empirical evidence for this expectation is lacking.

The use of parental diagnosis for the identification of children at risk requires careful documentation of the history of parental disorder and its onset and course. The change of diagnostic criteria from DSM-II to DSM-III, however, altered the focus of attention to different aspects of psychopathology. Information needed for DSM-III diagnosis may have been overlooked or not included in hospital charts or other records, therefore rendering data on premorbid functioning incomplete.

In summary, problems of adult diagnostic assessment with particular applicability to defining risk in the child center around four points: (1) the frequency and severity of the episode is often not taken into account, (2) affective symptoms such as depression are present in patients with a range of DSM-III diagnoses, (3) the temporal relation of the episode to critical periods of the child's development needs to be controlled, and (4) complete diagnostic data are often unavailable or unreliable because of the reliance on historical or retrospective materials.

|| Child Assessment Problems

At first glance, the assessment of the child in a prospective project seems to be a relatively easy task. One is interested in the effects of a parental condition such as depression or thought disorder and one attempts to assess the child's general or specific well-being or pathology. At second glance, however, the complexity of this task and our lack of tools and models for assessment become apparent.

First, most measurement instruments have been developed either to distinguish between health and illness or to scale individuals along a dimension of degree of illness or severity. It is to be remembered that in prospective research as we have defined it, however, the vast majority of children are presently healthy and functioning within the normal range. The use of most existing scales on such a sample would identify a very small group of poorly functioning offspring, and the remainder would display very little variance. Clearly, health defined as the absence of disease is not a very useful concept in this context. Yet we have not been successful in developing a theory of assessment, along with appropriate tools, that would scale individuals along dimensions encompassing both the normal and pathological range. We do reasonably well within the pathological sector but are sorely lacking with respect to the vast majority of children at risk who for the most part are functioning well.

To develop an adequate child assessment program, one needs to specify what shall be assessed, who shall assess it, and how it shall be measured. There are two general models within the "what to assess" domain. First, one can scale children on those dimensions that discriminate adults who display the syndrome for which the child is at risk. For example, adult schizophrenics display well-documented attentional deficits. In studying a sample of children at risk for schizophrenia, it might be helpful to assess the attentional skills of these youngsters to determine whether they display deficits similar to their adult counterparts, or at least deficits that indicate that they are at the initial stages of attentional problems. A problem with this approach is that it excludes other areas of potential strengths and deficits that might have etiologic implications. In other words, in some cases this approach can be too restrictive at the present stage of our knowledge, if taken alone.

A second approach is somewhat broader in its scope, but, it too, entails substantial measurement difficulties. Garmezy (1974d) has proposed that instead of assessing children at risk on variables which identify adult diagnostic groups, we assess offspring as to their level of age appropriate competency following White (1959). Garmezy's strategy was to assess children at risk on broadly based developmental skills that are age-specific and that reflect a continuum across several dimensions of growth, such as cognitive, physiological, and social.

Although this strategy is appealing in many ways, it introduces several problems. First, as mentioned above, we have poor techniques for assessing health, development, or competence. Garmezy's proposal has no implications for health or illness but instead refers to a continuum of functioning. Second, the model does not specify which aspects of behavior or development we should select. Clearly, we need to establish a broadly based evaluative battery, but a "shot-gun" approach at assessment is often nonproductive; providing overkill in some areas and underkill in others. Third, to compound the problem even further, because of cost most prospective projects are forced to select only a limited range of variables for study. Cost of assessment in terms of dollars and subjects' time compel most researchers to select only those variables that they feel will have the greatest predictive payoff. So some selectivity is required.

The "how to assess it" problem is one that confronts most measurement scientists, and we shall skim it only briefly. Some projects seem to focus on single-method assessments such as structured interviews or limited behavioral observations. In the broad-base measurement paradigm under discussion here, however, most investigators adopt a multimethod model using a variety of indexes. This methodological approach is adopted in an effort to reduce method variance so as not to tie a project to specific techniques that may unwittingly bias results. Developmental skills need to be measured from a variety of measurement viewpoints to maximize the possibility of gathering all relevant information.

The "who to assess it" problem is equally difficult. Briefly, child rating scales completed by parents are often biased by parental attitude and disorder, thus providing a distorted view of the child. Often, parental report of child behavior may have more implications for the parental disorder itself than for the child's growth. Clinical ratings using traditional diagnostic tools are often of little merit as the amount of clinical pathology displayed by the child is low, rater biases are high because it is often impossible to undertake ratings in a blind fashion, and the reliability of clinical ratings often goes unchecked. On the other hand, behavioral observations and in vivo measurements are often very expensive and logistically not feasible.

The last area to be reviewed in this section on problems of child assessment concerns the selection of the child cohort. In most cases, as mentioned above, risk is defined by the presence and degree of a particular characteristic in the parent. A question one needs to address is which of the parent's offspring should be studied: males, females, all children, or one child? Since statistically all offspring are at risk, it would be nice to include all of them in some way. Yet costs often preclude such an undertaking. Also, because costs tend to keep sample size small, is it wise to restrict the cohort to same-sex offspring of a narrow age range, or should both male and female children be included regardless of age? Restricted samples reduce generalizability, but at least the sample would be homogeneous, assuming that a sufficient sample is available for study to begin with. Also, at which ages should the children be assessed?

As can be seen, therefore, research decisions appear at every stage from defining risk, to selecting a sample, to establishing a measurement battery, and each of these issues must be directly addressed when planning a program of prospective research.

|| AN ILLUSTRATIVE PROSPECTIVE PROJECT

Given the varied and complex problems facing the prospective researcher, problems that are exacerbated by studying the interactions among variables so as to test hypotheses implying etiology and causation, how should one proceed in utilizing this potentially powerful approach? Although there are no clearly definitive answers to the questions and problems reviewed in the previous section, perhaps it might be helpful to describe one long-term prospective project in an effort to review how one such research team tackled each of these difficulties in turn. This is not to imply that the decisions of this group of investigators should be viewed as optimum; rather, these decisions seemed appropriate to the time and setting of this particular project.*

The University of Rochester Child and Family Study (URCAFS) is a long-term, prospective project, under the direction of Lyman Wynne, which seeks to study families and offspring of parents hospitalized for mental disorder. So far, approximately 145 families have been studied, and data collection on the first 3-year follow-up of the sample has been completed.

In studying the etiology of the severe mental disorders, the investigators selected a risk as opposed to a generic prospective strategy because incidence rates were far too low for a generic model to be feasible. With

*The project to be described in this section was designed and implemented by a large group of senior research scientists and consultants as outlined in the acknowledgment section at the beginning of this chapter. The present authors were contributory members of this team.

this in mind, the investigators collected a sample of families with a hospitalized adult who had a male child 4, 7, or 10 years of age at the time of the study. Male offspring only were chosen because they generally have a higher rate of mental health referral at this age range and because the costs of the project were so large that to divide the sample by sex of child, thus creating a smaller number per cell, was not feasible.

In an attempt to reduce the problems related to time and the longitudinal nature of the research, one of the first clinical applications of R. Bell's (1953) convergence technique was undertaken. The idea was to combine both longitudinal and cross-sectional strategies in the same project. The age of each male offspring selected for study at the start of the project was either 4, 7, or 10 years. At the 3-year follow-up, the ages of the children would be 7, 10, and 13 years. If we could demonstrate that over a 3-year period, previously designated aspects of the new 7-year-old group were like the old 7-year-old group and similarly for the new 10-year-olds and the old 10-year-olds, then we could begin to make some kinds of developmental statements on a cohort spanning from 4 to 13 years in a 3-year period.

The University of Rochester is situated in a highly stable upstate New York community in which the university and its medical and psychiatric services are positively viewed and highly valued. Patients were selected from hospital files to which the senior clinicians of the study had access. The previously hospitalized adult must have been discharged a minimum of 3 months prior to the initiation of the study, and in fact the average time span between initiation of the project and last discharge was 4.37 years. Each potential subject was contacted by letter and finally by telephone. A team undertook a home visit for purposes of recruitment and informed consent. The families had to contain an intact marriage, and the members had to agree to participate in over 40 hours of evaluation. For this they would receive transportation to the university as well as a moderate stipend for their effort. Most of these patients viewed the university and its health facilities positively and were cooperative.

Following this initial screening, the previously hospitalized patients underwent a detailed series of diagnostic procedures that have been described elsewhere (Kokes, Harder, Fisher, & Strauss, 1980). In addition to the assignment of each patient to a DSM-III diagnostic category, two diagnostic teams rated the key parent and spouse on global scales of severity of pathology and social and occupational functioning. Ratings also were made on the type of symptom displayed independent of diagnosis. The diagnostic assessment eliminated from study those families containing parents with severe alcohol, substance abuse, or organic problems. Social class V families also were omitted. These exclusion criteria prevented the kind of drop-out rate associated with families from this social class and from confounding variables associated with these factors.

Once the diagnostic evaluation was completed, the families participated in a series of individual, couple, and family procedures designated to assess a broad range of family- and individually based variables.

As mentioned earlier, there are two primary ways of assessing offspring at risk to mental disorder: on variables that identify pathological characteristics of previously diagnosed adults and on variables reflecting a developmental model. On variables that discriminate among groups of adult patients, the children and families were assessed on psychophysiological, consensus Rorschach, psychological testing, and on family interaction and clinical variables. Following a developmental or competence format, the children were assessed on school competence, parental report of child behavior and Piaget-type developmental criteria using referencial communication and egocentrism scales. Thus we selected a number of planned approaches to assessing these children at risk, making use of both models of assessment.

Our research was established to identify potential antecedent variables in groups of previously hospitalized adults using a prospective model. However, because the breakdown rate for children at these ages is very low, one could not expect to establish discriminative predictive criteria. One benefit of the prospective model is that it permits observation of the development of the disorder, and at this early state of the project we sought to document what we termed "intermediate" as opposed to long-term outcome. With this in mind, we decided to study the relationship between family and adult variables to child competence and vice versa. The questions we asked concerned what kind of families were associated with both low- and high-competence children, how such families were structured, and what the relative weights of contributory variables were.

Because child competence was the primary dependent variable for the assessment of intermediate outcome, we had to develop an assessment model that would scale children at risk along a dimension of competence–incompetence without reference to concepts of health or disease. Although parental report of child behavior (Jones, 1977) and clinical ratings (Yu, Prentky, Baldwin, Greenwald, Munson, Baldwin, & Fisher, 1980) were utilized, our initial efforts focused on the assessment of competence in the school setting; a relatively objective setting where the competence of children at risk could be recorded blindly. An assessment model was developed for both teachers and peers using the values and criteria for competence utilized by the participants of the setting itself, and not by outside researchers and clinicians (Fisher, 1980). The model led to the development of highly reliable instruments that yielded data at several measurement levels from molecular to global.

In summary, we attempted to deal with each major liability of the risk model in the following manner. A risk design rather than a generic model was utilized because of low frequency of the disorder in the general population. Risk was defined as being the offspring of a hospitalized adult, which while limiting in terms of generalizability of findings, provided us with (1) a point of entry for collecting the sample and (2) the possibility of comparing our data with other similar projects from several countries.

Diagnostic assessment of the hospitalized parent included not only categorization based on DSM-III criteria, but also on ratings of symptom expression, severity of disorder, frequency and duration of episode, and quality of episode with respect to its temporal relation to the child's development.

The measurement of competence and incompetence was utilized rather than a health–sickness model in an effort to assure our ability to scale the entire sample along a series of dimensions with a sufficient degree of within-group variance. Children were assessed utilizing a developmental model as well as utilizing dimensions on which diagnosed adult patients differed. We attempted a convergence technique in an effort to deal with the longitudinal nature of the research, and we chose a geographic area where the population was reasonably stable and the chances of losing families due to mobility were greatly reduced.

A review of our initial findings (Fisher, 1980; Fisher & Jones, 1980; Fisher, Harder, & Kokes, 1980; Fisher, Kokes, Harder, & Jones, 1980; Harder, Kokes, Fisher, & Strauss, 1980; Kokes, Harder, Fisher, & Strauss, 1980) indicates consistent and significant relationships between the school competence of children at risk and five sets of family and parental variables.

First, the child's cognitive skills in school were related to two family interaction variables derived from the Wynne–Singer consensus Rorschach procedure: communication deviance and nonacknowledgment (Fisher & Jones, 1980). These two variables also were related to offspring social–emotional behavior but were unrelated to compliance skills. The relationship of these family variables to school functioning emerged for the group as a whole, regardless of the diagnosis of the hospitalized parent: schizophrenic, affective disorder, or nonpsychotic.

Regardless of diagnosis of parent, the total risk group seemed to be functioning well in school, as predicted, and only a small number of children showed signs of clinical disorder (Fisher, Harder, & Kokes, 1980). Peers seemed more sensitive in discriminating among classmates along dimensions of social functioning whereas teachers were better able to scale students in cognitive areas. This was also somewhat expected since previous research (Cowen, Pederson, & Babigian, 1973) had demonstrated that peers were reliable and sensitive predictors of later psychiatric outcome and were more accurate in their prediction of interpersonal behavior than teachers.

These findings tended to hold only for mother patient families, and not for father patient families. However, only a small percentage of school-aged children had hospitalized fathers, and most of these tended to display more severe impairment than did the mother patient group. Consequently, whereas sex of patient parent would seem to be an important variable in considering the nature and type of risk to pathology in offspring, our data are inconclusive in this regard because of sampling biases.

As mentioned earlier, all patients were rated on the presence and degree of symptomatic behavior regardless of formal diagnosis. An analysis of these data indicated that high lability of mother patient affect was positively correlated with school competence in offspring; however, mother patients with high scores on withdrawal, depression, and incongruous affect had children who scored poorly on school competence measures. These findings did not emerge in father patient families. These data may indicate that maternal emotional availability across diagnoses may be a crucial predictor of competence in male offspring of this age range. Mothers who were emotionally withdrawn or depressed had male offspring who displayed low school competence. These findings held for the mother patient group as a whole regardless of formal psychiatric diagnosis.

|| CONCLUSIONS

It is premature to suggest that one primary parental variable is independently predictive of child competence, since, as we reviewed earlier, several parental and familial measures also were related to the functioning of offspring in the sample. What is needed in large-scale research where several independent variables all show significant relationships to several dependent measures is a series of multivariate analyses that will assist in determining the nature of the interaction between parental attributes and child behavior.

Focusing on only one attribute such as affective symptoms or diagnosis of parent out of the context of family, social, and psychological variables is like trying to describe the proverbial elephant on the basis of data gathered by a severely handicapped observer. Our experience in this prospective project has lead us to emphasize the necessity of tempering our enthusiasm for a particular theoretical precursor of psychopathology by broadening our perspective to include a range of other variables as well. Such an activity forces the researcher to rely more heavily on hypothesis testing as opposed to post hoc hypothesis generation and to increase dependence on multivariate procedures to handle the large number of potentially influential factors. With this in mind, we are now focusing on determining the relative contributions of individual, family, social, and other variables on intermediate outcomes in these children.

The prospective research strategy provides opportunities for identifying antecedent agents in mental disorder, but the degree of complexity of the research bodes a clear warning to the would-be investigator. Developing projects designed to assess the interactions between parent and child variables is a far more difficult task than the definition and assessment of individual components. As such, the temptation to rely on post hoc theorizing or to assess only individual components out of the context of the family setting is high.

In this chapter we have reviewed many of the potential difficulties of this kind of interactive research on a pragmatic level. Yet, from personal experience, prospective research presents a challenging and intellectually rewarding pursuit. It is a powerful approach, but one that needs continued, cautious development in order to overcome its drawbacks and to avoid its pitfalls.

5

Social Adjustment Among Schizophrenic, Depressed, and Well Mothers and Their School-Aged Children

Bertram J. Cohler, David H. Gallant, Henry U. Grunebaum, and Carol Kaufman

Study of the parent–child relationship among families in which a parent (principally the mother) has been mentally ill is of interest both from the perspective of primary prevention of subsequent psychopathology (Albee & Joffe, 1977; Caplan & Grunebaum, 1967), as well as from the perspective of socialization theory itself. The study of children of psychotic mothers has shown that genetic factors play a part in the development of serious psychopathology among these children "at risk" (Erlenmeyer-Kimling, 1975, 1977; Hanson, Gottesman, & Heston, 1976; Hanson, Gottesman, & Meehl, 1977; Mednick & Schulsinger, 1968; Meehl, 1962; Rosenthal, 1966, 1970, 1974). On the other hand, although detailed study has been devoted to the 10–16 percent of the children of these mothers who succumb to psychopathology, less careful study has been made of the large majority of these children who remain relatively invulnerable (Anthony, 1974a,b; Garmezy, 1974c, 1977, 1978a), particularly children of schizophrenic mothers who remain invulnerable and who, in addition, ap-

---

This research supported in part by a grant from the Grant Foundation, New York, New York, and by grants from the Social Science Divisional Research Committee, the University of Chicago, and the Spencer Foundation to the Department of Education of the University of Chicago.

pear to be more creative than children in comparison groups of well parents (Heston, 1966; Kaufman, Grunebaum, Cohler, & Gamer, 1979).

When considered in the context of complex interactions with genetic factors, socialization processes are of significance, more generally, in understanding the subsequent development of the children of mentally ill mothers. Maternal mental illness can be considered as a consequence of the failure to adapt successfully to the adult social roles of housewife, mother, and wife (Cohler, Grunebaum, Weiss, Robbins, Shader, Gallant, & Hartman, 1974; Cohler, Robbins, Hartman, Shader, Grunebaum, Weiss, & Gallant, 1975; Cohler & Grunebaum, 1982; Weissman, Paykel, & Klerman, 1972). Comparative study among mentally ill and well mothers of the impact of this role strain on both the mother–child relationship and the child's subsequent cognitive and social development provides important information regarding socialization processes, as well as better understanding of the problems experienced by both parents and children in contemporary society (Campbell, Converse, & Rodgers, 1976; Jacobson, Kaij, & Nilsson, 1965; Yalom, Lunde, Moos, & Hamburg, 1968). Even such factors as the inevitable separation accompanying maternal hospitalization for mental illness provide important information about the impact of parental separation on the child's development, not just in infancy, but across the preschool and school years (Rice, Ekdahl, & Miller, 1971). Such information is useful in understanding the dynamics of the parent–child relationship, as well as in understanding the impact of parental illness, including the separations that often accompany such illness, on the child's own development (Rutter, 1966).

Not only such factors as role strain or rehospitalization, but also factors associated with the very nature of the illness itself may have a significant impact on the child's development. For example, study of schizophrenic parents and their offspring provides a model for understanding more generally the impact of parental cognitive processes on the child's cognitive development. Since schizophrenia is viewed as essentially a disturbance of the thinking processes (Shakow, 1963; Silverman, J., 1964) and since the ability to selectively attend to stimuli (Freud, S., 1911; Gardner, Holzman, Klein, Linton, & Spence, 1959; Schachtel, 1954) and to sustain this attention over a period of time, has been shown to reliably differentiate between schizophrenic patients and both nonschizophrenic patients and well comparison groups, it has been assumed that genetic and environmental factors combine to increase the likelihood that the children of schizophrenic mothers would themselves show greater impairment than the children of well mothers on measures of attention. Indeed, a number of studies have found support for this hypothesis (Asarnow, Steffy, MacCrimmon, & Cleghorn, 1977; Erlenmeyer-Kimling, 1975,

1977; Fish, 1963; Fish & Alpert, 1962, 1963; Gallant, 1972a,b; Herman, Mirsky, Ricks, & Gallant, 1977; Marcus, 1972; Mednick & Schulsinger, 1968; Mednick, Schulsinger, Teasdale, Schulsinger, Venables, & Rock, 1978; Rutschmann, Cornblatt, & Erlenmeyer-Kimling, 1972).

In addition to this test of the attention hypothesis, there has also been some comparative study of general intellectual ability among the children within schizophrenic and nonschizophrenic groups that shows that the children of chronically schizophrenic mothers have both a lower intelligence quotient than children in nonschizophrenic and well groups (McClellan & Pugh, 1962; Mednick & Schulsinger, 1968), and also greater intra-test scatter (Gallant, 1972a).

Largely because schizophrenia is viewed as a cognitive disturbance, there has been much less concern with the socioemotional development than with the cognitive development among the children of schizophrenic mothers (Garmezy, 1978b). Reports from Mednick's research group (Higgins, 1966, 1968) do show increased social maladjustment among children of schizophrenic mothers as contrasted with the children of well mothers. Research reported by Beisser, Glasser, and Grant (1967), Rolf (1972) and Rolf and Garmezy (1974) failed to find very striking differences in social adjustment, as rated by classroom teachers, of the children of schizophrenic and psychiatrically ill neurotic mothers, although the adjustment of children in both groups was more impaired than that of children of well mothers. Rolf's study, which employed both teacher and peer ratings, did show that teachers tended to rate daughters of schizophrenic mothers as more antisocial, whereas peers rated sons of schizophrenic mothers as more antisocial and more like the group of antisocial children included in this study.

In addition to the nearly exclusive concern with the cognitive development rather than with the social development of the children of schizophrenic mothers, most research to date has used as a comparison group families in which the mother has not been psychotic. Such nonschizophrenic patient comparison groups seem to be comprised of mothers showing a neurotic affliction not necessarily serious enough to require prolonged hospitalization. The use of a group of psychotic comparison group comprised of women with an effective disorder (unipolar depression) and their children is of interest in determining the differential effects on the child's development of cognitive and affective maternal disturbance. A unipolar psychotic depressed group would control for the factor of psychosis and, quite possibly, for the factor of chronicity as well.

In one of the few studies explicitly using a comparison group of psychotic, multiply hospitalized, depressed mothers, Cohler et al. (1977b) report that the 5-year-old children of depressed mothers show even greater intellectual impairment than do the young children of schizophrenic mothers and also greater impairment on measures of both sustained and selective attention. In a subsequent report, based on the study of somewhat older (8- to 10-year-old) children, this research group reported essentially similar findings (Grunebaum, Cohler, Kaufman, & Gallant, 1978) regarding increased impairment in sustained and selective attention among children of depressed mothers as compared with the children of depressed and schizophrenic mothers; differences in intellectual functioning were not statistically significant, but children of depressed mothers still had lower scores on the Wechsler Intelligence Scale for Children (WISC) than did children of schizophrenic mothers.

To date, there has been little study of the social adjustment of the children of mothers with a psychotic affective disorder, and even less comparative study of the social adjustment of children of schizophrenic and psychotic depressed mothers. Using peer ratings of adjustment, Weintraub, Prinz, and Neale (1978) report few differences between school-aged children of psychotic depressed and schizophrenic mothers, with both groups of children more impaired in social adjustment than children of well mothers. However, the daughters of schizophrenic mothers appear to be particularly deviant in social adjustment.

Anthony has recently addressed the question of the development of children of depressed mothers in a number of provocative clinical papers (Anthony, 1975a,b, 1976a,b, 1977), and Weissman and Siegel (1972) have considered this question of the social adjustment of the adolescent offspring of depressed mothers. Their results suggest that the increased substance abuse within this group of offspring of depressed mothers may result from the attempt to provide stimulation and involvement that had been missing from the mother–child relationship. It is interesting to note that Weissman and Siegel's formulation is unique in focusing our concern away from group differences toward the question of the dynamics of the parent–child relationship itself.

Recent reports of the adjustment of school-aged children whose parents have been hospitalized for a unipolar psychotic disturbance show that these children also manifest depressive symptoms. Welner, Welner, McCrary, & Leonard (1977) report that, in contrast with the children of well parents, children of psychotic depressed parents (principally mothers) showed increased sadness, apathy, and both hypochondriacal and suicidal concerns. McKnew, Cytryn, Effron, Gershon, and Bunney (1979), studying the adjustment of a group of children of psychotic depressed parents but without any control group, report that the boys of depressed parents are particularly likely to show such sustained depressive symptoms over a 4-month period between interviews. Such findings are consistent with previous case reports that have suggested that depressed children are particularly likely to have depressed mothers (Pozanski & Zrull, 1970; Schechtman, Gilpin, & Worland, 1976).

The present chapter is concerned with the somewhat neglected question of the impact of maternal mental illness on the child's social adjustment and with the differential impact of schizophrenic and affective disturbance on childhood social adjustment. In addition, this chapter seeks to determine the relationship between aspects of maternal and child social adjustment among schizophrenic, depressed, and well mothers and their school-aged children.

|| METHOD OF STUDY

|| The Groups

The findings presented in the present chapter are based on data collected during the follow-up phase of a larger study in which intensive home nursing aftercare was provided for mentally ill (psychotic) mothers with young children following the mother's discharge from participating psychiatric hospitals (Grunebaum, 1977). The focus of this intervention study was on helping the mother to function more effectively in her adult roles as wife, housewife, mother, and member of her own extended family and on preventing rehospitalization (Table 5-1).

Mothers in the mentally ill and well comparison groups were contacted approximately 4 years after the original study regarding participation in the follow-up study, and 41 percent of the mentally ill and 45 percent of the well mothers agreed to take part in the follow-up study.* The groups of mentally ill and well mothers agreeing or refusing to participate were, in each instance, quite comparable. Among mothers in the mentally ill group, chronicity of adjustment or success in the previous intervention

---

*The present study includes eight children of mentally ill women and five children of well mothers who had originally participated in normative studies of measures of cognitive functioning, eight children of mentally ill women and six children of well mothers who had participated in a pilot study of an intelligence measure, and six children of mentally ill mothers and seven children of well mothers who had participated in other observational studies of mothers and children collaborating in the solution of various cognitive tasks as a part of a scheme for evaluating the mother–child relationship. In addition, eight children of mentally ill mothers had participated in studies of intellectual functioning in a variety of experimental mother-present and mother-absent conditions (Gamer, Gallant, & Grunebaum, 1976).

Table 5-1
Background Characteristics of Schizophrenic, Depressed, and Well Mothers and Their Children

	Groups							
	Schizophrenic ($N = 18$)		Depressed ($N = 12$)		Well ($N = 22$)			
Measure*	Mean	SD	Mean	SD	Mean	SD	Test	p
Mother								
Husband's occupation	4.3	2.2	4.0	1.2	3.7	1.6	$(F) = 0.34$	NS
Husband's education	3.3	1.6	4.1	2.0	3.5	1.6	$(F) = 0.93$	NS
Own education	3.7	0.8	3.9	0.9	3.5	0.8	$(F) = 0.80$	NS
Social status	3.2	1.4	3.0	1.3	3.0	1.0	$(F) = 0.07$	NS
Own age	4.4	1.1	4.2	0.8	4.3	1.5	$(F) = 0.08$	NS
Shipley vocabulary scale	27.0	10.1	30.0	4.9	32.6	4.0	$(F) = 2.50$	NS
Chronicity of adjustment	2.1	0.8	1.7	0.7			$(t) = 1.30$	NS
Prognosis/ rehabiliation	2.9	1.5	4.0	1.4			$(t) = 1.95$	NS

Proportion (number) rehospitalized past year	31 (5)		50 (6)				$(x^2) = 0.70$	NS
Days hospitalized	82.94	94.9	86.5	60.9			$(t) = 0.01$	NS
Total hospitalizations	1.6	2.2	1.5	1.7			$(t) = 0.02$	NS
Children								
Age in months	115.6	25.13	107.9	24.2	106.7	23.8	$(F) = 0.68$	NS
WISC verbal scale	115.6	15.46	105.9	16.09	114.2	13.88	$(F) = 1.54$	NS
Number boys/girls	8/10		5/7		13/9		$(X^2) = 1.28$	NS

*For the variables measuring husband and wife *education, occupation, and social status,* a 7-point scale was used (1 = higher status, greater educational attainment; for *own age,* an 8-point scale was used (1 = age less than 20, 8 = age 50 or greater); for mother's verbal *intelligence,* scores were based on the vocabulary scale of the Shipley Institute of Living scale; for scales of chronicity, a 3-point rating scale was used (1 = acute, 3 = chronic); for prognosis, a 6-point rating scale was used (1 = good prognosis, 6 = poor prognosis).

project was associated with agreement to participate in the follow-up study.† Within the group of well mothers, only the mother's own age differentiated between women participating and not participating in the follow-up research (t = 2.94; p <.01).

All the children had been seen at least once in the original study. However, since some of these children were brothers or sisters of the youngest or target child, as defined by the original research, slightly different kinds of information had been obtained from these children. Some children had participated in the pretest studies used to create the final instruments developed for the first phase of the research, whereas others had participated in studies of children other than the youngest who were within a particular age group and thus suitable for supplementary studies of mentally ill and well mothers and their young children. For this reason, the present chapter considers only data obtained in connection with the follow-up study.

The final group of mentally ill women included 18 who, 4 years previously, had been diagnosed as schizophrenic (8 boys and 10 girls), 12 women earlier diagnosed as having a unipolar affective psychosis (5 boys and 7 girls), and 22 well mothers (13 boys and 9 girls).‡ As Table 5-1 shows, the three groups are well equated in terms of maternal social class and age and, within the two groups of mentally ill mothers, regarding chronicity of illness. The groups of children were equated on age and verbal intelligence, and the proportion of boys and girls within each group was not significantly different.

|| The Measures

|| *Intelligence*

A brief screening measure of the mother's current level of intellectual functioning was obtained with the use of the Shipley scale (Western Psychological Services, 1963). This self-administered and objectively scored measure consists of 20-item vocabulary and abstraction scales in which the subject must determine a pattern of responses and complete the pattern. Several investigators have reported correlations between this mea-

†Copies of the table showing mean and standard deviations on these background characteristics for mentally ill and well mothers participating and not participating in the follow-up study are available without cost from the first author.

‡Each woman within the patient group had been seen individually by two psychiatrists who then used information obtained from this interview and hospital records to make independent appraisal of diagnosis and chronicity of disturbance. Interjudge agreement of at least 91 percent was obtained between these two independent assessments, and discrepancies between the two independent rathers were resolved by conference.

sure and the full-scale Wechsler Adult Intelligence Scale (WAIS) score in the 80 and 90 percentiles (Cohler, Weiss, & Grunebaum, 1970), making this a suitable measure for estimating verbal intelligence. Children in each of the three groups were individually administered the 1970 revision of the WISC. In the present study, this instrument was scored only for the verbal subscale.

|| *Social Adjustment*

Mothers were individually administered the Strauss–Carpenter interview (Strauss & Carpenter, 1972) of social functioning by a psychologist with several years of experience interviewing mothers for the larger project of which the present study is a part.§ Based on respondents' replies to a series of semistructured interview questions derived by Strauss and Carpenter for use in a large international study of diagnosis in schizophrenia, an outcome scale had been devised that reduced a large amount of information to five specific scales that can be reliably rated: (1) adjustment to occupational demands, including the role of homemaker; (2) fullness of life and use of recreation and leisure; (3) frequency of interpersonal contact; and (4) extent of satisfaction derived from interpersonal relationships. In addition to these four specific scales, an overall evaluation was made of the patient's present status.

These scales were complemented by an evaluation of present physical health and the scale developed by Strauss and Carpenter to tally the number of rehospitalizations (referring in the present study to those in the 4 years since the previous interview). The patient's own report of previous hospitalizations was tallied against information obtained for each patient from participating state and private psychiatric hospitals in the greater Boston area. Previous research with these scales of maternal social adjustment based on a semistructured interview has shown interrater correlations between .87 and .96.

Measures of social adjustment among the children of these mentally ill and well mothers were derived from structured interviews regarding the child's adjustment that were administered to the mothers themselves, together with structured interviews administered to the children in each group. The mother interview of child social adjustment was based on the Rochester Adaptive Behavior Interview (RABI) developed by Fred Jones (1978) for use in the "parent investigation" of the Rochester collaborative

---

§The interviewer was obviously not blind to the psychiatric status of the mothers in the study since women both volunteered information on their experiences since the last contacts with project staff in the Intensive Nursing Aftercare Study and were explicitly asked about the number of rehospitalizations at the conclusion of the interview. However, the interviewer *was* blind to the specific diagnosis of the particular mothers in the formerly hospitalized group.

high-risk study (Romano & Geertsma, 1978). This instrument consists of a series of items with forced-choice alternatives regarding the child's behavior at home, at school, and with friends. Summary scores are created on the basis of the sum of specific items in each of four areas of functioning: (1) school achievement, (2) sociability with friends, (3) behavior at home and with parents, and (4) evidence of specific symptoms of behavioral disturbance. Two additional scales were included for the present study along with these summary scales: extent of participation in family routines and creative individuality, based on the kind and number of hobbies and other activities that mothers reported for their children.

The childrens' interview was conducted by the project research assistant and focused on the child's own report, based on items with specified alternatives regarding school; most and least liked subjects; number of friends; most and least enjoyed games and active sports; nature and kinds of hobbies and other intrinsically satisfying activities; chief problems, worries, and concerns; and the child's perception of the nature and extent of problems at home, specifically, problems perceived with parents.[‖] The "three wishes" question traditionally used in diagnostic assessment of children was also administered. Wherever possible, findings are discussed separately for boys and girls within each of the three maternal diagnostic groups.

|| FINDINGS

|| Maternal Social Adjustment

It was expected that, as contrasted with the women in the well comparison group, both groups of formerly hospitalized women would show a less satisfactory adjustment. As can be seen from Table 5-2, which presents the findings obtained with the Strauss–Carpenter scales, the three groups were differentiated at a highly significant level. Only in terms of frequency of contact with significant others are there no significant group differences.

Of greater interest in the present context is the possible difference in adjustment within the two groups of formerly hospitalized mothers. Except in terms of physical health, ratings for the group of depressed mothers are lower on each scale than those for schizophrenic mothers; however, only in the case of the overall evaluation are the two groups differentiated at less than the conventional .05 significance level.

[‖]Copies of the interview used with the children are available without cost from the first author.

Table 5-2
Comparison of the Social Adjustment of Schizophrenic, Depressed, and Well Mothers

	Groups							
	Schizophrenic (N = 18)		Depressed (N = 12)		Well (N = 22)			
Measure*	Mean	SD	Mean	SD	Mean	SD	3 group† F Ratio	2 group‡ t test
Economic and occupation adaptation	3.0	0.9	2.8	1.1	3.5	0.7	3.42§	0.65
Recreation and use of leisure	2.3	0.9	2.3	1.1	3.1	0.8	4.71§	0.17
Reported physical health	1.9	0.8	2.4	0.7	1.4	0.5	8.53‖	1.63
Frequency of social contact	3.3	1.0	2.7	1.8	3.5	0.8	2.04	1.22
Satisfaction in interpersonal relationships	2.0	1.2	1.8	1.6	3.4	0.9	8.73‖	0.47
Overall evaluation of functioning	2.4	1.4	1.2	0.6	3.7	0.7	26.39‖	2.79‖

*For ratings of social adjustment, scores range from 0 to 4, with a higher score reflecting more satisfactory adjustment.
†Comparing schizophrenic, depressed, and well mothers.
‡Comparing schizophrenic and depressed mothers.
§$p < .01$.
‖$p < .001$.

Childrens' Social Adjustment

Maternal Evaluation

Maternal report of the child's social adjustment is shown in Table 5-3. Findings regarding social adjustment among the children are more complex than for the mothers, particularly within the two groups of children of formerly hospitalized women. With the exception of relations with friends, diagnostic group differences appear for each of these measures of social adjustment. Schizophrenic mothers report more adequate school adjustment than do those in the two other groups. On the basis of maternal report, boys of depressed mothers appear to be more impaired than girls in their adjustment both at home and at school and to show a larger number of symptoms overall characteristic of a behavioral disorder. Well mothers report an even greater number of symptoms for their boys than do schizophrenic mothers. Depressed mothers report their boys as participating much less in family life than do mothers in the two other groups, accounting for the diagnostic group difference on the measure of participation in family life. Finally, it should be noted that schizophrenic mothers rate their children as more creative than do either depressed or well mothers (Table 5-3).

Within the two groups of mentally ill mothers, there are a greater number of differences reported for the child's adjustment than for the social adjustment of the mothers themselves. Children of depressed mothers are described as significantly less well adjusted than children of schizophrenic mothers on those items that concern school and achievement, cooperative behavior at home, symptoms, and participation in family life. Within these two groups, as across the three groups, sex differences are also found in reports of adjustment to school, with boys showing greater difficulty in making a satisfactory adjustment than girls.

Considering the child's own report of behavior at school and at home, differences among children whose mothers were classified as depressed, schizophrenic, or well are much less clear than as reported by the mother herself. In Table 5-4, results are shown for the boy's own self-reported adjustment suggest little association between maternal diagnostic group and self-reported adjustment. Although all the boys of schizophrenic mothers have a hobby, only a majority of the boys of well mothers and a minority of the boys of depressed mothers have a hobby. All the boys of the schizophrenic mothers report problems at home, as contrasted with a small number of reports of problems at home among boys within the depressed group. A majority of the boys of well mothers also reported problems at home, showing that marital and intergenerational conflict is not limited to families in which a parent has been previously hospitalized for mental illness.

Table 5-3

Comparison of Boys and Girls of Schizophrenic, Depressed, and Well Mothers on Measures of Social Adjustment

	Group																	
	Schizophrenic				Depressed				Well				Comparison of Groups			Within Mentally Ill Groups		
	Boys (*N* = 8)		Girls (*N* = 10)		Boys (*N* = 5)		Girls (*N* = 7)		Boys (*N* = 13)		Girls (*N* = 9)							
Measure*	Mean	SD	Mean	SD	Mean	SD	Mean	SD	Mean	SD	Mean	SD	*F* Ratio Sex	*F* Ratio Group	*F* Ratio Sex by Group	*F* Ratio Sex	*F* Ratio Group	*F* Ratio Sex by Group
School and achievement	17.00	3.56	16.11	3.66	25.00	7.07	17.83	3.71	20.69	4.91	15.78	2.33	11.41‡	4.96‡	2.05	5.32‡	7.75†	3.23
Relationships with friends	16.57	7.32	15.33	2.12	16.00	2.92	15.83	2.14	16.62	3.93	15.67	3.20	0.43	0.01	0.07	0.01	0.17	0.10
Cooperative and social behavior at home	34.86	10.11	34.79	4.69	42.80	7.69	38.83	5.35	36.62	4.35	30.89	4.60	3.24	5.92‡	0.85	0.52	4.57†	0.48
Lack of symptom of disorders	49.43	10.57	48.22	6.28	59.40	10.60	56.17	6.65	55.92	10.62	49.89	5.01	1.82	4.00†	0.92	0.44	7.19‡	0.09
Participation in family life	6.14	1.95	6.57	1.42	8.60	1.14	7.17	1.17	6.69	0.95	6.22	1.64	1.42	5.61§	1.63	0.76	6.83‡	2.47
Overall creative individuality	2.75	0.71	2.30	0.68	2.00	0.71	2.14	0.38	2.08	0.49	1.89	0.33	1.04	4.33‡	1.13	0.41	3.60	1.54

*Summary Scores based on RABI; higher scores indicate less satisfactory adjustment; scores on creative individuality range from 1 to 4, with a higher score showing greater creativity.

†$p < .05$.

‡$p < .01$.

§$p < .001$.

Table 5-4
Present Adjustment and Behavior at School and at Home Among the Boys of Schizophrenic, Depressed, and Well Mothers

Child Interview Item	Mother Diagnostic Group				
	Schizophrenic % (n)	Depressed % (n)	Control % (n)	x^2	p
How are things at school?					
Good	63 (5)	20 (1)	31 (4)		
OK	25 (2)	80 (4)	39 (5)		
Bad	13 (1)		31 (4)		
				6.19	NS
Number of friends reported					
Few	25 (2)		31 (4)		
Some	38 (3)	80 (4)	54 (7)		
Many	38 (3)	20 (1)	15 (2)		
				3.61	NS
Whom do you play with after school?					
Others	63 (5)	40 (2)	31 (4)		
Alone	13 (1)	40 (2)	46 (6)		
Varies	25 (2)	20 (1)	23 (1)		
				2.89	NS
When seen best friend last?					
Within a day or so	38 (3)	60 (3)	32 (3)		
Within last week	13 (1)	40 (2)	31 (4)		
Longer than a week	50 (4)		46 (6)		
				4.86	NS
Favorite game					
Team	13 (1)	40 (2)	46 (6)		
Group	38 (1)	60 (3)	15 (2)		
Twosome	38 (3)		39 (5)		
Alone	13 (1)				
				8.34	NS
First of three wishes					
Person oriented wish			8(1)		
Magical or thing oriented	100 (8)	80 (4)	85 (11)		
Can't say		20 (1)	8 (1)		
				2.78	NS
Are there problems at home?					
Yes	100 (8)	20 (1)	62 (8)		
No		80 (4)	39 (5)		
				8.87	< .02

Child Interview Item	Mother Diagnostic Group				
	Schizophrenic % (n)	Depressed % (n)	Control % (n)	x^2	p
What do you worry most about?					
School problems	13 (1)	33 (1)	40 (4)		
Getting along with family	63 (5)		20 (2)		
Inner fears (phobias)	25 (2)	67 (2)	40 (4)		
				5.79	NS
Do you have a hobby?					
Yes	100 (8)	40 (2)	70 (9)		
No		60 (3)	31 (4)		
				5.83	< .06
Preference for doing things					
With others	63 (5)	60 (3)	69 (9)		
Alone	38 (3)	40 (2)	31 (2)		
				5.71	NS
Favorite kind of activity					
School related	25 (2)		8 (1)		
Outside of school	75 (6)	100 (5)	92 (11)		
				2.12	NS

Within the group of girls of schizophrenic, depressed, and well mothers, as Table 5-5 shows, there was only one item, preference for solitary versus shared activities, where there was a significant association with diagnostic group; a greater proportion of the girls of depressed mothers than of those in the two other groups preferred solitary to joint activities.

Relationship Between Mother and Child Assessments of Adjustment

Findings from maternal reports suggest that the children of depressed mothers are less well adjusted than children within the two other groups. It is not clear whether this finding is a result of maternal psychopathology itself. It is likely that the depressed mother's mood disturbance could lead her to be particularly critical of her child, viewing the child's adjustment as less satisfactory than among either schizophrenic or well mothers. The denial that is a defense so characteristic of schizophrenia might well lead the schizophrenic mother to underestimate the extent of the psychopatho-

Table 5-5
Present Adjustment and Behavior at School and at Home Among the Girls of Schizophrenic, Depressed, and Well Mothers

	Mother Diagnostic Group				
Child Interview Item	Schizophrenic % (n)	Depressed % (n)	Control % (n)	x^2	p
How are things at school?					
Good	56 (5)	43 (3)	44 (4)		
OK	22 (2)	14 (4)	22 (2)		
Bad	22 (2)	43 (3)	33 (3)		
				0.86	NS
Number of friends reported					
Few	22 (2)		22 (2)		
Some	67 (6)	71 (5)	67 (6)		
Many	11 (1)	29 (2)	11 (1)		
				2.85	NS
Whom do you play with after school?					
Others	70 (7)	71 (5)	67 (6)		
Alone	10 (1)	29 (2)	22 (2)		
Varies	20 (2)		11 (1)		
				2.25	NS
When seen best friend last?					
Within a day or so	50 (5)	14 (1)	44 (4)		
Within last week	10 (1)	57 (4)	22 (2)		
Longer than a week	40 (4)	29 (2)	33 (3)		
				5.16	NS
Favorite game					
Team	10 (1)	14 (1)			
Group	60 (6)	43 (3)	56 (5)		
Pair	30 (3)	43 (3)	33 (3)		
Alone			11 (1)		
				3.48	NS
First of three wishes					
Person oriented wish	10 (1)	14 (1)			
Magical or thing oriented	90 (9)	86 (6)	89 (8)		
Can't say			11 (1)		
				3.06	NS
Are there problems at home?					
Yes	60 (8)	100 (7)	67 (6)		
No	40 (4)		33 (3)		
				3.64	NS

Child Interview Item	Mother Diagnostic Group: Schizophrenic % (n)	Depressed % (n)	Control % (n)	x^2	p
What do you worry most about?					
School problems	25 (2)	29 (2)	43 (3)		
Getting along with family	25 (2)	29 (2)	29 (2)		
Inner fears (phobias)	50 (4)	43 (3)	29 (2)		
				0.86	NS
Do you have a hobby?					
Yes	60 (6)	43 (3)	44 (4)		
No	40 (4)	57 (4)	56 (5)		
				0.65	NS
Preference for doing things					
With others	40 (4)	29 (2)	89 (8)		
Alone	60 (6)	71 (7)	11 (1)		
				8.60	< .02
Favorite kind of activity					
School related	13 (1)	40 (2)			
Outside of school	88 (5)	60 (3)	100 (8)		
				4.05	NS

logy among her offspring. For this reason, a more detailed study was carried out on the relationship between maternal psychopathology and both maternal and child reports of adjustment.

Maternal Adjustment and Perceptions of Child Adjustment

The first issue concerns the association between present maternal social adjustment and psychopathology and maternal reports of child adjustment across the three groups (Table 5-6). Within the schizophrenic group, although overall maternal functioning is highly correlated with the several scales of psychosocial adjustment within the mother generation, there is little relationship between this summary measure and separate aspects of the child's functioning. Mothers rated as more successful in the use of leisure report better school adjustment for their children. Mothers rated as obtaining greater satisfaction from interpersonal relationships reported both the child's relationships with peers and the child's present adjustment as more satisfactory.

Table 5-6
Correlation Between Indices of Maternal Adjustment and Between Indices of Maternal Adjustment and Reports of the Adjustment of the "Target" Child Within Schizophrenic, Depressed, and Well Groups

	Measure of Maternal Adjustment						
	Economic and Occupational	Recreation and Leisure	Physical Health	Frequency Social Contacts	Satisfaction from Relationships	Overall Functioning	Rehospitalization
	Schizophrenic Group (N = 18)						
Mother Rating							
Economic/occupational							
Recreation/leisure	.51†						
Physical health	.55†	.39					
Frequency social contacts	.74‡	.56†	.42†				
Satisfaction from relationships	.62†	.32	.68‡	.65‡			
Overall functioning	.85§	.61†	.75‡	.56†	.71‡		
Rehospitalizations	−.26	−.36	−.35	−.08	−.38	−.45	
*Child Adjustment**							
School and achievement	−.06	.46†	.04	.10	.13	.18	−.24
Relations with friends	.26	.38	.06	.30	.49†	.28	.08
Cooperative behavior at home	−.08	.33	.61†	−.33	−.01	−.18	−.21
Lack of symptoms	.03	.19	−.08	.01	.56†	.21	.03
Participation in family life	.18	.03	.12	.22	.17	−.00	−.01
Overall creativity	.47†	.39	.06	.47†	.12	.31	.18

Depressed Group ($N = 12$)

Mother Rating							
Economic/occupational							
Recreation/leisure	.59†						
Physical health	−.21	−.03					
Frequency social contacts	.36	.39	.41				
Satisfaction from relationships	.56	.47	.40	.77‡			
Overall functioning	.76†	.52‡	.03	.24	.34		
Rehospitalizations	−.39	−.76‡	−.22	−.20	−.36	−.51	
*Child Adjustment**							
School and achievement	.06†	.69†	.14	−.01	−.15	.60†	−.80‡
Relations with friends	.49	.50	.15	.06	.22†	.78‡	−.63†
Cooperative behavior at home	.62† .	.56	.04	.36	.00	.39	−.07
Lack of symptoms	.42	.60	.33	.39	.23†	−.30	−.17
Participation in family life	.60†	−.31	.54−	−.59	−.51	.33	.14
Overall creativity	.49	.43	−.38	.23	.47	.17	−.23

(continued)

Table 5-6 (continued)

	Measure of Maternal Adjustment						
	Economic and Occupational	Recreation and Leisure	Physical Health	Frequency Social Contacts	Satisfaction from Relationships	Overall Functioning	Rehospitalization
			Well Group (N = 22)				
Mother Rating							
Economic/occupational							
Recreation/leisure							
Physical health	.46†						
Frequency social contacts	−.25	−.05					
Satisfaction from relationships	.14	.55†	.37				
Overall functioning	.16	.56‡	.39	.78§			
Rehospitalizations	.48†	.63‡	.49†	.18	.14		
*Child Adjustment**							
School and achievement	.30†	.01	.31†	.29†	−.24	.10	
Relations with friends	.18	.23	−.21	.50†	.42†	.06	
Cooperative behavior at home	.24	.03	.24	.05	−.02	.22	
Lack of symptoms	.21	.19	−.02	.27	.17	.17	
Participation in family life	.06	.02	.42‡	−.05	−.15	.40†	
Overall creativity	−.26	.05	.44‡	−.18	−.15	.31†	

*Scores on the RABI reflected so that a higher score indicates more successful adjustment.

†$p < .05$.

‡$p < .01$.

§$p < .001$.

Within the group of depressed women, not only is the relationship less significant between the composite mother measure of overall functioning and the separate scales of maternal adjustment, but also, these scales show correlations with reports of the child's adjustment quite different from those within the schizophrenic or well groups. More satisfactory adjustment regarding the roles of worker and homemaker is associated with reports of more successful child adjustment both at school and within the family. The greater the number of social contacts reported by the mother for herself, the less she sees her child as involved in ongoing family life. Finally, in contrast with the schizophrenic group, both evaluation of overall maternal functioning and tally of the number of rehospitalizations are significantly related to the reported success of the child's adjustment, with the children of depressed mothers more often rehospitalized and showing less satisfactory overall adjustment reported as showing less successful school adjustment and greater conflict in establishing satisfactory relationships with friends.

Within the well group, greater maternal satisfaction in the use of leisure time and in relationships with others was associated with increased social contact and also with better overall maternal functioning. Increased satisfaction with the homemaker role was also associated with reports of increased social contact, as well as with better physical health. Indeed, this dimension of maternal physical health emerged as more important within this group of well mothers and their children than within either of the two other groups. Better perceived health was associated with more satisfactory adjustment reported for the child both at school and at home and also with increased creativity among these children of well mothers.

Interrelationships Among Child Adjustment Measures

Within the schizophrenic mother group, as well as within each of the two other groups, that maternal report of child adjustment most highly intercorrelated with other child adjustment dimensions was lack of symptoms of a behavior disturbance. This dimension was particularly associated with peer relationships within the schizophrenic group; with social behavior within the depressed group; and with school, peer relationships, and behavior at home within the well group. At least as seen by the mother, adjustment at home, at school, and in peer relationships was much more a unitary phenomenon within the well group than within the two other groups (Table 5-7).

Six dimensions of child self-report were selected, referring to adjustment at school, at home, and with friends, together with the number of

Table 5-7
Intercorrelation Among Social Adjustment Items for Children Within the Groups of Schizophrenic, Depressed, and Well Mothers*

	Rochester Adaptive Behavior Item					
Rochester Adaptive Behavior Item	School and Achievement	Relations with Friends	Behavior at Home	Lack Symptom of Disorders	Participation Family Life	Creative Individuality
Children of Schizophrenic Mothers (N = 18)						
School and achievment		.33	.00	.30	.29	−.18
Relations with friends			.44	.76§	.11	.44
Cooperative behavior at home				.47	.53†	.19
Lack of symptoms of psychological disturbance					.23	.06
Participation in family life						
Overall creative individuality						
Children of Depressed Mothers (N = 12)						
School and Achievement		−.55	.67†	.57	.39	−.08
Relations with friends			.40	.29	−.13	.11
Cooperative behavior at home				.81‡	.17	−.49

Lack of symptoms of psychological disturbance				−.08	−.23
Participation in family life					−.07
Overall creative individuality					
Children of Well Mothers (N = 22)					
School and achievement	.37	.48†	.52†	.11	−.08
Relations with friends		.45†	.70§	.05	.07
Cooperative behavior at home			.68§	.33	.26
Lack of symptoms of psychological disturbance				.19	−.03
Participation in family life					
Overall creative individuality					

*Scores on the RABI reflected so that a higher score indicates more successful adjustment.
† $p < .05$.
‡ $p < .01$.
§ $p < .001$.

Table 5-8
Intercorrelation Among Measures of Child Self-Reported Adjustment for Children of Schizophrenic, Depressed, and Well Mothers

	Child Self-Report of Adjustment					
	Problems at School	Number of Friends	Number of Close Friends	Problems at Home	Hobbies	Seeking Solitary Activities
Within Schizophrenic Group						
Problems at school		−.23	.04	.12	.05	−.04
Number of friends			.08	−.22	.00	−.04
Frequency of contact—closest friend				−.14	−.14	.15
Problems at home					.36	.19
Number of hobbies						.36
Seeking solitary activities						
Within Depressed Group						
Problems at school		−.19	.13	−.15	−.79†	−.48
Number of friends			−.14	−.40	−.29	−.12
Frequency of contact—closest friend				−.60*	−.20	.25
Problems at home					.24	.14

Number of hobbies					.46
Seeking solitary activities					
Within Well Group					
Problems at school	−.10	.07	.04	−61†	−.08
Number of friends		−.06	.01	.03	−.29
Frequency of contact—closest friend			.14	.12	−.47*
Problems at home				.23	.02
Number of hobbies					.03
Seeking solitary activities					

*$p < .05$.
†$p < .01$.

Table 5-9
Correlation Between Child Reports of Social Adjustment and Reports by Mothers of Own and Child Adjustment Across the Three Groups of Schizophrenic, Depressed, and Well Mothers

	Child Self-Report of Adjustment					
Mother Report of Adjustment	Problems at School	Number of Friends	Number of Contacts Best Friends	Problems at Home	Hobbies	Seeking Solitary Activities
Within Schizophrenic Group						
Self						
Economic/occupational	−.26	−.00	.62‡	−.50†	.33	−.27
Recreation and leisure	−.53†	−.29	.50†	−.21	−.21	−.29
Physical health	.18	−.24	−.19	−.46†	.04	−.37
Frequency of social contacts	.17	−.12	.64‡	−.33	−.03	−.40
Satisfaction from relationships	.00	.16	.35	−.39	.12	−.58†
Overall functioning	−.22	.03	.48†	−.37	−.27	−.27
Number of rehospitalizations	.63‡	−.21	−.18	.00	.00	.47†
Child						
School and achievement	−.65‡	−.31	−.18	−.35	.26	−.13
Relations with friends	−.28	−.29	.42	.01	.11	−.30
Cooperative home behavior	.03	.21	.04	.10	−.28	.04
Lack of symptoms/disturbance	−.20	.12	.07	−.25	.22	−.36
Participation in family life	−.43	.50†	.02	−.49†	−.01	−.20
Overall creativity	−.08	.01	.38	.09	.47†	.25

Within Depressed Group						
Self						
Economic/occupational	−.03	.49	.50	−.59†	.35	−.14
Recreation and leisure	−.52†	.62†	.18	−.45	.80‡	−.36
Physical health	.07	.08	−.03	−.18	.02	−.35
Frequency of social contacts	.22	.58†	.10	−.17	.27	−.33
Satisfaction from relationships	.05	.72‡	.20	−.35	.14	−.31
Overall functioning	.03	.17	.29	−.31	.37	−.31
Number of rehospitalizations	.54†	−.22	.22	.09	.29	.03
Child						
School and achievement	−.21	.17	.27	−.76‡	.67†	−.42
Relations with friends	−.38	.11	.66†	−.30	.20	−.31
Cooperative home behavior	−.11	.26	−.40	−.57†	.40	−.38
Lack of symptoms/disturbance	−.34	.33	.03	−.34	.48	−.78‡
Participation in family life	.06	.23	−.44	−.44	.16	−.38
Overall creativity	−.19	.59†	.14	.00	.29	.12

(continued)

Table 5-9 (continued)

Mother Report of Adjustment	Child Self-Report of Adjustment					
	Problems at School	Number of Friends	Number of Contacts Best Friends	Problems at Home	Hobbies	Seeking Solitary Activities
Within Well Group						
Self						
Economic/occupational	.04	.18	.33	−.48†	.15	−.35
Recreation and leisure	−.28	.13	.31	−.45†	.54‡	.07
Physical health	−.20	.44†	−.02	−.08	.03	−.11
Frequency of social contacts	−.17	.06	.13	−.17	.23	.03
Satisfaction from relationships	−.44†	.18	.11	.18	.45†	.05
Overall functioning	−.29	.20	.13	−.34	.39	.05
Child						
School and achievement	−.46†	.30	.39	−.17	.15	−.38
Relations with friends	.06	.06	.51†	−.15	.54‡	.00
Cooperative home behavior	−.31	.18	.12	.11	.03	−.10
Lack of symptoms/disturbance	−.29	.07	.34	.08	.23	.03
Participation in family life	−.29	−.33	.30	−.23	.45†	.05
Overall creativity	−.17	.33	.15	.09	.36†	.05

*Higher scores on the measures of mother adjustment (Strauss & Carpenter, 1972) and reports of the child's adjustment on the Rochester Adaptive Behavior Inventory (Jones, 1978), reflect more satisfactory adjustment. Scores on the child reports of problems at home and at school and of seeking solitary activities reflect less satisfactory adjustment.

†$p < .05$.

‡$p + .01$.

hobbies and interests. The intercorrelations among these measures are shown separately in Table 5-8 for each of the three mother diagnostic groups. Overall, these dimensions appear more independent of each other as reported by the child than as reported by the mother. Among children of depressed mothers, report of problems at home was associated with decreased social contact, and a smaller number of hobbies was associated with a greater number of school problems. Among children of well mothers, this relationship between hobbies and school adjustment shown among children of depressed mothers was replicated; a significant relationship was also reported among children in the well group between the preference for more solitary activity and fewer contacts with friends (Table 5-8).

Child Self-Reports of Adjustment and Both Ratings of Maternal Adjustment and Maternal Report of Child Adjustment

Using the several ordinal measures of child adjustment, together with ratings of maternal psychosocial functioning and the child's adjustment to home and school, it is possible to determine the association within each diagnostic group between child self-report and both staff ratings of maternal adjustment and maternal reports of child adjustment. Particularly within the schizophrenic group, as Table 5-9 shows, there are a number of significant correlations between rated maternal psychosocial adjustment and childrens' self-report, particularly frequency of contact with the best friend. Mothers within this schizophrenic group rated as having a greater number of social contacts have children who report increased contacts with the best friend. Within this group of schizophrenic mothers, rehospitalization is associated both with an increased number of school problems and also with increased preference for solitary activities. Finally, it is interesting to note the correspondence within this group of schizophrenic mothers and their children between the child's school adjustment; mothers who view their children as more creative have children who report a larger number of hobbies and other interests.

Within the group of depressed mothers and their children, maternal report of child adjustment shows some association with the child's own self-report, particularly within the area of social adjustment. Both ratings of the extent of maternal satisfaction in interpersonal relationships, as well as frequency of maternal social contact, are associated with the number of friends that the child reports. Mothers rated as more effective in their use of leisure time have children reporting a greater number of hobbies and interests. Finally, it should be noted that, just as within the other group of mentally ill mothers, frequency of maternal rehospitalization is associated with the child's report of an increased number of problems at school (Table 5-9).

It was expected that the reduced variation in self-reported adjustment problems among children within the well group would lead to lower association between child self-report and both staff ratings of maternal adjustment and maternal reports of child adjustment. A number of interesting correlations between mother and child adjustment, however, were found regarding both problems at home and also hobbies and other interests. As was true within the depressed group, children of mothers rated as having a greater number of intrinsically satisfying activities (recreation and leisure) also reported a greater number of hobbies and other interests. Children of mothers reporting increased problems as homemakers also reported the presence of problems at home. Mothers and children within the well group agreed in their perceptions of both whether the child was having trouble at school and of the extent of the child's social network. As was true within the schizophrenic mother group, the mother's judgment of the child's creativity was significantly related to the child's report of extent of hobbies and interests.

|| DISCUSSION

A major problem in understanding the results we have presented concerns the validity of ratings of maternal adjustment and also of maternal reports of child adjustment. Although Miller (1960) states in his review that mothers can be accurate reporters of the extent of symptoms among their children, he does not take into consideration maternal psychopathology as a factor mediating the accuracy of the report. Particularly within the group of depressed mothers, the guilt and self-accusations so characteristic of this disturbance would be expected to lead these women to overestimate the extent of disturbance present among their children; it is likely that these women consider themselves to be particularly "bad" mothers and having a particularly adverse impact on their children's development. For this reason, it is difficult to know whether the results reported for the RABI are a reflection of real differences among children of depressed, schizophrenic, and well mothers or are largely a function of maternal psychopathology as it affects the accuracy of the mother as a reporter of her child's development.

Reliance on interviews with mothers themselves regarding the child's development poses other problems in addition to those due to the interaction of maternal psychopathology and accuracy of report (Herjanic and Reich, 1982). A number of investigators (Burton, 1970; Mednick & Schaeffer, 1963; Robbins, 1963; Wenar, 1961; Yarrow, Campbell, & Burton, 1968, 1970) have noted the distortions introduced into maternal reports of child behavior due to time itself; selective distortions due to memory are further influenced by such factors as parity and education. In the present research, by emphasizing the present rather than the past as the subject of discussion, by asking for explicit behaviors, and by relying on maximal cooperation of women who have participated in the research over a period of many years, we hoped to minimize such biases.

In projects such as the present one, the New Haven depression in study (Weissman, Orvaschel, & Padian, 1980; Orvaschel, Weissman, Padian, & Lowe, 1981), the high-risk research being carried out by the Rochester colloborative study (Romano & Geertsma, 1978) or the Stony Brook study (Neale & Weintraub, 1975) which also rely on parent interviews of child behavior, problems of method cannot easily be separated from actual findings. One alternative is to use teacher and peer ratings of adjustment, but, as is clear from the findings summarized in Glidewell's (1966) review, teacher ratings also present problems. Teachers are often unreliable judges of child mental health. Since they quickly learn of such potentially troubling events in childrens' lives as maternal hospitalization for mental illness, this knowledge, itself, may bias the teacher toward seeing a larger number of adjustment problems than would exist if the teacher were truly "blind" to the child's home situation.

It is interesting to note that, consistent with Heston's (1966) findings that children of schizophrenic mothers may be more creative than children of well mothers: a higher proportion of boys within the schizophrenic group report hobbies and other interests than boys in the two other groups. In addition, schizophrenic mothers view their boys as more creative than do mothers in the two other groups. This finding points to the need to consider not only possible areas of vulnerability, but also reserves of coping and invulnerability among these offspring of formerly psychotic mothers. Apparently, at least the boys of the schizophrenic mothers are able to make use of their mothers' highly idiosyncratic manner of viewing the world and to integrate this uniqueness in a way that leads to increased talent. In other respects, wherever it was possible to examine findings separately for boys and girls within each of the three maternal diagnostic groups, there were few clear findings suggesting that boys and girls were differently affected by the presence of maternal mental illness, type of disturbance, or frequency of rehospitalization.

Finally, it should be noted that, although the correspondence between maternal and child reports is not extensive, there appears to be greater agreement than might be supposed between mothers and children regarding such basic issues as presence of school difficulties or ease in making friends. Certainly, the correspondence between mother and child report is no greater among well mothers and their children than among mothers and children in the two other groups, suggesting that psychopathology may not necessarily render maternal perceptions of the child's adjustment less accurate than would be expected among well mothers and their school-aged children in the community.

SUMMARY AND CONCLUSION

On the basis of staff ratings of present maternal psychosocial adjustment, maternal reports of the present adjustment of the 8–10-year-old children and the child's own self-reports within families in which the mother had been hospitalized for a schizophrenic or unipolar affective psychosis, and reports of a comparison group of well families in which the mother had never been hospitalized, depressed mothers were rated by interviewers "blind" to specific maternal diagnosis as showing the greatest conflict in their childrens' adjustment as less satisfactory than within the groups of schizophrenic or well mothers and their children. On the basis of child self-report, differences in adjustment across the three groups appear less striking than in consideration of maternal ratings of the child's adjustment at school, at home, and with friends. Boys of schizophrenic mothers report a greater number of hobbies than do boys within the two other groups but also acknowledge a greater number of problems at home.

Although there was not complete agreement between maternal and child reports of the child's adjustment at home, at school, and with friends, there was sufficient correspondence between maternal and child reports to suggest some agreement regarding areas of possible problems. Finally, it should be noted that even though depressed mothers evaluated their childrens' adjustment as less satisfactory than did mothers in the two other diagnostic groups, there were no striking differences across these three mother diagnostic groups in the overall correspondence between mother and child reports of adjustment.

There were few differences reported by the children of schizophrenic, depressed, and well mothers in their own adjustment, although, within each of the two groups of mentally ill mothers, increased frequency of maternal rehospitalization is associated with child reports of increased impairment in school adjustment. However, there was little evidence that maternal psychopathology, itself, had a particularly notable impact on the self-reported social and school adjustment of the children in these groups.

Additional study of this issue of the subsequent adjustment of children whose mothers have previously been mentally ill is of great importance for our understanding of both primary prevention and a means of increasing our understanding of the variety of both genetic and environmental factors that affect the child's psychosocial development. However, it is important to study in greater detail such issues as the means by which the children of mentally ill mothers remain invulnerable to psychopathology rather than only to consider possible evidence of increased vulnerability among these children. At least with regard to schizophrenia, there is some evidence that, rather than merely interfering in the child's adjustment, aspects of the mother's disorder may in some complex manner be related to the development of increased creativity among the children of these schizophrenic mothers. However, more extensive study of this issue, with much larger groups of mothers and children followed over a longer period of time is required to better understand the impact of maternal psychopathology on the child's subsequent development.

6

The Depressed Mother and Her Rebellious Adolescent

Myrna M. Weissman

Depression in a mother can have a serious impact on the entire family and particularly on the adolescent children. Moreover, maternal depression is relatively common. A review of the epidemiologic literature finds few exceptions to the observation that clinical depression is more common in women (Weissman & Klerman, 1977). Its incidence may be increasing, and it is no longer a disorder predominantly of the older woman or the hospitalized. Today, the typically depressed patient is apt to be a woman in her most productive years, married, living at home, and rearing children—often adolescent children. Depression affects the capacity to enjoy life and to carry out the vital tasks of being a parent; however, insufficient attention has been paid to the family dynamics of depressed patients in general or to the relationships with their children in particular. Even less has been written about the relationship between the adolescent children and depressed mothers.

During the course of studying various treatment approaches to depression, we became aware of the social and interpersonal problems of the depressed woman (Weissman & Paykel, 1974). Following these observations we undertook a systematic comparison study of the social adjustment of a group of depressed women, both at the height of illness and at the point of their recovery, and compared them with a group of women who had never been depressed (the controls). All the acutely depressed women's relationships were found to be impaired, but their most intimate relationships, particularly those with their children, were the most impaired when compared with the matched control group. We concluded that an acute depressive illness significantly affected the depressed woman's capacity as a mother. A more intensive clinical study of the depressed mothers and their children at different stages of the family life cycle was then undertaken. This study indicated that a substantial amount of deviant behavior was found in the adolescent children of depressed mothers.

This chapter describes the impact of a depressed mother on her adolescent children and the implication of these findings for treatment intervention. The focus is on the mother because we have studied these problems only among women. Further work is urgently needed in understanding the impact of paternal depression on children.

DEPRESSED PATIENTS AND "NORMAL" NEIGHBORS

The observations were derived from a study of the social functioning of 40 depressed women who were compared with a group of 40 controls in their neighborhood ("normal" neighbors). All the subjects were women between the ages of 25 and 60 years who lived in the greater New Haven (Connecticut) area. The depressed women were the first 40 consecutive patients admitted to a research clinic for the study and treatment of depression. These patients were judged by the treating psychiatrist to have moderate to severe depressive illnesses and no other prominent psychiatric syndromes. The symptoms of depression included feelings of sadness, worthlessness, a tendency to cry, guilt, suicidal feelings, weight loss, and sleep disturbance and were present for at least 2 weeks prior to the interview. The large majority of the depressions met the DSM-II criteria for depressive neurosis. If these patients were to be classified according to the more recent DSM-III, they would receive a diagnosis of nonbipolar, nonpsychotic major primary depression.

The normal-neighbor group was selected from the city directory and resided on streets adjacent to those where the patients lived. They were matched for sociodemographic variables with the patient group. Also, those included were without overt psychiatric disturbance or previous psychiatric history or treatment or serious medical illness.

Clinical data on the mother–child interaction were obtained in the course of the psychiatric treatment of the mothers and during research assessments. Some clinical interviews were obtained with the adolescents of the depressed sample in the course of the mothers' treatment. Information on the adolescents of the control group was obtained during the mothers' research assessments.

Parental role performance of all 80 women was assessed by the Social Adjustment Scale (SAS), which contains 42 questions that measure either instrumental or expressive role performance over the past 2 weeks in six

Table 6-1
Relationship Between Depressed Women and Their Adolescents

Less involved
Impaired communication
Increased friction
Loss of affection
Overall more impaired as parents

major areas of functioning: work as a worker, housewife, or student; social and leisure activities; relationship with extended family; and role as a spouse, a parent, and a member of the family unit. This report focuses on the parental role.

In general, the questions in each area fall into four major categories: the subject's performance at expected tasks, the amount of friction with others, finer aspects of interpersonal relations, and inner feelings and satisfaction. Each question is rated on a 5-point scale with a higher score indicating impairment.

Details of the sampling method, structure, reliability, and scoring of the rating scale can be found elsewhere (Weissman & Paykel, 1974). The depressed and normal women were similar in age, sex, social class, religion, race, marital status, and numbers and ages of children. They were predominantly middle-aged (mean age 42 years), white, Catholic, married, living with their spouse, and from the middle and lower-middle social classes. The average number of children per family was 2.5.

DEPRESSED AND NORMAL WOMEN AS PARENTS

Sixteen of the 40 depressed women and 17 of the 40 normal women had at least one adolescent child living at home. The typically depressed person is sad, apathetic, and listless. Juxtapose these symptoms with the demands of parenthood that require energy, interest, emotional involvement, and affection. As one might expect, acutely depressed parents had considerable difficulties with their children. Compared with the normal neighbors, the depressed women were quite impaired as parents. They were only moderately involved in their children's lives, had difficulty in communicating with the children, reported considerable friction, and expressed a loss of affection toward their adolescents (Table 6-1). The mothers were guilty about their inadequacy but were unable to control these feelings or to change their behavior, and there was anger and resentment at the entire family for making what was interpreted as unfair demands.

In contrast, the normal women usually reported relatively harmonious, involved, and affectionate relationships with the adolescents. We have identified at least four areas of parental dysfunctioning in depression: emotional involvement, communication, affection, and hostility.

|| Involvement and Interest

Acute depression impaired the parents' ability to be involved in their children's lives. For adolescents, this included interest and involvement in school progress, social activities, friends, and the dispensing of discipline.

Irritability, self-preoccupation, and anergia prevented the parents from meeting their children's normal demands for attention. Involvement was limited by the emotional or physical distancing of the parent or by overcontrol; for example, one mother retired to her room when the children came home from school; another regimented household activities, and any deviation from the schedule was met by her harsh reprisal.

|| Communication

Adolescents became less inclined to discuss events or deeper feelings and problems with the depressed parent whose troubled affect and self-preoccupation conveyed disinterest and an unwillingness and inability to listen.

Parent–child relationships became disengaged, and the children either took their problems elsewhere or allowed them to build up. One 14-year-old youngster abruptly stopped attending school during the height of her mother's illness. She had been having academic difficulties, felt that her teacher was unsympathetic to her, and was embarrassed by her own poor performance in the class. She had not discussed the problem at home as she did not wish to overburden her mother and felt that she would not understand. The mother was totally perplexed at the girl's sudden refusal to attend school.

|| Affection

Depressed parents reported a lack of affection for their children that produced feelings of guilt and inadequacy. The mothers worried about these feelings of not being able to love their children or to feel spontaneously warm emotions. Some mothers became frightened about their own hostile feelings toward all the children or, at times, toward one child who was singled out.

Hostility

Contrary to older writings on depression, we have found that acutely depressed patients show increased rather than decreased hostility. This hostility is directed toward intimate family members, spouse, and especially children, and less so toward casual acquaintances or the professionals who are carrying out their treatment. The compliant and obsequious patient in the office can be quite hostile at home. The discrepancy in the patient's affect at home and with strangers may account for the discrepancy in the literature regarding hostility and depression.

Most of the hostility toward the children took the form of irritability; however, at times overt and intense conflicts and physical violence were reported. The conflicts could become quite serious with the adolescent child, especially if the child exploited the parent's helpless state and became rebellious and demanding. As is described later, a substantial minority of adolescents developed problems in school, with friends, or with the law or had an intensification of ongoing problems that predated the parent's depression.

We also observed children who became withdrawn and sad, such as one 14-year-old boy who was afraid to make any comments or requests that would disturb his mother. She had spoken so openly of the helplessness of her life that he was afraid she might kill herself.

At times, the depressed parent's intense rage toward the children was frightening to both the parent and the child. When Mrs. W. came for her weekly appointment, she could barely speak. With a trembling voice she described an incident the evening before. Her daughter had been deliberately defiant and challenging, and the mother couldn't take it any longer. In a fit of rage she held a knife to her daughter's throat, and when she considered the impact of what she had done, the mother felt weak, terrified, and full of remorse.

In general terms, the acute symptoms of depression conflicted with the demands of being a parent. Depression has been described as a signal for nurturance, assistance, and succor. These are the very demands made on parents by their children. At the simplest level, apathetic, sad, and anergic depressed parents are placed in an untenable position of having demands made on them by their children for the help, care, and affection that they themselves require.

ADOLESCENT CHILDREN

What meaning do the parental depressive symptoms have for the child? The writings of Bowlby (1951, 1958, 1960, 1961, 1968, 1969, 1970, 1973, 1977) provide the best conceptual framework for understanding

Table 6-2
Women Reporting Problems with at Least One of Their Adolescent Children

Depressed women	81%
Normal women	12%

both the short-term impact and the long-term consequences of parental depression on children. Many forms of psychiatric disorders result from the malfunctioning of a person's capacity to make and maintain affectional bonds. The pattern on which personal affectional bonds are modeled is determined to a significant degree by events within the family, especially—but not exclusively—during childhood. Many of the intense human emotions arise during the formation, disruption, and renewal of affectional bonds.

Applying these concepts to the depressed mother–child interaction, the eruption of a clinical depression in a parent can be experienced by the child as a disruption of affectional bonds. A number of children developed symptoms in association with the parental depression. For the older child, the parent's withdrawal was felt as a loss of guidance and boundaries and a loss of a model of behavior. Depending on the pervasiveness, severity, and recurring nature of these symptoms and the availability of alternate caretakers, the impact on the child's development could be short-term, subsiding with the parental recovery, or it could be long-term and resistant to change.

Thirteen of the 16 depressed women with adolescents (81 percent) had problems with one or more of their adolescent children; however, only two of the 17 normal women (12 percent) reported having problems with their adolescents. The differences were highly significant (Table 6-2).

The depressed women had 23 adolescent children, 17 (74 percent) of whom had problems (Table 6-3). By contrast, the normal women had 31 adolescents, 3 (10 percent) of whom had problems. The difference between the number of the depressed women's adolescent children and the normal women's adolescent children who had problems was also highly significant ($p<.001$).

Table 6-3
Adolescent Children Reported to Have Problems

Depressed women	74%
Normal women	10%

Table 6-4
Problems in Adolescent Children of Depressed Mothers

Problem	Number of Adolescents Involved* (N = 17)
School difficulties	8
Parental conflicts	8
Involvement with law	5
Drug use	3
Sexual involvement	3
Total	27

*The number of adolescents involved in various problems exceeds the number of adolescents since some adolescents were involved in more than one problem.

In summary, substantially more depressed than normal women had problems with at least one of their adolescents, and substantially more adolescents of the depressed women as compared to the normal women had problems. The kind of problems reported by the mothers varied. In the normal group, one adolescent was illegitimately pregnant, and two were involved frequently in severe verbal clashes with the mother.

The normal women were not without problem children, and some of them discussed how they averted potential difficulties with their adolescents. A 44-year-old woman, the wife of a factory worker, with five children aged 11–18 years living at home, described how she and her husband had dealt with the problems presented by their oldest child. The youth had befriended a group who had prison records and were jobless. He claimed that his parents did not understand him. The parents responded with genuine concern, indicated their strong interest in understanding him, and suggested that they sit down and talk. Several lengthly and emotion-laden discussions ensued. During that time and subsequently, the parents reported an outstanding improvement in his appearance, attitude, and choice of friends.

By contrast, a substantial number of serious behavior problems was found among the adolescents of depressed mothers during the height of the mother's illness (Table 6-4). Some adolescents were involved in multiple problems. School problems and conflict with parents occurred frequently. Eight adolescents were having serious school problems such as truancy, sudden failing grades, and dropping out of school.

Some parent–child conflict might be expected in association with an adolescent's increasing independence; however, extreme conflict was reported for eight of the depressed mothers' adolescents. This conflict included physical or persistent verbal clashes that resulted in three adolescents leaving the home temporarily and one 13-year-old running away for 1 month after an argument with her mother. Five adolescents were involved in legal problems. One, a 15-year-old boy, was put on probation for stealing a bicycle, and four other adolescents were arrested for various difficulties including possession of drugs or weapons and glue sniffing. Three adolescents were involved with drugs, including heroin, LSD, and frequent marijuana use. Three adolescents were involved in sexual difficulties that included promiscuity and homosexuality. A 16-year-old girl became involved in a homosexual relationship during the height of her mother's illness, leaving home to live with an older single woman. Despite all these problems, only two adolescents were receiving psychiatric treatment.

The depressed women displayed little resilience and had difficulty in controlling their own hostility and aggression. They alternated between episodic explosive outbursts and withdrawal. They frequently directed their hostility toward the child. They were unable to define or set limits for their adolescents and either overcontrolled or undercontrolled them. Some mothers were envious of their teenage daughters' developing sexuality and were even competitive with the girl for the attention of the spouse. Rather than providing stability and nurturance to the children, the mothers, when ill, made demands for themselves.

THE DEPRESSED WOMAN AS A PARENT DURING RECOVERY

Clinical data indicated that the adolescent's deviant behavior in most cases was highly related to the mother's acute depression. Statistical assessment of the changes in the behavior of the adolescents as the mothers improved was not available; therefore, we examined the depressed mothers after 8 months of treatment for depression when they were asymptomatic. Comparisons of the parental role performance of the depressed women at the height of symptomatic illness, after treatment when asymptomatic, and with the normal women are shown in Figure 6-1. Only 13 of the 16 depressed patients were assessed at the end of the 8 months since 3 patients had been withdrawn from the study because of clinical relapse.

As shown in Figure 6-1 and described in Table 6-1, the patients at the height of illness (00) were significantly more impaired parents than normal women on all variables. The changes in the parental role performance of the depressed patients from the height of illness (00) to the recovery phase after treatment (08) were not significant on any variables other than the raters' global judgment. When the recovered patients (08) were compared with the normal group, the differences were not significant on any varia-

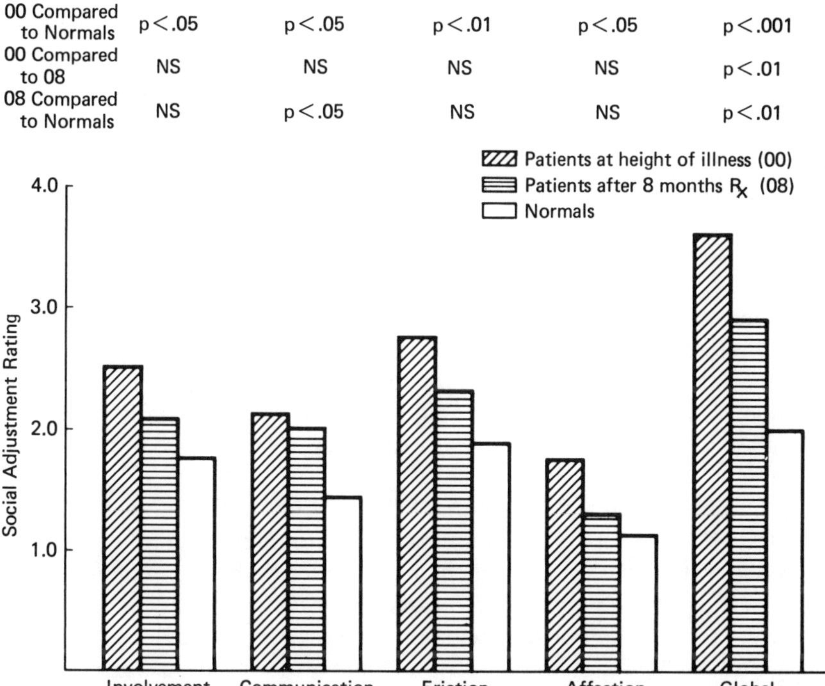

Figure 6-1. Social Adjustment Scale scores at height of illness and after 8 months of treatment: a comparison with normals. (Reprinted with permission from Weissman, M., & Siegel, R. The depressed woman and her rebellious adolescent. *Social Case Work,* 1972, *18,* 563–570. Published by *Family Service Association of America.*)

bles except communication with the adolescent and the raters' global judgment, where the patients were still rated as more impaired.

Figure 6-1 offers a presentation of these results and shows that the depressed patients were somewhat less impaired as parents after 8 months of treatment than they were at the height of their illness but were still more impaired than the normal mothers, especially in communication with their children. After treatment, the depressed women were intermediate in parental performance between their acute illness and the normal state.

After 8 months of treatment for depression, when most of the women were symptomatically recovered, their parental performance had improved considerably in all areas. However, they were still somewhat more impaired than the normal women, especially in their ability to communicate with the children. The adolescents in many cases did respond to the mother's recovery with some decrease in acting out.

Adolescents' Response to Mothers' Improvement

As the depressed mothers recovered, many, but not all, of the problems with their adolescents improved, and many of the children's problems diminished. The ability of the mother to pull herself together, to set limits, to negotiate with the adolescents, and to show genuine interest usually had a salutary effect on the child. Obviously, the youth on heroin did not stop the habit when the mother recovered but did curtail physical abusiveness toward the mother when she had enough energy and self-confidence to make it clear that she would not tolerate it. One 14-year-old had refused to return to school during her mother's illness. When the mother felt better, she began to listen to what was disturbing the daughter in school. The mother was then able to discuss the problem with school officials and worked out a more satisfactory school placement for her daughter.

Another 17-year-old girl responded to her mother's recovery by mobilizing herself to look for employment. The depressed mother's pessimism about the girl's future and chances of ever finding employment had deterred the girl from making any plans for herself. The boy on probation for stealing a bicycle took a paper route to buy his own bicycle and joined a boy's club. The girl involved in a homosexual relationship returned home when the mother was well enough to encourage her to return. Although the girl continued the homosexual relationship, she ceased to live with the woman and began involving herself in heterosexual relationships as well.

A small number of the adolescents who were not involved in deviant behavior did, in fact, become nurturing and maternal to the mother in her illness. The adolescent took over the housework and care of siblings and sometimes intervened between the mother and the more rebellious siblings. Most of the adolescents, however, did not respond to the mother's request for help but were threatened by this request; they tended to exploit her helplessness by further rebellion. A considerable amount of deviant behavior, including problems with school and law, drug abuse, sexual acting out, and hostile clashes with the mothers, was observed in the majority of the adolescent children of the depressed mothers. The extent of this behavior was in sharp contrast to that of the adolescent children of the normal women, where few problems were observed.

Questions can be raised about the temporal relationship between the mother's illness and the adolescent's deviance. Would any mother not become depressed with such problems? In this sample, many of the women had been treated previously for depressive episodes, when the children were younger and without observable problems. Although many of the adolescent problems may not have occurred directly in conjunction with the mother's illness, many of the children had not had a previous history of behavior problems. Much of the children's acting-out behavior increased with the mother's acute illness, and the major part of it decreased with her improvement.

The depressed woman's spouse should be mentioned, as his role was crucial in the perpetuation of a conflictual mother–child relationship. If the spouse aligned himself with the adolescent against the mother, the child's abusive behavior toward the mother increased and was difficult to control even when the mother recovered.

Is the Adolescent Deviance a Masked Depression?

The frequent association of adolescent deviant behavior with adolescent depression has been described by a number of investigators. It has been suggested that acting out and sociopathic manifestations in adolescents are likely to mask underlying depression and take the form of temper tantrums, school drop-outs, truancy, running away, drug use, disobedience, underachievement in school, and promiscuity. Delinquency, especially gang contacts, may combat feelings of helplessness and prevent these feelings from becoming overt. The adolescent's antisocial behavior may be a deliberate attempt by the child to provoke parental condemnation. It allows the parent to focus on such behavior while ignoring long-standing hostilities and allows the child to ward off feelings of loss. Aggressive behavior may be used to ward off depressive feelings and may be considered justified by the adolescent for past grievances toward the parent.

The loss of a parent through death has been observed to interfere with the development of an effective superego since the identification process is considered critical in preventing delinquency among adolescents. Although the depressed mother may be physically present, her withdrawal and detachment may be experienced as a loss by the vulnerable adolescent, a loss not only of her nurturing and interest, but of her direction and control as well. Indeed, she is not psychologically available to guide, lend interest, or comfort. Her pessimism is conveyed and can be assumed by the adolescent, suggesting that the adolescent problems described here may be a form of masked depression.

Because contacts were primarily with the mother, it is beyond the scope of this study to determine the degree of covert depression in the adolescents; however, certain trends are suggestive. The adolescents did experience an object loss previously and might be vulnerable to depression themselves. A number of the adolescents did appear to have a quality of hopelessness characteristic of depression. Although it was suggested that the deviance was a form of masked depression in many of the adolescents, more intensive clinical studies are necessary to confirm this.

|| CLINICAL IMPLICATIONS

There is substantial evidence in this research and in others that maternal depression can have a detrimental effect on children of any age and especially on the developing adolescent. The depressed mother's withdrawal, disinterest, and hostility can exacerbate serious adolescent behavior problems that may not be easily reversible. Therefore, early detection of the maternal depression as well as prompt and appropriate treatment can have an important preventive impact.

|| Detecting Depression in the Parent

Who can detect depression, and how is depression detected? Early detection usually occurs directly with the parent, often by a nonpsychiatric physician or a professional who is not a physician. A case of depression that reaches the psychiatrist is usually not in its earliest stages. Physicians other than psychiatrists, mental health personnel of all disciplines, and those professionals not involved in mental health clinics per se, therefore, are in excellent positions to do early detection. There are many clues to help in the detection of depression. The parent who seems apathetic or listless, has multiple complaints, or is extremely irritable may be harboring depressive symptoms. Direct inquiries such as "Have you felt sad, moody?" or "Have you had difficulty in sleeping?" or "How has your appetite been?" or "Have you felt life is worth living?" are all useful.

If a large-scale, systematic approach to screening for depression is required, there are a number of simple paper–pencil tests for depression that have been widely used and can be incorporated routinely into clinics. These screening tests can be quite useful for detecting persons who may be depressed, but they are not diagnostic tests. They are useful for isolating those persons who are likely to have the disorders from those who most likely do not. All screening tests have a certain chance of failing to detect persons who really are depressed and are falsely negative, or of classifying as depressed those who really are not and are falsely positive. All such screening techniques thus require active clinical follow-up for a more intensive, diagnostic assessment of possible cases.

DETECTING MATERNAL DEPRESSION THROUGH THE CHILD

Personnel who deal with children should be alert to abrupt changes in the child's behavior. These changes may be indicative of a change in the parent's clinical state. The important indicators for children might be development of academic or social problems, a drop in grades, repeated absences, deviant behavior, promiscuity, truancy, and fighting. Although none of these is necessarily specific to parental depression, their sudden presence in a previously well-functioning child may indicate a change in the emotional state of the parent. These signs should be followed up by inquiry with the parent and the child.

Indirect evidence gained from a study of depressed women has shown that hostility directed toward the children, either verbal or physical, is frequent and pervasive during the parent's acute depressive episode. Inquiry into symptomatic status of parents of abused children should be made. If the parent is depressed, another mode of treatment and possible prevention of future abuse may be available.

TREATMENT OF THE PARENT: ACUTE EPISODE

The most promising advance in the treatment of depression has been in the availability of a range of effective antidepressant medications that have demonstrated efficacy (Hollister, 1978). There are now a number of such medications widely available that are relatively safe and can be administered by most physicians, although patients with concurrent medical problems or previous unresponsiveness or who present special diagnostic or management problems should be seen by a psychiatrist. These medications are particularly useful in reducing the acute symptoms of depression, improving mood and sleep, and restoring appetite and energy. Drug-induced remissions take 1–4 weeks, and with symptom reduction comes a resumption of social functioning, although often at a slower pace over the next 2 months.

The antidepressants have by no means replaced psychological treatments (Weissman, 1979). Indeed, there is evidence that one important function of the antidepressant is to sufficiently alter the symptoms so that the patient can begin to engage in psychotherapy, which is the treatment aimed at improving social adaption. In practice, some form of psychological intervention is usually combined with antidepressants, although either treatment may be used independently. There is a wide range of psychological treatments that differ in aim, intensity, duration, and the professional training of the therapist. Generally, the purpose is to provide emotional support and the opportunity for ventilation, to help in dealing with the consequences of the disorder, and to provide an understanding of the maladaptive patterns or antecedents that may have predisposed the parent to the depression.

Whether or not formal psychotherapy becomes part of the treatment plan, there are certain practical issues in the patient's daily life and with the family that should be considered with all patients. Two immediate issues with the acutely depressed parent are the care and the involvement of the family. Detailed questioning about the children and their daily care and the other available caretakers is important. The enlistment of the family may be required, especially if small children are also at home. Families of outpatients may not realize the extent of the patient's incapacity and may perceive the apathy or anergia of depression as laziness and irresponsibility. Clarification of the nature of depression, the treatments used, and the time span for recovery may help to involve the family positively in the treatment and help them to assist in the care of the children. Although families of outpatients may be tolerant of the patient's decreased performance and hopeless affect, daily confrontation with these disorders can be a trying experience, and many families require support.

The astute clinician will realize that the compliant obsequious depressed patient can be quite irritable and hostile at home. Discrete questioning such as "Do the children get you down?" or "Do you tend to pick on them?" or "Can you tolerate the children's noise?" can lift the burden of secrecy from the patient, establish the treatment relationship on a firmer ground, and assist the patient and family in arranging the care of the children.

This type of questioning and planning can be handled by any mental health professional responsible for the care of the patient. The term "approach model" frequently employed in clinics is appropriate. In this model the physician provides and supervises the medication; a nurse, social worker, or other nonmedical professional carries out the psychological counseling.

TREATMENT OF THE PARENT: CONTINUING CARE AND TERTIARY PREVENTION

There is good evidence now that a 6–8-month course of maintenance treatment is valuable in preventing relapse after recovery from the acute symptoms of depression. There is evidence that depressions tend to reoccur so that most patients who have suffered a depression will require continuing available care even beyond the maintenance phase. The care required may be intensive for sustained durations or periodic and not intensive.

During the period following symptomatic recovery, there is opportunity for tertiary prevention that is rehabilitation and achievement of maximal functioning. For most patients, a return to an asymptomatic state and a resumption of normal parental caretaking reduces the parent–child problems and alleviates symptoms in the children. For others, however, where the parent–child relationships have been seriously and chronically impaired or where the adolescent symptoms have become persistent, more is required. It is during this rehabilitative period that parents can begin to consider dealing with the longer-term problems of their children.

It is not uncommon for child guidance referrals to be made or family therapy to be undertaken during this recovery period, as the parents can focus away from their own despair and begin to consider underlying problems in the family or the special needs of a particular child. Social services as well as other social supports that relieve family tensions and pressures should be considered. Mental health workers should recognize the importance of this period for repair, rejuvenation, and reorganization within the family. The dramatic effects achieved by medications quickly and inexpensively can divert the clinician away from helping those families who still require the longer social and psychological interventions. Even among those patients who recover rapidly and whose accompanying family problems resolve, the tendency for depressions to reoccur requires that prompt treatment be available as needed.

7

Depressive Potentials: Interface Between Adolescence and Midlife Transition

Craig L. Johnson and Floyd S. Irvin

Emphasis on the unique demands of certain developmental phases has become fashionable over the last several years. Occasionally the attention paid to these phase-specific analyses has left the arena of fact and bordered on overstatement if not sensationalism; nonetheless, there have been some very useful results from our efforts to recognize those developmental tasks that arise during the life-span. Two phases that have received particular attention are adolescence and what has come to be called "midlife transition," which is a period between early and middle adulthood. What is of interest for this chapter is the recognition that the timing is such that adults who are attempting to negotiate the demands of midlife transition are often the parents of youth who are either amid or approaching adolescence. It is important to recognize the timing of the two transitional periods because the demands of each stage to assess, align, and integrate fundamental issues of identity such as body image, role expectations, and shifting self and object representations can generate substantial turmoil in family systems. Also, since both adolescents and their parents are highly vulnerable during these phases of development, uncharacteristic and often pathological resolutions to the conflicts that each is experiencing can occur at the interface in the family system. For example, it does not seem coincidental that parents who become depressed or angry during this transition often have adolescents who act out by using drugs, becoming delinquent, or running away. Likewise, it does not seem accidental that parents of adolescents often become anxious and uncertain about themselves at a time when this is precisely the struggle that their adolescent offspring is experiencing. Consequently, this chapter represents an attempt to explore more fully the unique interactions that can occur between adolescents and their midlife parents as each seeks resolution to their own developmental conflicts. The discussion is divided into three parts. The first two sections are brief overviews of some of the development demands of adolescence and midlife transition, with special emphasis on the tasks that make each particularly vulnerable to the other. The final section offers a perspective for recognizing and understanding how a series of maladaptive and even destructive resolutions can be forged as the two systems interface.

ADOLESCENCE

Adolescence is often referred to as a crisis stage where a child is suddenly victimized by the growth process. Words such as "tumultuous" and "turbulent" have been used in an attempt to capture the quality of the experience for many of these young people. Although a sizable number of teenagers do have difficulty with at least some phase of the transition, there is an even larger percentage who negotiate the developmental tasks without serious trouble (Offer, 1969). Nonetheless, for those who do struggle, the journey can be long and trying (Lamb, D., 1978).

Like all developmental life stages, adolescence can be arduous, painful, and very frightening. Although the physical attributes of teenagers are admirable in that they reflect the values of the larger adult culture, physical maturation among adolescents is often both deceptive and misleading. As nature would have it—that is, psychological nature—internal self-representations seldom progress at the same rate of development as physical traits (Blos, 1962). Thus many youths who are physically attractive, strong, alert, and charming are at the same time internally perplexed, uncertain, confused, even helpless, immobilized, or permanently incapacitated psychologically.

Adolescence is too often misled by the biological model and hence has been oversimplified by the notion that it is merely that period of life that begins with puberty and ends with the arrival of adulthood. If, however, we avoid the trappings of considering adolescence along chronological parameters, perhaps we can be more sensitive to, even empathic with, the psychological issues germane to this phase of life. Perhaps only then can the internal richness, diversity, and complexity of adolescence be appreciated. Conceptually, adolescence should be considered a frame of mind characterized essentially by the onerous task that one relinquish one's nuclear support system, replacing it with new object attachments.

Although the psychological potential for tolerating the loss of a basic support system may be available during the teen years, the effective integration of the mourning process into one's internal set of self-representations often extends beyond the teen years, even into adulthood. Although the task of accepting another support system is at times eased by the newly arrived powers of abstract reasoning and future-oriented thinking that begins to occur during this phase of the life cycle, it often complicates matters and creates an imbalance that either unnerves or overwhelms the adolescent.

What follows is an attempt to briefly identify some of the tasks that the adolescent must encounter and master in order to continue to grow. The synopsis is not offered as an exhaustive statement regarding all the developmental demands of adolescence. Instead, hopefully it highlights some of the adolescent's developmental challenges in such a way that a comparison can be drawn between similar struggles that their parents may be encountering in their own transitional work.

There is some agreement among clinicians and scholars who work with adolescents concerning the major developmental tasks that confront youth. The psychological requirements for "rite of passage" into young adulthood demands that teenagers trade in the fantasy life of their latency years for a more reality oriented, productive, and practical use of their energies (Erikson, 1968). Moreover, adolescents must relinquish their infantile omnipotence, innocence, and irresponsibility so that they may recognize their limitations, culpability, and duty to the community (Blos, 1967). It is generally agreed on also that youth must learn to negotiate the nuances of both homosexual and heterosexual relationships (Freud, A., 1958). Also, they must learn how to cultivate increasing intellectual capabilities and how to manage their adult bodies, which have reproductive and destructive capabilities dramatically different from when they were children (Inhelder & Piaget, 1958). There is as well the prevailing expectation that youth consolidate the divergent aspects of their experiences into a somewhat consistent and adaptive identity (Erikson, 1950). Finally, adolescents are expected to become increasingly independent by moving beyond the protection and safety of their parents and families to become members of a larger and more diverse society (Anthony, 1969).

The consequences of mastering these phase-specific psychological tasks is that adolescents become adults, a reward that many youth accept with understandable ambivalence. The ambivalence for the adolescent results from the mutually occurring experience of feeling thrilled with the increased opportunity for freedom and expression, yet being frightened by the loss of familiar objects and surroundings. Another change that may be experienced as particularly dangerous is the rapid increase in sexual and aggressive drives. Puberty heralds the emergence of secondary sexual characteristics and an increased height and weight that equips the adolescent with a body capable of adult sexual functioning and aggressiveness. What was once available to them only in fantasy can now actually be enacted both sexually and aggressively. This obviously changes the nature of their relationships, not only with their peers, but especially with their parents. The revival of the well-known oedipal struggles during adolescence takes on a much different flavor as all members of the cast are now capable of playing for keeps. The emergence of these new characteristics, which forces a realignment of the relationship within the family system, may not be welcomed by either the child or the parent (Cohen, D. J., 1974).

An equally ambivalent and potentially disruptive experience is the increasing consolidation of an autonomous identity that is both exciting and frightening for the adolescent. The ability to think, judge, and act on their own is usually welcomed and tenaciously guarded. Although this new autonomy represents the opportunity for freedom, which has never been available to either the parent or the offspring before, it is also a harbinger of the impending separation of the progeny from the childhood role and eventually the nuclear family structure. This is a fragile and precarious time that is marked by anxiety, indecision, and potentially significant loyalty conflicts. It is, psychologically speaking, an "in-between" time for adolescents where they feel pulled in contradictory directions; this conflict is often manifest in the adolescent's erratic and confused behavior. It is as though the exercise of the adolescent's new autonomy in the service of developing object ties outside the family brings a paradoxical sense of loss and fearful insecurity. If the adolescent does not make this motion to the outside, however, the regressive pull of the infantile ties is experienced, which is equally frightening because it threatens to annihilate the meager beginning autonomy. The conscious experience for the adolescent during this back-and-forth time can be one of not belonging anywhere, which is translated into feeling of estrangement, alienation, instability, and perhaps even insufficiency.

The ambivalence, confusion, and instability inherent in the adolescent process can render adolescents particularly vulnerable to outside influence. In an effort to find stable ground amid a sea of freedom and opportunity, they may invite or participate unwittingly in maladaptive behavior along with their parents. If one considers that the parents may also be struggling with their own developmental concerns, the opportunity for pathological interaction increases dramatically. We turn now to some of the themes of midlife transition that affect parents as well as their offspring.

|| MIDLIFE TRANSITION

Like adolescence, midlife transition during adulthood has been referred to as an "in-between" stage. Where adolescence is seen as a passageway between childhood and adulthood, midlife transition is regarded similarly as a passageway between early and middle adulthood. It occurs roughly between the ages of 38 and 48 years, and as with the period of adolescence, words such as "turbulent" and "crisis" have been used to describe the emotional experience. Also, it has been noted that many of the developmental tasks that are characteristic of this midlife transition parallel the tasks of the adolescent transition. This is particularly evident in the midlife adults' struggle to rework their body image, redefine their responsibilities, and reassess their identities. The similarities between the scale and focus of the two transition periods has led some writers to suggest that the term "middle-essence" be coined to describe this period between young and middle adulthood (Stevenson, 1977). Little seems to be gained by adopting such a term except to emphasize that there does seem to be some significant similarities between the two developmental phases.

The reaction of midlife adults to this transition is as varied as that of adolescents (Levinson, Darrow, & Klein, 1978). Many negotiate the stage with little difficulty. For some, however, the developmental demands are quite anxiety producing, perhaps even overwhelming. Stories abound of midlife parents very abruptly making major life changes in reaction to the conflicts aroused during this stage. Some become involved with younger lovers, others totally abandon their homes and family responsibilities, and yet others opt for complete career changes. Overall, recent research has indicated that there is a peak vulnerability during these years to depression (Gurland, 1958; Horn, 1970; Silverman, C., 1968), psychosomatic illness (Blumenthal, 1959; Steiner, 1973), sexual difficulties (Pfeiffer, Verwoldrt, & Davis, 1972), alcoholism (Moon & Palton, 1963), and marital problems (Pineo, 1968; Thurnher, 1976; Wasserman, 1973). Undoubtedly, the increased incidence of these disorders, as well as the sudden appearance of uncharacteristic behavior, is testimony to the intensity of the anxiety connected with the developmental demands of midlife transition.

The literature on midlife transition is relatively new, and there remains a fair amount of disagreement regarding what is believed to occur and what in fact does happen during these years. There is, however, some consensus regarding several psychological tasks associated with this stage. For example, it is generally agreed that midlife adults must reintegrate their body images and accept in this process that the resilience and stamina of their youth is less available to them and that their physical reproductive and destructive potential is waning (Gutmann, 1976; Neugarten & Gutmann, 1968). Moreover, midlife adults must accept increased responsibilities for leadership in their extended families, and in society at large (Levinson, Darrow, & Klein, 1978). Also, they must trade in their pipe dreams, which in effect means giving up the grandiosity and omnipotence of their younger days for a realistic assessment of both their accomplishments and limitations (Cohler, 1978b; Lewinsohn, 1974). Finally, midlife adults must recognize the eventuality of their own mortality (Jacques, 1965) and begin to mourn the loss of their youthfulness, their unrealized dreams, and perhaps even more concretely, the demise of their own parents (Cytrynbaum, Patrick, Stein, & Wilk, 1978).

The rewards for successfully navigating these psychological tasks is that the adult is viewed as more established, mature, and settled. The ambivalence these parents often feel encountering this transition is paralleled only by the ambivalence their adolescent offspring may be simultaneously experiencing about becoming young adults. Some of the anxieties, narcissistic injuries, and grief that are experienced by midlife parents in reaction to these developmental demands bear further exploration.

With age comes a decline in the body's functioning that is particularly evident in its decreasing resilience and recuperative capacity. Both men and women in this age group must find some way to accept the fact that they are becoming more prone to illness and that the length of time for recovery following an illness or injury is longer than it has ever been before in their lives. Also, they must adjust to the fact that they tire more easily, are more forgetful, find it more difficult to learn large masses of information, and have less acute hearing and vision. They gain weight more easily, and once they become out of shape, it takes much more time and effort to regain their muscle tone and fitness than when they were younger. Overall, for most, the abounding energy and resilience of youth is undeniably less available to them. This can be a devastating experience for individuals who have relied in some way on their bodies to demonstrate a sense of mastery in the world or who have received substantial gratification from their appearance.

One hears much these days about professional athletes who become distressed or lost in their late thirties or early forties when it becomes evident that they can no longer contend with younger athletes. Professional athletes only represent the extreme, however, as many middle-aged weekend warriors, tennis hacks, and sandlot stars must grapple with similar issues as they learn that they have lost a step to younger people. The experience of envy, jealousy, competitiveness, and loss, stirred by the realization of the aging process, can be equally devastating for the woman who has always prided herself on her firm figure and unlined face. The slowing of the metabolic process, the natural aging of the skin, and the approach of menopause can often result in added weight, facial lines, and hormonal shifts that these women find difficult to integrate. The pain and even despair connected with these realizations can be exacerbated by the presence of sons or daughters who are at, or approaching, the zenith of their beauty, strengths, and intellectual capabilities. Some of the pathological solutions to the competitive and narcissistic issues that arise between parents and their adolescent offspring during this time are explored more fully in the following sections.

With the increasing awareness of growing older comes a heightened sense of mortality that is often prompted by a shift in time perspective that occurs during these years (Jung, 1969). At this point, the midlife adult generally changes from viewing life in terms of time since birth to time until death (Neugarten, 1979). This can be a dramatic realization. Both the shift in time perspective and heightened sense of mortality that results are often further intensified by the naturally occurring deaths of contemporaries. For the midlife adult, it ever so gradually becomes less shocking when friends near their age die of coronary disease, cancer, or other non-accident-related causes. The deaths of contemporaries and the sense of lost youth can toss the midlife adult into a lengthy and stressful mourning process.

Equally devastating and stressful can be the caretaking of aging parents and the helplessness and sorrow that middle-aged adults experience in watching their own parents progressively deteriorate. The multiple responsibilities of caring for increasingly dependent parents, their own children, and perhaps other members in the extended family, often leave midlife parents feeling overwhelmed and as though the weight of the world is on their shoulders. As a consequence, many parents we see in clinics and hospitals are exhausted, depleted, and angry during these years. Amid these multiple responsibilities, they are often particularly vulnerable to seeking relief from the pressure either through delegating their burdens to others or perhaps more dramatically, escaping them by running away. As we examine in the following section, their adolescent offspring may be likely candidates to aid in this search for relief, either by prematurely assuming adult responsibilities or by enacting the parent's more repressed wishes to act out.

Along with the midlife shift in time perspective and heightened awareness of mortality comes an increased sense of introspection or a turning inward to examine one's situation. This "review," as some writers have labeled it, usually involves an overall midlife assessment. In particular, this period represents a point in one's life where one has a fair idea of what the scale of one's contribution will be and what will actually be accomplished in one's lifetime. For many, this is a period of disillusionment or *de*illusionment, as the discrepancy between the pipe dreams of youth and the reality of one's circumstances is now more difficult to deny or rationalize by projecting dreams into the future. Substantial depression and anxiety can result from the narcissistic injury experienced as a result of this significant assault on the last vestiges of infantile grandiosity and omnipotence. Ambitious and aspiring men and women are anything but invincible during this period, especially if they have become stalled in some career progression (Rosenbaum, 1979). Career changes, divorces, family abandonment, and other efforts to radically redefine their identities are often seen among those individuals who cannot, or have chosen not to, reconcile these conflicts or mourn the loss of their youthful dreams. Although these dramatic changes in life-style can be acted out directly by the parent, it is possible also that adolescent sons or daughters can quickly be enlisted to fulfill these aspirations and thus spare the parent from the pain of disillusionment.

Overall, midlife transition and adolescence both require a variety of somewhat dramatic shifts that can generate substantial anxiety, depression, ambivalence, and impulsivity. Both periods represent an opportunity for reintegration and growth; however, they essentially require also a multiple mourning process. The protest and despair that has been associated with such a process can be observed as adolescents struggle to relinquish their childhood irresponsibilities, innocence, fantasies, and the protection and safety of their families (Bowlby, 1961). A similar process can be observed as their midlife parents attempt to mourn the loss of their youthful bodies; dreams; omnipotence; and perhaps, in fact, the actual loss of their own parents. The mutual vulnerability, disruptive potential, and opportunity for destructive influence between these two groups is significant during these stages and are the focus of the following section.

|| THE INTERFACE

Throughout this section an attempt is made to clarify how these two distinct developmental phases interface and how pathological resolutions to the conflicts inherent in each stage can emerge. A note of caution seems important at the outset. In the process of exploring how individuals become embroiled in growth-inhibiting relationships and how systems become deadlocked, it often appears that there are clear-cut villains as well as victims. It is usually a mistake to assume this position. Instead, the more productive line of inquiry seems to lie in the investigation of how any behavior simultaneously meets the needs of several members in the system.

Steirlin (1974) proposes a transactional model for understanding psychosocial interactions between parents and their adolescent offspring. His three major constructs include binding, delegating, and expelling. Essentially, binding interactions or resolutions occur when either the parent or offspring becomes enmeshed in the system with the hope that the established equilibrium within the family will be preserved. Delegating interactions take place when the offspring are enlisted to make a decision or to lead their lives in such a way that it serves to repair or relieve inadequacies, anxieties, or unfulfilled dreams of the parents. Finally, expelling interactions exist when either a parent or offspring is physically or psychologically removed so that whatever tension that had been created by the mutually occurring developmental stages is finally eliminated. An elaboration of these constructs follows.

|| Binding Interactions

Amid the throes of change, either the parent or the offspring may unwittingly initiate or participate in a process whereby change is minimized and the status quo in the system is preserved. Binding is one mechanism that can be employed by either in such a way that time is frozen and old systems are perpetuated. An offspring can bind a parent through two manuevers that are not mutually exclusive. One is through open invitations, and the other is through a more subtle manipulation of parental guilt. Likewise, a parent may bind an offspring through separation guilt or through a process whereby regressive behavior is gratified. What is most important to understand in these interactions, however, is the developmental conflicts that each participant is experiencing that leads to the binding resolutions.

The binding of a parent by a child often seems to become more observable as the process of separation becomes more sharply focused during adolescence. For youth, the separation means that it is time "to make it on their own," which necessitates giving up most of the luxuries of childhood. Also, the separation process ushers in feelings of ambivalence, loyalty conflict, and perhaps fear of abandonment. Youth often sense that they are unprepared for this step or may be reluctant to relinquish the safety and gratification of their childhood role. If they feel overwhelmed by the conflicts and loss inherent in this step forward, they may unwillingly create scenarios that require parents to very actively and perhaps intrusively invade their lives. Delinquent behavior and psychosomatic symptoms are often irresistible invitations for parents to continue, or become reinvolved, in their offspring's life. Guilt over the child-rearing process, or conflicts that parents are encountering in their own midlife transition, is what often motivates them to respond to their children's invitations to remain attached. When parental guilt is being leveraged by the adolescent, the parent is made to feel that they have inadequately prepared the adolescent for separation, and consequently the parent must either continue to protect the adolescent or be punished.

As mentioned, midlife parents can be particularly vulnerable to such manipulations because of their own developmental crises. Several of the developmental demands that they themselves may be encountering can result in their unwitting participation in their offspring's efforts to bind them. One of the reasons that the midlife parent may participate in a binding interaction is that the increasing autonomy and eventual separation of their adolescent is concrete evidence that parents are getting older. Not only are they no longer parents of young children, but are now capable of being grandparents. Since these same parents are being confronted also with watching their own parents become increasingly debilitated as they near death, the prospect of facing the same fate is an ambivalent experience at best. Their adolescent's invitation to continue to be actively involved, if not enmeshed, in their lives may be a welcome opportunity because it forestalls the separation and, hence, postpones the transition toward middle adulthood. Also, as their adolescents become increasingly autonomous, the amount of time necessary for child-rearing functions sharply decreases. For some midlife parents, the increase in freedom of time and mobility is welcomed. For many, however, the increase in free time simply becomes a void and a phenomenon that has been labeled the "empty nest syndrome" develops (Bart, 1971). Women whose lives have been organized around the child-rearing process and who have relied on it for a sense of usefulness and meaningfulness often show signs of depression and anxiety and identity confusion as their offspring grow up and leave. Also, marital problems that were obscured by the child-rearing process or deflected by the child's presence often surface again and can threaten the stability of the marriage. Midlife parents, then, are vulnerable to participating in binding resolutions for several reasons. Faced with the prospect of growing older, the possibility of no longer feeling needed, and the potential threat of having to confront long-standing marital problems, these parents may not only accept the invitations of their adolescents to maintain the attachment, they may also initiate such behavior.

The binding of the adolescent by the parent can be accomplished through several means. Two that are readily observable in most clinical settings is the binding through guilt, or through encouraging regressive dependency. Adolescents who are being tied to the family by guilt are made to feel that if they separate from the family, something terrible will happen to the parents or family. The covert psychological messages that adolescents receive from parents are that they are their parents' whole being or life blood or the sum total of their parent's existence. It is usually made clear to the adolescent that life without their presence will be nothing and that the parent will be left useless if the teenager leaves. Among other factors, this presents a tremendous loyalty conflict for the adolescent in that the choices that once seemed to be available now no longer exist. Adolescents must either sacrifice their own continued development by remaining tied to the parents or pursue their own lives at the expense of parental pain and grief. The adolescent's ambivalence and insecurity about the separation makes them especially vulnerable not only to being exploited by guilt, but also to offers to continue to bathe in the familiar waters of the family.

The adolescent who has been encouraged to remain dependent often appears depressed and helpless, which may reflect to some degree the disappointment or disillusionment that the midlife parent is experiencing. What has happened is that in the transition, the midlife parents may come to feel that they have been exploited in their careers, marriage, or other relationships. Thus they may have come to feel that the dues that they have had to pay to reach this point in their lives have not been worth the reward. Consequently, in subtle ways the parents may have related to their adolescents that the world on the outside is a cruel, ruthless, and disappointing place and that they would be much safer and happier remaining within the confines of the family. In this ultimately destructive process, it is important to note that it is not usually a malevolent act for the parents; on the contrary, they may feel that their overprotection is not only benign but facilitative. Often, in fact, the protection, soothing, or regressive gratification offered to their children is an attempt to provide for them what they feel is no longer or never was available to them. In addition to providing a compensatory function for the parents, the regressive binding can also serve to minimize competitive issues between both parties.

The following cases were selected because they contain several aspects of binding interactions. As the cases unfold, it becomes increasingly clear how the symptomatology and binding resolutions help each party manage their own developmental conflicts.

||| Case 1

Ann was a 19-year-old female who was the only child of a middle-class Jewish family. Throughout her life she had been an excellent student, who according to varied sources had been a very well-behaved if not compliant adolescent. Near the middle of her senior year in high school, she began to eat excessively and abuse laxatives on a regular basis. She had binged on food occasionally in the past, but as she neared the end of her senior year, she began a routine of gorging herself at least once a day and then taking laxatives to avoid gaining weight. The binges would last anywhere from 45 minutes to 2 hours, and following the binge, she would ingest several laxative tablets. Once she selected a college, and as the date of her departure neared, the eating disorder worsened and she became less and less discreet about her difficulty. She later became aware of her ambivalence surrounding the upcoming separation and how this was manifest by her alternately wanting her parents to find out about her problems, with the hope that they would prevent her from leaving, and at the same time she did not want them to know. The eating difficulties were not acknowledged, however, and she left for college as planned.

At school, she felt lost and reportedly felt no confidence in her ability to judge things for herself. After several months her anxiety and despair reached panic proportion, and she informed her parents through long distance telephone conversations of her eating disorder. Her mother, in particular, quickly became reinvolved, and although Ann remained at school, a rather maladaptive system was developed between her and her parents. Ann would phone regularly and desperately report the extent of her binging episodes and the details of her laxative abuse. Her mother, although alarmed, would attempt to console her and would send detailed meal plans to Ann in an effort to regulate her eating. This arrangement persisted for many months until Ann requested psychological treatment at the urging of a roommate.

Initially, Ann complained of her parent's intrusiveness but gradually realized how she participated, if not invited, the intrusiveness by phoning them and elaborately describing her symptoms. She also became more aware of her anger at being in what she called an "overprotective" family. She realized also how she simultaneously punished her parents and yet kept them bound to her by repeatedly making them feel guilty about how poorly they had prepared her to be on her own. As she became more involved in psychotherapy and more aware of how she was binding her parents to her, she gradually quit telling them about her struggles with food and laxatives. Almost immediately, Ann's relationship with her parents acquired a more adult tone. Although somewhat frightened by her new status, Ann prospered for several months until she learned that her mother had become quite depressed. Ann's bingeing and laxative abuse promptly worsened, and she felt pulled to renew her earlier arrangement with her mother. Family sessions were initated, and her mother's developmental struggles became more sharply focused.

In the family session it was learned that Mrs. K.'s mother had been an alcoholic who had both criticized and neglected her children. In Mrs. K.'s struggle to survive her own mother's outright neglect and criticism, she vowed that she would never treat her children in the same manner. When she became pregnant with Ann, she reported that she felt a sense of purpose and self-worth that she had never experienced before in her life. She acknowledged that she had always felt a pressure to do things for her daughter and came to realize that the pressure she felt was from her need to provide, protect, and soothe Ann in a way that had been denied her. When Ann began to separate from her, she suddenly felt empty and useless. Equally important, however, was that without Ann to soothe and protect, she herself felt vulnerable and insecure. It was a shocking discovery and a painful loss for her to realize how much she relied on the nurturance she provided for Ann to soothe herself and compensate for her early experience of neglect. Mrs. K. eventually entered individual treatment, and with the separation guilt relieved, Ann began the process of learning how to manage her own life again.

|| Case 2

Betty was also a girl who throughout her early development showed no signs of difficulty. She had always been the bright, attractive, and responsible daughter of her father, who was a mildly successful businessman, and her mother, who had always been regarded as a beautiful and seductive woman. Betty was the only child in the family and had a close relationship with her mother. Her mother had always delighted in buying expensive clothes for Betty and was always subtly schooling her in the art of feminine intrigue.

When Betty reached menarche, she quickly blossomed into a shapely adolescent. Older boys started pursuing her, which she later admitted frightened her. Around this time her mother began to enter menopause and became overweight, angry, and depressed. Mrs. B. began to criticize her daughter about her appearance and flirtatiousness in a way that undermined Betty's self-esteem. At the same time she began to subtly relate to Betty her discontent with how things were turning out for her. She would comment on how she felt she had made a bad choice in her marriage and how she felt she had been used by her husband and other men. Near this time, to everyone's surprise, Betty began starving herself until she became an emaciated, amenorrheic girl who appeared like a child. She was referred for treatment, and both individual and family therapy were begun.

During the course of family therapy, Mrs. B.'s envy and jealousy of her daughter's youthful beauty emerged. She admitted that it was particularly hard for her to see Betty receive the amount and type of attention that had always been so important to her, especially since she now felt "over the hill." She also acknowledged that she was disappointed with her life, particularly because she felt she was never able to recreate or recapture the sense of specialness that she had experienced as a child in her family. She had always hoped that her husband would provide this for her, but he had either been unwilling or unable to do so. Betty had in some ways been her salvation in this regard until she became a competitive threat rather than a cute but benign narcissistic object.

Betty had obviously deciphered her mother's painful messages, and her anorexia offered an interesting solution to the suffering she saw her mother experiencing. Her extreme weight loss served several purposes simultaneously. For example, it eliminated Betty's secondary sexual characteristics, which relieved the competitive issues between her and her mother. It also relieved the male pursuit that had frightened her. Having seen her mother's despair in reaction to becoming overweight and having heard her complaints about men, Betty was convinced that there was nothing particularly attractive about growing up and becoming a woman. Consequently, she was actively turning her back on further development. And finally, her extreme thinness and frail condition certainly lowered the expectations on her to separate from the family, which she was equally frightened about. Once both mother's and daughter's developmental crises were addressed, the way was cleared for each to begin to unlock the system.

|| Delegating Interactions

As outlined earlier, delegating occurs when the offspring are enlisted to make a decision or lead their lives in such a way that repairs or relieves inadequacies, anxieties, or unfulfilled dreams of the parents. In addition to this restitutional function, delegating may serve also to provide the parents with stimulation that they feel was never available to them. The delegating process is actually a subtle form of binding in that the offspring appear to be acting autonomously. On close inquiry, however, it is clear that their actions are intimately tied to the parents' needs. Essentially, adolescents are being sent out with all the trappings of independence, but their success or failure is being utilized vicariously by the parents. The offspring almost always sense that they are living for two separate parties and not acting autonomously.

Once again the understanding of the mechanism of delegating lies in appreciating how this process can serve both the parent's and adolescent's needs. Midlife transition parents often report that they feel caught "in between." As mentioned earlier, these parents feel committed to continuing to consolidate the direction of their lives, which means proceeding with matters as they exist: family, friends, career, and so on. On the other, hand, some parents experience such disenchantment at this juncture that they would like to effect a radical change and flee the status quo. This can create a significant and painful dilemma. Do they sacrifice the security of what they have and risk the fear, guilt, and disapproval of others for what could be a more exciting and free existence, or do they press onward with business as usual? Loyalty conflicts, helplessness, depressive resignation, rageful protest, and a sense of being trapped are but a few of the feelings that can result from the perceived dilemma. One solution that may represent compromise and offer a sense of relief is for the adolescent to become delegated to enact the parent's ambivalent and conflicted wishes.

The adolescent may be particularly vulnerable to this type of interaction because of the insecurity and indecision endemic to the process of identity formation. It is not unusual for adolescents to feel overwhelmed by the opportunity to shape their own destinies. In confusion, teenagers may consciously or unwittingly welcome the chance to borrow from the structure of their parents' wishes.

There are many delegating resolutions that can evolve between parent and offspring. Delegated behavior generally can be identified according to the type of needs it serves for parents, whether it be affective needs, ego-supportive needs, or super-ego needs (Steirlin, 1974).

Affective Needs

If the behavior of the adolescent reflects some repressed or suppressed sexual or aggressive thought for the parent, it may have been delegated in order to meet a parent's affective needs. The following three cases are examples of how an adolescent can be delegated to express some affective need of the parent.

Case 3

Carolyn was a 17-year-old who had a history or promiscuous behavior and who was the daughter of rigorous Catholic parents. Initially, her chief complaint was that she was feeling very uncertain about who she was and that she felt that her behavior was being dictated by someone other than herself. Individual and family psychotherapy were recommended. One particularly important aspect of her relationship with her mother emerged during treatment. Early in the sessions, Mrs. C. condemned Carolyn for her sexual behavior, referring to it as adventurous and hedonistic. She would thoroughly chastise her daughter and attempt to make her feel guilty by reminding her of her Catholic upbringing. Carolyn initially absorbed these tirades without protest. As the family treatment continued, it became clearer that she really didn't enjoy the relationships she had with boys and was perplexed about why she continued to engage in the sexual behavior. She gradually began to reveal that her mother had always been very inquisitive about the boys who were around the house. In fact, she would even walk through the room where Carolyn would be heavily petting without saying a word. Carolyn had always been confused by what appeared to be contradictions in her mother's messages to her. Even though she scolded her, Carolyn felt that her mother was giving her permission to actively behave sexually in front of her by not stopping her in the family living room. When this contradiction was revealed, Mrs. C. became guilty and depressed. Shortly thereafter with only mother and father in the sessions, Mrs. C. began to talk about her own frustration and disappointment with her inability to enjoy sex. She had been raised in a very strict family and had married very early in an effort to escape her home. She felt deprived, naive, and enraged that she had never been able to explore her own sexuality. Now that she was becoming older, she felt that this was one aspect of experience that would be denied her. Unbeknown to her, Carolyn had sensed her despair and was enacting her mother's wishes in an effort to provide for her what she felt she had missed. Once the delegating had been acknowledged by the mother in the sessions without Carolyn, she was able to give her daughter nonambivalent messages about her sexual conduct.

Case 4

Joe, a 16-year-old who had never been in trouble before, was brought to a therapist by his family following a sudden decrease in his school performance and a precipitous episode of running away. The father was particularly concerned because he and Joe had always been extremely close. Joe had great difficulty explaining his behavior and, in fact, reported that he had just been out driving when he felt an urge to just continue to drive. When he was discovered, he was three states away. The therapist was not impressed with Joe's commitment to running away, so he arranged a meeting with his parents. Almost immediately, the father began to complain that "this was all he needed, another problem and another expense." Apparently, his own father than recently become quite ill and had been hospitalized. Also, it appears that the eldest daughter wanted to enter college and the parents were not sure that they could afford it. Mr. S., in particular, felt pressured. He did not know how he could pay for his daughter's schooling, and it was clear that his own father was near death. He felt overwhelmed and as though the weight of the world was on his shoulders. He felt powerless and helpless in the face of the events and had been losing a fair amount of sleep as well as having difficulty in concentrating on his work. The therapist asked the father if he had ever entertained fantasies of just taking off and leaving his problems behind. He admitted guiltily that he had felt that urge strongly but could never do such a thing. He was surprised by his admission, and it had not dawned on him prior to this that his son's behavior could have been related to his own troubles. Joe's running away and poor school performance in fact were both very related to his father's struggles. Joe had detected his father's sense of burden and had also recognized his wish for relief in running away. He had been serving a restitutional function for his father by performing that which his father felt was unavailable to him.

|| Case 5

David was the 14-year-old son of a city engineer. He was brought to an inpatient setting following repeated incidents of extreme defiance and vandalism. Over the course of several months, he had become increasingly rebellious and openly hostile and aggressive toward authority figures. He was finally referred to the hospital by the courts because he was vandalizing public buildings. Apparently, he had been apprehended several times spray-painting obscene words on the walls of these buildings.

After a stormy entry, David settled into the unit, and his oppositional defiant behavior abated dramatically. He attended school on the unit without difficulty and was found to be likable by both staff and patients. His behavior, however, would always predictably take a turn for the worse the day before his parents would arrive for regularly scheduled visits, when his father and mother would always be greeted with news of his rageful and defiant behavior. The mother was always alarmed and confused, but the father would absorb the stories in passive resignation. The pattern and object of David's destructive behavior seemed too consistent to be coincidental. Consequently, the family therapist began probing into the dynamics of the family system. What was learned was that David's father was a frustrated and enraged 47-year-old city engineer who had been repeatedly passed up for promotion. His most recent lack of promotion had convinced him that he would never rise above staff engineer. He was extremely dissatisfied, disillusioned, and infuriated with a system that he felt was arbitrary and exploitive. He felt stalled and helpless. After all, he complained, what could he do? He was a responsible and law-abiding community member who had bills to pay. He felt that he could not find work elsewhere, which prevented him from protesting his case and risking losing the job. Outwardly, it appeared that he had resigned himself to the situation, but it was obvious that he was narcissistically wounded and angry. It was not surprising to learn that the beginning of David's acting out had coincided with the father's last failed promotion. Apparently, what had developed between David and his father over the months was a system whereby David would cause trouble and then come home to confess the details of his crimes to his father. Mr. M. would listen intently and then unconvincingly request that David stop vandalizing city buildings and creating such a ruckus. David sensed his father's ambivalence, if not enjoyment, of his behavior and continued because he felt he had power, autonomy, and importance in his destructiveness. Nobody could tell him what he could not do or could stand in his way. David had much less autonomy than he believed and, in fact, was unwittingly protesting his father's grievances. Once Mr. M. became aware of the connection between David's behavior and his own feelings, he decided to enter treatment himself, which, predictably, relieved David also.

|| *Ego-Supportive Needs*

In addition to being delegated to express some unacceptable affect or impulse for the parent, the adolescent may be enlisted to meet more ego-supportive needs. Parents who become depressed or overly stressed during midlife transitions may resort to delegating parental responsibility to their offspring in an effort to cope with what may be a developmental crisis. Delegating in this instance again serves to bind the offspring to the system while giving the appearance that autonomy is being encouraged. An adolescent who increasingly assumes household duties or child-rearing responsibilities may obstensibly appear to be learning or practicing skills that will be beneficial in the future. When separation arises, however, the true function of the delegated behavior is often revealed.

Adolescents with low self-esteem or who are particularly threatened by life outside the family often readily accept these responsibilities because it offers an opportunity to feel worthwhile and useful. Even if they sense that their parent's motivation for turning over the responsibility is less than educational, the opportunity to feel a sense of importance usually outweighs the more subtle threat to their autonomy.

|| Case 6

Ellen was admitted to a medical unit to determine whether she had multiple sclerosis. She complained of a series of symptoms that included a low degree of energy, fatigue, and loss of appetite. Multiple sclerosis was suspected because both her mother and younger brother had been diagnosed as having this disease several years earlier. The medical workup revealed that there was nothing particularly wrong with Ellen, and in fact her symptoms had improved dramatically after her admission. A psychiatric consultation was requested. It was learned that Ellen was coming home immediately after school everyday to prepare dinner for the family and to care for her younger brother, who required special attention because of his illness. Ellen's mother, after having delegated most of these duties, had increasingly withdrawn to her bedroom. Although Mrs. R. had always been a conscientious and responsible person, it emerged that she had become profoundly depressed at about 43 years of age when one day she felt that her choice to marry her husband and to raise a family had been wrong. She revealed that her husband was alcoholic and that he abused her on occasion. Some months after she became depressed, it was suggested that she also might have multiple sclerosis. Although the symptoms were quite nonspecific and nondebilitating, Mrs. R. no longer had much desire to be in charge of the home. This responsibility was gradually assumed by Ellen. She performed well, and everybody commented on her efficiency and the great experience she was acquiring. Ellen felt important and grown up. As her mother withdrew further, however, Ellen found that she no longer had time for school or her friends. Even more confusing and upsetting to her was how her relationship with her father had begun to change. As her mother continued to withdraw, Ellen found herself alone more and more with her father, in the early mornings and late evenings. It progressed to the point that she and her father would be the only ones up after her mother and brother had retired for the evening. Ellen became quite uncomfortable with this, and we learned sometime later that one evening her father, while drinking, had made a sexual advance. It was shortly after this incident that Ellen became symptomatic and was admitted to the hospital.

In her disillusionment and depression, Mrs. R. had unwittingly delegated Ellen to take over her role as mother and wife. Ellen, in her self-doubt and insecurity, had reveled initially in the sense of importance. Gradually, however, she had become aware of the consequences of accepting the invitation and became psychosomatically ill in an effort to escape the danger of the situation.

|| *Superego Needs*

The "life review" that is characteristic of midlife transition generates the setting for a final type of delegating. It is during this time that the midlife parent undeniably realizes that the special fantasy, dream, or ideal that thus far had been held throughout life may not materialize. Rather than mourn the loss of the dream or suffer the narcissistic injury of unachieved ideals, these parents often turn to their offspring with the expectation that they perform or achieve in the way that they themselves were unable to. Daughters who must be beautiful, witty, and successful and sons who must be presidents and quarterbacks often labor hard to protect their parents from the dashed hopes and depressing disillusionment they may feel regarding unrealized ambitions. Again, however, the key to the delegating process is that the adolescent must not actually exercise autonomy in such a way that results in separation from the parents. Instead, the adolescent must attempt to accomplish the delegated roles close enough to home so that parents may vicariously participate.

Adolescents become engaged in these scenarios for several reasons. Some sense the psychic danger that shattered dreams present for their parents, and out of guilt or fear of the parent's collapse, they attempt to serve a restitutional function by taking over the dreams. Other adolescents participate out of the fear of separation or inability to decide for themselves what they would like to pursue. Regardless of the motivation, the essential ingredient that must be present is that the actions of the adolescent remain intimately tied to the parents.

|| Case 7

Dan was a bright and ambitious 17-year-old who was shy and somewhat withdrawn. This shyness, however, changed dramatically when he entered a baseball field. He was an all-city baseball player who showed moderate promise to make the pros. He was referred to an outpatient clinic by an alert family physician who had been concerned about Dan's accident-proneness. He had apparently incurred several broken bones, sprains, and muscle strains over the last 12 months, and the injuries were beginning to occur more frequently as he entered his senior year. Dan offered little resistance to the notion of visiting a psychiatric clinic. On the other hand, when his father learned of his planned visits, he protested vehemently that there was nothing wrong with this son and that the appointments would interfere with baseball practice. The therapist, sensing the delicacy of the situation, simply offered an alternative time that would not conflict with the practice and recommended that Dan consider that option. Dan entered treatment, although his father was not informed.

Initially, Dan talked a lot about baseball and his future with the pros. He presented the prospect matter-of-factly, and there appeared to be little passion or enthusiasm connected to the goal. In contrast, when he was with his father, it was reported that he was very enthusiastic and eager to pursue a baseball career. Gradually, in the sessions, he talked more and more about how he had never known anything but baseball and how so much emphasis had always been placed on doing well on the field. He told stories about how his father used to tie his hands behind his back and with the catcher equipment on, make him block pitched baseballs with the inside of his thighs. He was 10 years old at the time. The purpose of tying his hands was to ensure that he would use his legs rather than his hands to stop the ball. Although it hurt, he learned not to be afraid of the ball and to use the inside of his legs. Also, he recalled that his father would push him to run wind sprints until he vomited from exertion. As he pressed further into these stories, he was surprised to find that he really did not like the game and that he felt immense pressure to be an outstanding catcher. He actually did not feel that he was pro material and became curious at one point about whether his injuries might be a subtle way of defaulting on the task that had been laid out for him. The therapist subsequently learned that the father had been a promising young catcher but that his chances for the pros had been eliminated when he became blinded in one eye as the result of an automobile accident. Apparently the pressure had always existed for Dan to be a ballplayer. When his father had his forty-fifth birthday, however, Dan felt that something had changed. His father began telling more stories about his old baseball friends, some of whom made it to the pros. Simultaneously, he started really pushing Dan even harder to practice and to do well. He pushed him to be the field captain and to keep the team fired up. Dan had done these things, but with little genuine enthusiasm, and he had now come to feel that he was perhaps doing it more for his father than for himself. He requested help to tell his father that this perhaps was not what he wanted to do. His father had actually already sensed this, and although it was disappointing for him, he accepted his son's request to explore some other possibilities for his life. It should also be noted that Dan was quite frightened by the freedom to explore his alternatives and in his frustration on many occasions considered returning to baseball because of its familiarity.

|| Expelling Interactions

Expelling represents the final pathological resolution that can occur between parents and adolescents. Unlike binding or delegating, the ultimate goal of expelling is to physically cast out or psychologically exclude some member in the system to eliminate undesirable tensions or conflicts. A parent or offspring can be vulnerable to this type of process, depending on the nature of the tension and where allegiances in the system are most firmly rooted.

The two most clinically observable tensions that lead to an expelling resolution are where competitive issues are stirred or where the adolescent is seen as a hindrance or burden. In the first instance, adolescent daughters who become attractive and accomplished or sons who become virulent and successful may pose such a narcissistic threat to the midlife parent who is struggling with the decline in body functions and perhaps shattered dreams that the offspring must be physically cast out so that the parent's esteem can be preserved. The adolescent must either be driven out or must leave prematurely so that the parent's equilibrium can be maintained.

Also, as mentioned earlier, the adolescent struggle to master developmental demands is often accompanied by erratic, defiant, and delinquent behavior. If this uproar occurs at a time when the midlife parent is feeling disillusioned or overwhelmed by additional caretaking responsibilities, such as ill parents or other responsibilities in the extended family, the adolescent may be expelled in an effort to relieve some of the burden. Or, more frequently, the adolescent may be viewed as an obstacle that is preventing the midlife parent from making a new start and having more fun.

The actual expelling can be accomplished through either overt or more subtle processes. The adolescent who is being actively expelled is constantly criticized, informed of their undesirability, or in some cases actually assaulted. The only course of survival is to flee the home. Adolescents who are being expelled through a more subtle process are either grossly neglected so as to feel nonexistent in the family or to feel that they are such a burden that things would be better if they left.

This type of process may serve several needs for the adolescent as well. For the adolescent who is having difficulty with ambivalence around separation, the process of being expelled usually preempts the possibility of loyalty conflicts. Also, if the adolescent is cultivating a representational world in which feelings of inadequacy and unworthiness arise, the expelling by the parent may serve to confirm this emerging belief in such a way that a sense of control and predictability is experienced by the adolescent.

|| Case 8

Mark was a 16-year-old who was the eldest son in a first-generation Italian family. He was admitted to an inpatient service on recommendation of the court because of repeated school truancy, drug use, and running away from home. The acting-out behavior had reportedly begun rather abruptly following a fight between Mark and his father in which Mark had knocked his father to the floor. The circumstances surrounding the quarrel were somewhat vague, and the entire family had great difficulty in talking about the incident.

During the course of the family treatment, it was learned that Mr. H. had a volatile temper and that he had always run the family with an "iron fist." Apparently, he had always been very critical of Mark and relied heavily on physical intimidation to "keep him in line." When Mark entered puberty, he grew quite tall, although he remained thin. At 16, he was several inches taller than his father, and he began to fill out substantially as a result of a weight-lifting program he had begun. Mr. H., on the other hand, was in his midforties and had become quite out of shape. Finally, on one occasion when Mr. H. was trying to physically intimidate Mark, he was knocked to the floor by his much stronger son. Mark remembered the event and recalled that it seemed as though "a hush fell over the family." Shortly after this, Mr. H. became quite sullen and depressed. He refused to speak with his son, and Mark felt compelled to leave the family, which was the beginning of his difficulty.

This is not a particularly unusual theme in families where fathers rule by physical coercion. What made the case unique was that after many months of family work, the parents disclosed, without Mark present, that the incident of Mr. H. being knocked to the floor coincided with a temporary bout of impotency that Mr. H. had been experiencing. Seeing Mark becoming stronger and more virulent at a time when he was feeling weaker and less vital had been very difficult for him. Consequently, when he was actually overpowered by Mark, the insult was more than he could bear. He was feeling quite threatened, and in his anger and hurt he had driven his son away from the family, thus relieving the threat.

|| Case 9

An alert, bright, and conscientious student, Jeffry passed successfully through his first 3 years of high school. The summer before Jeffry's senior year, his mother was hospitalized for drug and alcohol abuse. His father, a prominent and successful businessman who was generally aggressive and outspoken, became temporarily despondent, if not morose. Verbal confrontations between father and son crescendoed, and Jeffry's academic work during the first part of his senior year plummeted. He experienced his living situation as intolerable and his school work as totally ungratifying. Just as Jeffry was making plans to move away from home and drop out of school, he was referred for psychotherapy. During the course of psychotherapy Jeffry related his bewilderment, confusion, and uncertainty regarding graduating from high school and going off to college. Also, he expressed his rage concerning his father's frequent verbal assaults. At times the father attempted to intimidate Jeffry's therapist by demanding accelerated progress. Furthermore, the father would demand family sessions so that he could have the opportunity to vent his chagrin at both Jeffry and the therapist. The therapist in this case delicately but firmly avoided the potential destructiveness of family encounters by electing to work individually with Jeffry while soothing the father through frequent and lengthy telephone conversations. In treatment, Jeffry reviewed his fears about breaking away from home and was able to examine his feelings of uncertainty over individuating. He was also able to acknowledge that many of his father's angry outbursts had been unwittingly provoked by him in moments of despair over the future. As Jeffry learned to express his doubts and fears in psychotherapy, his academic work returned to normal, hostile interchanges between father and son dissipated, and the expelling process was abated.

Mr. G. was able to acknowledge during a crisis interview with Jeffry's therapist that in spite of his success in the business world, he felt like a sham and wanted out. His fantasy was to leave his business, friends, and perhaps even his wife and son and retreat to an easier, less demanding life-style. When his son performed below his potential in school, Mr. G. experienced guilt over his own wish to be fickle and carefree. In effect, when Jeffry was on the brink of academic failure, the threat of capriciousness was too stimulating for the father. In his efforts to purge himself from his own wish to act irresponsibly, Mr. G. doggedly attempted to extricate his son from the home, thereby eliminating the fear of undependability once and for all.

|| SUMMARY

In an attempt to contribute to the overall understanding of parents of depressed children, this chapter has addressed itself specifically to the issues resulting from the interface between adolescence and midlife transition. The ecology of two mutually occurring developmental life phases has been elaborated, and the point at which these independently potent if not volatile stages interjoin has been emphasized. Although we have made an effort to preserve the unique qualities of both adolescence and parents in midlife transition, the parallels or similarities between both developmental phases clearly have not been minimized. Further, we have proposed that biological and chronological models be replaced by psychosocial or transactional paradigms in order to better understand adolescence as well as midlife transition. In this regard, a particular psychosocial model was developed, one in which binding, delegating, and expelling interactions or resolutions could be expected to occur. It was demonstrated further that the outcome of these interactions all too frequently results in pathological consequences for parents and their adolescent offspring alike. Finally, with the use of clinical case material, the overt as well as the covert maneuvers of parents and their adolescent offspring were traced as we endeavored to clarify the potency of family systems as they interconnect during two independent and highly vulnerable, perhaps even potentially explosive, phases of human development.

8

The Spouse in Depressed Families

Henry U. Grunebaum, Enid Gamer, and
Bertram J. Cohler

When the mother of young children is hospitalized as a result of psychiatric illness, major responsibility for child care shifts to the father. Although his role within the family is an important one, it is true that, particularly during the years when there are young children at home, the wife and mother typically assumes primary responsibility for the care of these children (Chodorow, 1978; Cohler & Grunebaum, 1981). Of necessity, when his wife is hospitalized, the father assumes responsibility for raising the children and supervising the household. He must make appropriate child care arrangements during the hours when he is at work, as well as at those times when he visits his wife in the hospital.

In spite of the father's central role in maintaining the household when the wife and mother is hospitalized, with the exception of reports by Clausen and Yarrow (1955), Keritman (1964), Kaplan and Blackman (1969), Hopkins (1980), and Clausen (1981; in press), there has been very little study of these husbands and fathers whose wives have been hospitalized and of the manner is which they adapt to their additional responsibilities. The present chapter reports on differences in domestic and child-centered activities among fathers whose wives have been hospitalized for psychosis as contrasted with families in which the wife and mother is well-func-

This research was supported in part by a grant from the Grant Foundation, New York, and a grant from the Social Science Divisional Research Committee, the University of Chicago. The authors would like to thank Dr. Justin Weiss for his assistance with all aspects of the study and Drs. Carol Hartman and David Gallant for their suggestions regarding revisions of this manuscript.

tioning at home and in the community. Unfortunately, too little is known about the imprint of parental depression on the spouse to focus solely on that problem.

|| BACKGROUND OF THE STUDY

When a parent is hospitalized for mental illness in our society, more often it tends to be the wife and mother. In part, this is because courtship and marriage require greater activity and social competence for the man, who must show initiative, than for the woman, who accepts the proposal of marriage. Thus, whereas less socially competent men tend to remain single, it is more frequent for less socially competent women to get married and even have children. These same dynamics are likely to operate during the course of family life, so that men who cannot provide for their families because of mental illness, alcoholism, or inability to obtain work are likely to be extruded from the family unit, leading to a very common downwardly mobile single-parent family.

In addition, the father's important role as the primary provider, particularly during the early years of the family life cycle, means that he is more likely than his wife to receive psychiatric treatment without hospitalization, for the loss of income subsequent to hospitalization would have a serious impact on the stability of the family unit as a whole. It is, thus, no coincidence that in a discussion of families with a psychotic parent, that parent is usually the woman. When the designated patient is the man, the result is more likely to be a single-parent family. In addition, since there is some tendency toward homogamy, it is not surprising that families with a psychotic parent will often include a less than competent mate. In addition, it is important to emphasize that more prepsychotic and psychotic women marry and more have more children than do mentally ill men (Clausen and Yarrow, 1955). Psychotic women are more likely to be in the home and involved in the care of children than are psychotic men. The adverse effect of midlife depression on men, or its equivalent—which may well be manifest in alcoholism, underemployment, and criminal activities—is probably equal to the effect of depression on children. Men who are seriously depressed are more likely to be led to extrusion from their homes than is true for equivalently depressed women. (Clausen, 1981; in press).

When a wife and mother is hospitalized, the husband and father must make a radical adjustment in his schedule. Even though his wife may also have held a job at least part-time, the primary wage earner in the contemporary family is the man, and if there is one job to be preserved, it is typically the man's job. Gutmann (1975) has argued that the very fact of parenthood tends to distribute tasks within the family on a sex-role stereotyped basis. Referring to the parental phase as that part of the life cycle that engenders "a sense of chronic emergency," Gutmann suggests that it is during this phase of the life cycle that men are most likely to emphasize their role within the family as the instrumental leader, following the well-known paradigm by Parsons and Bales (1955), whereas women are most likely to emphasize their role as the expressive leader. When his wife is hospitalized, the husband and father must learn the household routine and provide for the direct care of the children in ways that previously were the responsibility of the wife and mother during those hours in the day when he was at work, which are the hours when the children must be supervised and cared for.

Multiple hospitalizations for episodes of a recurrent psychotic disturbance (Zubin & Spring, 1977), characteristic of most schizophrenic women who succumb to mental illness during the years when there are young children at home, further disrupt the family's stability and gradually wear down the morale of the husband and father. Work disruptions, isolation from friendships and important leisure time activities, and the role overload and strains that result from having to be both parents for the children, the sole family provider, and an important source of support for the wife and mother during her hospitalization, all take additional toll on the father's personal resources. Temporary efforts at providing child care fail to work over extended periods of time; relatives become increasingly wary of caring for the children and find the inevitable requests for babysitting to be burdensome. The husband and father finds himself increasingly resentful and angry; over time he may even decide to separate from his wife, resulting in additional strains for both parents and children. Gradually the family unit begins to implode itself, unable to resolve enduring conflicts, and becomes increasingly isolated from community resources as sources of assistance in such times of crisis.

Most information to date regarding the impact of recurrent mental illness on the family has come from studies in which the vulnerable family member is schizophrenic (Anthony, 1977, 1978a; Garmezy, 1978b). Although this form of psychosis presents dramatic symptoms that are most clearly socially unacceptable, depression is a symptom that is far more ubiquitous and has a nonpsychotic equivalent that is more frequently encountered by persons in the community (Zetzel, 1965). However, the impact of parental depression on the family has been less carefully studied; just as it may be more pervasive within the community, many more seriously depressed than schizophrenic parents may be continuing in the parental role.

Although the schizophrenic mother gives reasonably clear signs that a break is impending and hospitalization is required, the psychotic depressed mother may give few such signs. Rather, she becomes increasingly sad and apathetic, gradually withdrawing from her husband and children until some specific event, such as a suicide gesture, forces the hospitalization. Weissman and Paykel (1974) have discussed this impact of the psychotic depressed woman as parent and note the feeling of inner deadness and emptiness that these depressed mothers engender in their children. This depression spreads across the family unit and has additional adverse impact on the husband and father, who may also experience an increased sense of lethargy and lack of inner resources as a response to his wife's profound depression.

Not only has depression been less carefully studied than schizophrenia in terms of its impact on the family, but also, regardless of the mother's diagnosis, much less is known about the impact of the mother's illness on the life adjustment of her husband and that of her children. There has been considerable study of children at "risk" or vulnerable as a result of maternal mental illness (although typically concerning schizophrenic rather than psychotic depressed mothers); however, very little is known about the impact of either schizophrenia or depression on the adaptation of the husband and father (Kreitman, 1964; Kaplan & Blackman, 1969; Hopkins, 1980). Comparative study of these husbands and fathers whose wives have been hospitalized, as contrasted with well families, in which the wife and mother is well-functioning in the community, is made even more difficult as a result of the scarcity of information more generally regarding the father's perception of his roles as husband and parent.

Little of the detailed normative study of the father's role within the family has been reported regarding the role of wife and mother. Most such studies to date regarding the father's role within the family are concerned either with the demonstration that fathers *do* spend time with their children or with the differential response of infants and toddlers to their fathers and mothers as observed in systematic laboratory studies (Lamb, 1976a,b). There have been three studies that do report on father's perceptions of their roles, as well as a recent psychodynamically informed collection of essays concerning the impact of fatherhood on the lives of men (Cath, Gurwitt, & Ross, 1982); however, two of these studies are somewhat dated and provide information that is not very relevant to contemporary issues within the family.

Gardner (1943) interviewed 300 fathers in the community with a particular interest in the activities that these men were involved in with their children. In this study, less than 10 percent of the fathers reported giving "plenty of care," whereas over a third of these fathers reported giving little or no care at all. The majority of the fathers in this earlier study did report some consistent activities with their children in the course of the children's development. These findings also showed that fathers were more involved in specific child-care routines in caring for children under the age of 6 years than for somewhat older children. In their relationship with children from the age of 6 through adolescence, these fathers reported a shift in emphasis from concern with specific aspects of child care to the role of counselor, providing guidance and advice regarding money, school achievement, and choice of friends. Discipline of the school-aged child was reported to be more the responsibility of the mother than the father.

Tasch (1952) interviewed 85 fathers in an effort to collect information regarding their involvement with their children. Fathers reported that over one-third of their activities for children under 4 years old was directed toward routine daily care such as feeding, bathing, and dressing. As the children entered school, fathers became involved in teaching them intellectual and social skills. Still later, fathers assumed the task of instilling responsibility through chores and allowances. By senior high school, fathers engaged in more recreational activities with their children. About three-fifths of the fathers reported that the task of disciplining the children was shared by both parents.

Pederson (1969) studied fathers' involvement with their first-born infants. Material was gathered through observation of infants at 8 and 9½ months, together with interviews with their mothers. No father was directly observed or interviewed. The investigators reported that, on the average, fathers spent slightly less than 8 hours a week in active play with the infant. Some fathers participated little in routine caretaking, whereas an equal number participated substantially. The experimenters concluded that each father was "highly involved" with his child but that, as a group, they demonstrated great differences in their child-centered behavior.

These studies suggest that the extent of father–child interaction varies widely when there is a well-functioning mother attending to the household. The activities a father chooses to engage in are largely determined by the age of his child. Routine care takes precedence until the child enters school. Fathers then see themselves as teachers responsible for guiding their children socially and morally into adulthood. We should take note of the fact that these are somewhat dated studies in an area in which social change has been quite rapid. Fathers today are understandably more involved with their children than in past generations (Parke, 1977).

In a unique study, and one of the very few concerned with the father's role among families in which the wife and mother has been hospitalized, Merrill (1969) interviewed 34 fathers whose wives were admitted to a psychiatric hospital. The children in these families ranged in age from 1 month to 22 years. The focus of the interview was on the family's adaptation to the mother's illness. Merrill did not detail actual caretaking activities but stated that fathers were highly involved with the whole family unit and assumed many domestic and child-care responsibilities. Merrill also observed that the children in each family seemed to align themselves with their father rather than their mother because of his "more consistent and protective position." This alignment kept family life predictable and ordered but had the effect of excluding the mother after her hospital discharge as an active, participating family member.

Merrill's findings may be compared with those of Gardner and Tasch. First, it appears that the majority of men with wives hospitalized for psychiatric illness are highly involved in domestic and child-care activity, whereas fathers with emotionally healthy wives vary considerably in the extent of their involvement. Second, fathers in the Gardner and Tasch studies of well families report a shift in their activities from child care to teaching as their children grow older, whereas men with emotionally disturbed wives are described as remaining active primarily in basic domestic and child-care routines. The present exploratory study is an attempt to gather specific information regarding domestic and child-care routines engaged in by the husband and father whose wife has been hospitalized and, also, to compare their activities with those of men married to stable, well-functioning women.

METHOD OF STUDY

The Groups

The men interviewed were husbands of women participating in a larger study investigating the value of psychiatric nursing home visits for discharged psychotic mothers and their children (Grunebaum, 1977). Two groups of fathers were interviewed: Group I consisted of 10 men married to women who had been hospitalized at least one time for psychosis, generally with affective features, and who had at least one child under the age of 5 years. The women in this group had once been diagnosed as psychotic, although all were discharged from the hospital and functioning with varying degrees of competence at home at the time of this study. Group II consisted of 10 husbands of women in the well control group; these women had never been hospitalized for emotional illness. Within each group, the first 10 men were interviewed who were willing to participate in the study, were cooperative, and were available.

The average for Group I fathers was 35.4 years, in comparison to 33.8 years for Group II. Ages in both groups ranged from midtwenties to midforties. Educational attainments ranged from elementary school to graduate work. The following weights are assigned to the educational levels: 1 = elementary school; 2 = high school; 3 = some college; 4 = college graduate; and 5 = graduate work. The mean for Group I is 3.1, versus 3.6 for Group II. Social class based on the Hollingshead two-factor classification system showed an average of 3.0 for Group I and 2.6 for Group II. The average age of the youngest child was 30 months for Group I and 39 months for Group II. The age range for the children in Group I was 6 months–18 years and for Group II, 7 months–18 years. There was a mean of 2.8 children per family in Group I and 3.0 children per family in Group II.

The Interview

The interview procedure was first explained to the wife over the telephone, and she was asked to discuss it with her husband. Chances of talking to a receptive father were likely to be increased if the project was first described favorably by an interested wife. Appointments were made at the father's convenience. All interviews were held at the Massachusetts Mental Health Center except for two that were held at the father's place of work and two that were held at the father's home.

The interview for all fathers consisted of five sections covering (1) the father's weekly work and recreational schedule; (2) a "typical weekday" interview that focused on the activities the father engaged in with his children; (3) additional questions covering broad areas of father–child interaction and paternal child-care responsibilities, (4) a "typical day" interview for a weekend, and (5) family-planned practices used by the couple and fathers' attitudes toward having further children. Each father in Group I was specifically asked about child care and household management during his wife's most recent hospitalization.

RESULTS

Both groups of fathers were involved with and concerned about their families, taking time for their children and letting their children know that they were available. The types of interaction described by the fathers were grouped as follows: (1) routine caretaking activities; (2) activities that demand an extended period of social interaction between the father and his child; (3) situations initiated by the father that allow for, but do not demand, social interaction; and (4) situations initiated by the child that allow for, but do not demand, social interaction (see Tables 8-1 and 8-2).

The results allow the following conclusions: (1) men with emotionally ill wives participate with their children in more of the routine child-care activities; (2) these men show a lower number of activities that demand an extended period of social interaction with their children; and (3) men with

Table 8-1
Number of Group I and Group II Fathers Reporting Weekday Activities

	Number of Fathers	
	Group I	Group II
Routine Care		
Father takes primary responsibility for discipline	8	3
Father attends to night care of children	5	1
Father wakes children up	4	1
Father helps at evening bath time	3	6
Father puts children in bed	1	5
Father gives children medical attention	2	1
Father helps children dress	1	0
Father prepares breakfast	1	3
Total	25	20
Father–Child Interactions		
Father plays with children	6	6
Father teaches children or gives them information	5	4
Father reads to children	3	6
Father helps children with homework	3	2
Father takes children outside for recreation	2	2
Total	19	20
Situations Allowing Father–Child Interactions (Father-Initiated)		
Father has dinner with all or some of his children	7	7
Father has breakfast with all or some of his children	6	6
Father drives children to an activity	4	3
Father sets up toys or gives play material	4	3
Father takes children on an errand	3	3
Father takes children to school	2	2
Total	26	24
Situations Allowing Father–Child Interactions (Child-Initiated)		
Children ask father to fix toys	5	6
Children watch father	3	1
Children help father with his activity	3	0
Children show father homework	2	1
Children ask father for money or goods	1	1
Children approach father for help	0	1
Total	14	10
Total of C and D	40	34

Table 8-2
Number of Group I and Group II Fathers Reporting Sunday Activities

	Number of Fathers	
	Group I	Group II
Routine Care		
Father helps dress the children	3	1
Father gives children a bath	1	1
Father wakes children up	1	0
Father undresses children	1	0
Total	6	2
Father–Child Interactions		
Father takes children on a Sunday outing often	5	6
Occasionally	1	3
Father plays with children	1	4
Father reads to children	0	1
Total	7	14
Situations Allowing Father–Child Interactions (Father-Initiated)		
Father has Sunday dinner with all or some of his children	9	9
Father has breakfast with all or some of his children	8	7
Father drives his family to an event	1	2
Total	18	18
Situations Allowing Father–Child Interactions (Child-Initiated)		
Children are "around" father	7	5
Children help father with his activity	3	0
Children watch TV with father	3	1
Total	13	6
Total of C and D	31	24
Summary of Tables 1 and 2		
Routine Care	31	22
Father–child interactions	26	34
Situations allowing father–child interactions (father-initiated)	44	42
Situations allowing father–child interactions (child-initiated)	27	16
Total	71	58

psychotic wives are sought after by their children more often than are men with well wives.

During the work week, fathers from both groups engage in roughly the same number of extended social interactions. However, Group II fathers report a greater number of shared activities on Sunday. It seems likely that on Sunday, when all fathers have more available time and the option to choose activities, Group II fathers choose to interact more often with their children than do Group I fathers.

Category D in Tables 8-1 and 8-2 show for Group I fathers a greater number of child-initiated activities that allow for, but do not demand, father–child interactions. Although this is a finding about children's behavior that is reported by their fathers and hence subject to possible distortion, it suggests that children of emotionally disturbed mothers demonstrate a greater interest in seeking out their fathers and maximizing their opportunities to be near them.

The fathers were specifically asked about child discipline and middle-of-the-night care. The answers revealed two problem areas faced by Group I fathers: the wife's ineffectiveness in discipline and her withdrawal from the family. Eight fathers with a psychotic wife versus only three fathers with a well wife reported either taking all the responsibility for the discipline or being the dominant parent with only occasional attempts by the wife. Husbands in Group I made comments such as "She's soft with the children" and "My wife has a problem in disciplining the children." It is striking that not one Group I father, versus four in Group II, reported the mother as taking primary responsibility for discipline. These findings are consistent with the Gardner and Tasch studies, which indicate that the emotionally stable mother plays a major role in discipline. Disciplinary actions were divided between both parents in two Group I and three Group II families.

The responses to the question "Who does your child call for when he wakes at night?" indicated that these formerly hospitalized women were less available and less responsive to their family than are the nonhospitalized wives following a psychotic episode. Five men in Group I either attend to their children or must prod their wives into action. Only one father in Group II attends to his children at night, and this occurs because his wife suffers from a severe visual deficiency. It is notable that this father does not perceive getting up as a man's responsibility but rather is compensating for his wife's disability. Another Group I father, in addition to the five discussed above, described how he, too, used to care for the children when they cried at night. He began to feel that this was his wife's job and so made the effort to wake her. Now his wife does hear the children and tends to them, but this husband stressed that she responded only after several years of training. Contributing to the lack of response of

Table 8-3
Birth Control Practices of Group I and Group II

	Number of Fathers	
Birth Control Device	Group I	Group II
Intrauterine device	3	0
Abstinence*	2	0
Prophylactic	1	1
Diaphragm	1	2
Pill	1	2
Rhythm	0	2
Total	8	7

*One father stated that he will not continue to practice abstinence after his wife receives her IUD.

Group I women is the effect of the medication they are taking. One Group I father specifically mentioned the deep sleep of his wife due to medication.

The fathers' involvement with domestic activities show patterns comparable to those already described in relation to child care. That is, fathers with psychotic wives are more involved in the daily household routine and exercise their judgment over domestic matters to a greater extent than do men with healthy wives. Group I fathers usually supervise food purchasing, which consumes a significant portion of the weekly income. Seven Group I fathers, as compared to only two of the controls, buy the weekly provisions. Two reasons for this involvement were given: (1) the husbands considered themselves better judges of good quality and prices; and (2) the wives' emotional problems included a reluctance to mix with large groups of people.

As might be expected, fathers with psychotic wives are home more hours during the week than are the fathers whose wives function well. This finding helps to account for the fact that "bedtime routine" was the only child-care activity in which Group II fathers showed greater involvement than Group I. Group II fathers reported that soon after they came home, it was time for the children to be put in bed. In order to spend time with their children, they specifically looked for ways to share the bedtime hour.

The greater domestic responsibility shouldered by Group I fathers is reflected in their attitudes toward having additional children. They clearly do not want to increase the size of their families. All the husbands with formerly hospitalized wives either did not want or were ambivalent about having additional children, whereas husbands with small families whose wives were well did want more children.

The choice of birth control techniques bears out the extreme reluctance of Group I fathers for further children and their disinclination to rely on their wives to act consistently and responsibly (see Table 8-3). Group I fathers undertook family planning by using abstinance or a prophylactic. These couples generally avoid the pill or diaphragm, which depend on the wife's intact ego function. Instead, the intrauterine device (IUD), which requires a one-time decision, is a preferred method.

|| DISCUSSION

It is clear that the husbands of psychiatrically ill wives feel a greater pressure to take on domestic and child care functions than do husbands of well women. The former are involved in aspects of child care that are routinely left to the healthy mother, and in addition they help to run the household. The clear desire of these men not to have further children reflects the demands on them of added duties and responsibilities.

Problems created by having to provide the care of both parents for the children are increased by the responsibilities involved in caring for the formerly hospitalized spouse. Frequently, particularly when the wife and mother is depressed, she is angry and resentful, and family members must accept a good deal of hostility. Weissman and Paykel (1974) have reported that, next to the children, the husband is most often the object of such hostility; communication is often impaired, as a result of mutual nagging, sarcasm, and physical violence; sexual intimacies are likely to be very limited and provide little pleasure for either husband or wife. Clearly, neither spouse receives the kinds of support and affection that are part of the "give and take" of marriage. Nor can differences be discussed and arguments resolved in the usual ways. The presence of a depressed wife does not involve simply the absence of a partner but, rather, a major shift in the nature of the marriage itself.

The present findings are reported for the groups of fathers whose wives are either hospitalized or well, functioning within the community. In the present study, it was not possible to examine these findings within the group of families in which the wife and mother had been hospitalized for depression separately from those in which the wife and mother had been hospitalized for schizophrenia. While focusing primarily on these families in which the wife and mother is depressed, it is necessary to carry out additional study by using larger numbers of families in which both the severity and form of the wife and mother's illness is systematically varied. On the basis of the findings from the present study, some observations can be made regarding the role of these husbands and fathers with their children that can provide the basis for subsequent inquiry.

In addition, these findings provide some guidelines for intervention among families in which a parent has been hospitalized for mental illness that are of particular relevance for primary prevention.

|| Fathers and Children

One generalization that can be made regarding the quality of the social and playful interactions between Group I fathers and their children is that they do not make as great an effort as do the fathers with healthy wives to be involved in recreation and child-oriented play. Group II fathers (those within the well families) reported a greater number of Sunday and holiday outings for pleasure and gave more instances of reading or playing with their children. The reasons for these differences may result from the situation and personality of Group I fathers. Men having wives who need their aid and support in child care may not have the desire or the energy to create situations that center around the child, while at the same time making father an important companion. These men already feel involved in the child-rearing process. One man married to a woman with a long history of mental illness was asked "What part of the children's upbringing do you feel is your responsibility?" He replied, "I guess all of it is." Also, fathers, with psychotic wives may be more withdrawn and isolated themselves thereby making them less sensitive to their children's need for companionship and social interaction. We can speculate that the children help to compensate for their father's lack of initiative by becoming part of his activity, thus creating situations that may result in some attention being paid them. Perhaps this is a reflection of the father–child alliance discussed by Merrill (1969).

What is the impact of this style of family organization on the children? Overall, the children whose mothers have been mentally ill experience their father as a protector and caretaker. Even though these children see their father more hours during the week, they are not often the center of his playful attention and tend to be neglected in terms of social interaction with their father. On the other hand, children of well mothers who have little difficulty in receiving basic care receive extra playful attention and interest from their fathers.

In spite of this focus on fathers and their activities, we cannot overlook the mother's activities and influence. All the men in Group I were employed, which means, in effect, that the mother was still the primary caretaker and parent. One of the most important ways a father can aid family stability and good child care is to support and discuss problems with his wife. After talking at length to the Group I fathers, we were impressed with the differing amounts of emotional support that they offered to their wives. Since these families were involved in a program of psychiatric nursing care, we were able to obtain independent ratings of the degree of emotional disturbance of the father by a graduate psychiatric nurse closely involved with the treatment of the family. As might be expected, there was considerable association between the severity of the father's pathology and the family's adjustment, with the healthier fathers showing good family coherence and harmony and the more disturbed fathers describing an empty or chaotic home life.

The unique adaptations shown by these healthier fathers vary considerably and depend on aspects of the wife's household disorganization as stemming from her illness. He will make suggestions as to how domestic activities could be rearranged or structured. Often his advice is carried out by the next day. Another example is Mr. L., who was a very active man both at work and in community affairs. Since his wife's hospitalization, he has discontinued his evening commitments in order to be home and available.

On the other hand, there are fathers who demonstrate a low level of adaptation to their wife's disturbance. Often they, too, have been hospitalized or treated for psychosis. They may scapegoat their wives and blame them for household disorganization while in fact they share much of the responsibility. Thus Mr. B. explains his refusal to help his wife, a chronic schizophrenic, with any household affairs by saying, "I have peculiar ideas about responsibility—each one has to carry out his own." However, Mr. B. repeatedly turns the children against their mother, at times even encouraging them to attack her physically. The father's activity can be understood both in terms of what the father directly does for the children and how he indirectly assists the mother in helping the children.

It is of interest to note that hospitalization of their wives leads to a positive change in marital attitudes among the more mentally healthy of the Group I fathers, a finding also noted by Morrow and Robins (1964). Both Mr. C. and Mr. L. felt strongly that they and their wives were closer following her illness. They commented that each of them was making a greater effort to communicate and to express feelings.

In a study of 44 couples in which one partner had been diagnosed as psychotic, DuPont, Ryder, and Grunebaum (1971) found that 70 percent of all respondents reported the psychotic experience as having had some positive impact on their marriage. They further found that the nonhospitalized spouses of those couples who reported high levels of marital satisfaction and recognized positive aspects of the psychotic experience showed much less psychological impairment on the Minnesota Multiphasic Personality Inventory than did the "healthy" spouse of those couples reporting low levels of marital satisfaction. This finding is consistent with our clinical impression of the mentally healthy father and his positive adaptation to his wife and family. Stated simply, the healthier the nonhospitalized spouse, the healthier the marriage and more positive the posthospitalization adaptation of both the couple and the marital family.

IMPLICATIONS FOR INTERVENTION AND PREVENTION WITHIN FAMILIES "AT RISK"

The findings from this study suggest the following guidelines for the clinician when a woman is hospitalized for psychosis. First, the husband should be regarded as an ally rather than an enemy of the therapeutic process. Many of these men are emotionally stable and competent and are highly motivated to keep their family intact and functioning well. Often psychiatrists have only minimal contact with these well family members. According to Deasy and Quinn (1955), limited time, uncertainty of prognosis, and the attitude that the psychiatrist is aligned with the patient against the spouse all contribute to this lack of contact. With men who can understand and help to make the necessary domestic adjustments, however, the "buffer" aspect of the psychiatrist's attempt to help the patient is not in the interest of better posthospital adjustment and clearly not in the interest of the children's future development. Second, husbands can benefit from counseling at the time of discharge, which will inform them as to how their wives are likely to function at home. Counseling should aim at alerting these husbands regarding such particular problem areas as the wife's extreme drowsiness due to medication, her reduced capacity to perform daily chores, and her inability to set limits for the children. Many men expect their wives to function well after hospitalization and are not prepared for the continuing signs of illness. Since the mother often remains withdrawn after discharge from the hospital, the father's social role with his children is especially critical.

Let us now turn to consideration of interaction among those children and their psychotic parents. There are three potential concerns for such interventions: (1) the patient, (2) the child, and (3) the spouse. It seems likely and is borne out both by the experience of Pasamanick's group (Angrist, Lefton, Dinitz, & Pasamanick, 1968) and ourselves, that a considerable number of psychotic mothers are relatively unresponsive to psychotherapeutic or psychoeducative intervention in changing their mothering role. They remain chronically disabled and function at a rather minimal level, able to do housework or to be employed at a diminished level, but having little in the way of interaction with their children. It is possible that the greater the genetic vulnerability and the biological basis of psychosis, the less difference an interpersonal approach to therapy will make. Weissman and Paykel (1974) in their study of depressed women have documented in detail the impact of parenting by depressed women.

They found that depressed women were inordinately involved in their children's daily lives, had difficulty communicating with them, and were aware of their own loss of affection for their children. They also reported considerable friction between those depressed mothers and their children, who were the most frequent objects of their mother's hostility.

It may be that children of depressed mothers are more vulnerable prior to adolescence whereas it is only at adolescence that the children of schizophrenic mothers become most vulnerable (Mednick & Schulsinger, 1968; Mednick, Schulsinger, Teasdale, Schulsinger, Venezles, & Rock, 1978). It is plausible, however, that long-standing parental psychotic depression could have a more pervasive impact on parenting and child care than schizophrenia, an illness in which symptoms are often confined to a single sector of the personality. In addition, a child may feel more responsible for the mother being sad and "down" and rather less responsible for her being irrational and "crazy."

Increasingly, we have come to believe that the children of psychotic parents should be offered psychiatric assistance on a continuous basis as Anthony (1972, 1974a,b, 1977, 1978a,b) has already undertaken. The advantage of such a program is that efforts are brought to bear directly on the family member at greatest risk and who is most malleable and likely to change. It is well known, however, that such psychotherapeutic work is often undermined by features of home environment, particularly if the changes that occur are threatening to the parents. The possibility of weaning the child from dependence on a psychotic parent or of immunizing the child against the influence of parental distortions may be accompanied by the unwillingness of the parent to permit the child to become independent or an unbeliever. Finally, there is the fact that the child will be with the parents for more of the time than with the therapeutic team.

Focusing efforts on the husband and father, in addition to the child, offers certain clear advantages, however. First, the father is with the child far more than any other single person. Clearly, one goal of a preventive intervention program among families in which the mother is mentally ill should be to encourage the father to increase the amount of time he spends with his children. Second, the spouse should be encouraged to intervene directly and protectively between the children and their mother when it is felt that the relationship between them is likely to be harmful. This goes against current practice in which the spouse of the psychotic patient is encouraged to become more understanding of their partner, rather than being oriented to prevention of disability to the children. The effort should be to help the spouse understand which interactions with the child are likely to be pathogenic and then to foster the ability to intervene effectively, but not punitively. To the extent to which this intervention is seen as undermining the parental coalition or "driving the other person crazy," by invalidating them, work must be done with care and is perhaps best undertaken in the context of the home, where observation rather than report is the source of the data.

We are impressed that all the spouses in the families we have studied are themselves greatly overburdened and in need of support. They report feeling depressed and helpless, seek "peace at any price," and often experience the mental health professional who is assisting the patient as blaming them for the illness. These feelings may lead to their withdrawal from their family or their failure to take an active role with their children. Clearly, psychoeducative work that emphasizes the vital role the husband and father can take in their children's lives, together with psychotherapeutic work, assisting to clarify the nature of the family pathology including feelings that interfere with parental action, will be of great importance.

Our clinical experience in working with families in which the wife and mother is mentally ill suggests that children function better in those families where the father is playing an active role with them. In the course of our current follow-up study (Grunebaum, Cohler, Kaufman, & Gallant, 1978), we have heard from a number of fathers who have been separated from their wives but have maintained custody of their children; they report that the children are doing well, although there has been little systematic study of families in which husbands and wives are together and separated. In those rare cases where a child was doing well whose father was not involved in parenting, there was not one instance of significant improvement in a family in which father was seen as inadequate.

The development of a program of preventive intervention, with fathers in particular, will demand changes in accepted practice. The traditional psychodynamic view of mental illness suggests that relatives should be supported during the period while the patient is "working out her problems" and should be encouraged to be understanding of the patient. The accepted family therapy approach to mental illness suggests that the healthy partner has just as much investment in the pathology as does the so-called ill partner and must also change. Often the change encouraged is in the direction of greater self-awareness of psychopathology by the healthy family member. Although the healthiest member of the family is often the person most capable of fostering creative change, it is also important to support that family member in determining which interactions are pathological and intervening directly to prevent them.

Provision of family-planning, counseling, and contraceptive services should be an essential task of mental health professionals who work with families under the stress of mental illness. Research has shown that mentally ill women have a large number of unplanned and unwanted pregnancies and that their children are likely to be at risk for psychological, social, and educational impairment (Abernethy, 1973, 1974; Abernethy & Grunebaum, 1973; Abernethy, Grunebaum, Hunt, & Groover, 1976; Abernethy, Robbins, Abernethy, & Grunebaum, 1975; Grunebaum & Abernethy, 1975; Grunebaum, Abernethy, & Rofman, 1971; Grunebaum, Abernethy, Clogh, & Groover, 1975).

Additional births provide an additional stress for an already burdened woman and her family and may lead to a recurrence of her illness. With the widespread therapeutic use of psychotropic drugs that render the patient socially functional, we are faced with an increasing birth rate among the mentally ill. A 12 percent increase in the birth rate was found by Erlenmeyer-Kimlind, Ranger, and Kaillman (1966) between 1934–1936 and 1954–1956, and we suspect that this trend has continued. In addition, the mentally ill population has special difficulties in making informed and balanced decisions about sexual behavior and fertility since many patients are at only marginal functional levels. Many are impulsive and immature adolescents. Recent work suggests that these very young parents represent an increasing proportion of the psychotic mothers of young children. Referral to community-based family-planning clinics is rarely successful; family-planning counseling should be an integral part of treatment.

These studies show that psychiatric patients desire contraceptive assistance. Such assistance is rarely suggested by mental health professionals, and it is certainly not a routine part of treatment planning. When family-planning counseling and services are provided in the mental hospital, however, they are welcomed and used; with ongoing support from the staff, available findings show that responsible family-planning practices are continued after discharge. Resistance is more likely to come from the staff than the patients. With the aid of a grant initially from the Office of Economic Opportunity, and now from the Office of Family Planning, we have counseled and provided contraception for more than 1000 women in three state mental hospitals in Massachusetts in the last 3 years. In this day of rapid discharges, short-term hospitalization, and community-based care, helping a woman to plan her family should be part of total care. It is, in addition, a safe and effective form of prevention.

Even if we were to undertake all these measures, it is not at all certain that we would significantly reduce the incidence of psychosis. Perhaps we will have a positive influence only on the level of milder psychopathology, and perhaps not even that. Manfred Bleuler's (1974) report of children who grew up in homes in which a psychotic parent was present offers an eloquent comment regarding the future of intervention efforts with psychotic parents and their offspring: "In short, the sufferings that the children endure can continue to affect their lives even when they do not interfere with their health or professional attainment. Any horrible experience remembered from childhood continues to hurt and to cast its shadow over life's happiness." Hopefully, continuation of clinical efforts may mitigate this human tragedy as we accompany families through their struggle with madness.

9

Depressive Reactions During Separation Period: Individuation and Self Among Children of Psychotic Depressed Mothers

Sandra Bemesderfer and Bertram J. Cohler

Psychic development across the first 3 years of life involves achievement of a stable representation of self and others, increasingly successful regulation of inner tension, and increasing sense of inner autonomy, described by Mahler and her colleagues (Mahler, 1968; Mahler, Pine, & Bergman, 1975) as the process of separation–individuation. As a result of the availability of reliable maternal care, the "ordinary devoted mother" (Robertson, 1962) provides a range of care that permits the child to develop a concept of an "average expectable environment" (Hartmann, 1939).

Gradually, children learn to communicate their needs to their mother and to anticipate and experience the mother's generally satisfying response to their needs (Sander, 1962, 1964, 1969, 1975). Gradually, the child develops the ability to experience self-soothing, which is parallel to his mother's caretaking activities (Tolpin & Kohut, 1980). With the realization of object and person permanence (Piaget, 1937), which provides the basis for establishing relationships with others, together with increasingly successful regulation of inner tension, the child is able to take the next important developmental step, experiencing sustained satisfaction in

Preparation of this chapter was supported by a grant from the National Institute of Mental Health (MH-28143) and a grant from the Joyce Foundation of Chicago. The authors would like to thank Dr. Jerry Dincin, Executive Director, The Thresholds for his continuing support of the program and Ms. Rose Ann Clark, project psychologist, for her many helpful comments and observation of the development of these and other children participating in the "mother's project."

relationships with others on an enduring basis, based on the successful resolution of the conflict associated with the separation individuation process across the first years of life, leading to the establishment of "libidinal" object constancy (Fraiberg, 1969; Freud, A., 1960; Hartmann, 1952; Mahler, Pine, & Bergman, 1975).

This overview of psychological development in early childhood assumes that the mother is capable of rendering consistent and appropriately dosed care that provides the basis for the child's developing sense of inner regulation. Study of families in which this care is unavailable or uncertain provides important information regarding the course of the developing mother–child relationship (Winnicott, 1965). Previous research has focused primarily on deprivation of maternal care, either in situations where environmental events enforce such a separation, as in the English studies of the war nurseries (Freud, A. & Burlingham, 1943, 1944) or where children have been orphaned or neglected (Spitz, 1945, 1946). Much of this literature has been summarized by Bowlby (1951, 1958, 1969, 1973, 1980), Ainsworth (Ainsworth, 1969, 1973; Ainsworth, Blehar, Waters, & Wall, 1978), and Rutter (1972).

Study of mothers hospitalized for mental illness and their young children provides another opportunity for examining the impact of mothering on the child's psychological development. First, the mother's illness (typically either a schizophrenic or unipolar affective psychosis) means that she may be unavailable to her child for periods of time because of symptoms related to the illness, and also because of physical separation from the child as a result of more or less brief hospitalizations (Grunebaum, Weiss, Cohler, Gallant, & Hartmann, 1982). In addition, the fact of the mother's illness means some increased genetic "loading" for serious psychopathology in the child, suggesting that these children of seriously mentally ill mothers may be both genetically and environmentally "at risk" or "vulnerable" (Anthony, 1974a,b, 1978a,b; Garmezy, 1974, 1977, 1978b).

|| BACKGROUND OF THE PRESENT RESEARCH

Over the course of the past decade, there has been considerable study of the children of schizophrenic mothers. Starting from an interest specifically in the development of schizophrenia, investigators have studied offspring of schizophrenic parents as a relevant population. The increased genetic loading for schizophrenia among these children of one schizophrenic parent (10–12 percent versus less than 1 percent among children of well or nonschizophrenic parents) is believed to increase the probability that the study of some of these offspring vulnerable or at risk over long periods of time will reveal some who will eventually become identified patients, so that the etiology of the schizophrenic illness can be more readily understood, (Anthony, 1978a,b; Garmezy, 1978b; Garmezy & Devine, 1977; Shakow, 1973).

Beginning with Shakow's (1946, 1963) pioneering studies of attentional processes, attention has been viewed as a cognitive function that has a specific causal relationship in the etiology of schizophrenia (Garmezy, 1978b; Mednick, S., 1958). Since deficits in attention and information processing have been reported to differentiate between adult schizophrenics and nonschizophrenic groups (including both other psychiatric patients and well comparison groups) (Shakow, 1963; Silverman, J., 1964) and, since the offspring of schizophrenic parents show increased genetic risk for this disorder, long-term study of these offspring would be expected to yield important information regarding antecedents of adult thought disorder, together with the related impairment in social competence so characteristic of process schizophrenia in adulthood (Garmezy, 1974a, 1977, 1978b). Mednick and Schulsinger's (Mednick & Schulsinger, 1968, 1970; Mednick et al., 1978) pioneering reports have provided some evidence for this hypothesis, suggesting that deficits in information processing were central to the development of vulnerability among the offspring of schizophrenics.

As a result of this more specific concern with the transmission of an attentional disturbance from mother to child among schizophrenic patients and their offspring (Garmezy, 1978b), interest has shifted away from the larger issue of the impact of parental personality on the child's development, including the particular vicissitudes of parental psychosis on the child's psychic development. With the exception of Anthony's pioneering clincal studies (Anthony, 1975, 1976b, 1978a,b), little study has been given to this later issue in the literature on children "at risk" as a result of parental psychosis. Furthermore, the literature on risk has focused almost entirely on schizophrenia because of the relevance of this disturbance for the brain sciences, and because schizophrenia is a more visible disturbance on which to focus efforts at intervention and prevention. Even serious depressive disorders fail to attract attention until the prospective patient becomes so immobilized that routine daily tasks remain unfinished.

The impact of a mood disorder of psychotic proportions is likely to have as significant an effect on the child's development as a schizophrenic disorder. First, the "risk" as a result of genetic loading is roughly the same for each disorder (Erlenmeyer-Kimling, 1977; Rosenthal, 1970). Second, the apathy and withdrawal characteristic of the depressed patient is likely to have as profound an impact on both the child's cognitive and socioemotional development as the more clearly characteristic cognitive disturbance that is so much a part of the schizophrenic syndrome. Not only are the children of depressed mothers likely to receive inadequate supervision (Cohler, Grunebaum, Weiss, Hartmann, & Gallant, 1975), but also the mother's inability to respond to the child's need for empathy contributes to the child's problem in the development of a nuclear self. Third, recent developments in our understanding of depression suggest a significant cognitive component in disorders of mood as well as in disorders of thinking. As a result of a redefinition of the concept of affect (Basch, 1976; Schmale & Engel, 1975), mood itself may be understood as a form of cognition. Recent formulations of the dynamics of the depressive syndrome emphasize the cognitive nature of this disturbance, including Beck's (1967, 1974) explicit cognitive formulation and the more recent concept of "learned helplessness" as described by Seligman (1974, 1975) and, more recently, by Abramson, Seligman, and Teasdale (1978). Such reformations of depression as a cognitive disturbance points to the likelihood that parental depression may affect the child's cognitive development to the same extent that schizophrenia does.

Within the tradition of high-risk research, most study has been devoted either to infancy (Fish, 1963; Fish & Alpert, 1962, 1963; Fish & Hagin, 1973; Sameroff, 1978; Sameroff & Zax, 1973a, 1978; Schachter, Elmer, Ragins, 1977) or to children of school age (Beskow, 1955; Garmezy, 1974, 1978b; Mednick, 1966, 1978; Mednick & Schulsinger, 1968; Mednick, Maura, Schulsinger, & Mednick, 1973; Mednick et al., 1978; Rolf, 1972; Rolf & Garmezy, 1974; Weintraub, Liebert, & Neale, 1978; Weintraub, Prinz, & Neale, 1978). There has been relatively little attention paid to the development of the young children of mentally ill mothers in the period referred to by Mahler and her colleagues (Mahler et al., 1975) as junior toddlerhood, during which time the child is involved in the resolution of conflicts regarding separation and individuation, which are so central to the achievement of inner autonomy. Even less attention has been paid to the nature of mother–child interaction during this developmental period. Anthony (1968, 1978a,b) has devoted some study to this period of development and recognizes the importance for the child's own development of resolving the mother–child symbiosis. Anthony discusses the additional problems posed for the toddler of resolving this issue of individuation among families in which the mother has an affective disorder, although little systematic data are provided in support of this formulation.

The present chapter documents the impact of the presence of a psychotic depressed mother on the child's resolution of issues associated with separation individuation process. Observations from two mother–child pairs studied systematically in an intervention program over an extended period of time illustrate the unique problems in the child's development of a cohesive self resulting from being cared for by a psychotic depressed mother during the second year of life.

MATERNAL DEPRESSIVE AFFECT AND PSYCHOLOGICAL DEVELOPMENT OF CHILDREN OF DEPRESSED MOTHERS

Affect Theory and Psychoanalysis

There is fairly general agreement that psychoanalysis has had difficulty in defining the concept of affect (Basch, 1976). David Rapaport, in his classic paper on the subject, says, "We do not possess a systematic statement of the psychoanalytic theory of affects" (Rapaport, 1953, p. 476). Rapaport traces affect theory through three separate phases: "In the first theory, affects were equated with drive catheses; in the second theory, they appeared as drive representations serving as safety valves for drive cathexes the discharge of which was prevented; in the third theory, they appear as ego functions, and as such are no longer safety valves but used as signals by the ego" (Rapaport, 1953, p. 493).

This third formulation of affect as a signal used by the ego has resulted in contributions from investigators in the field of signal and communications theory. Once the concern is with a mechanism of communication rather than a quantity of cathected libido, it is possible to study levels of messages being sent and received at different stages of psychological development. There has been considerable controversy as to whether depression is theoretically possible in the earliest stages of an infant's development. Observations on newborn infants and their parents document the range of affective behavior available to the neonate. Parents can identify the infant's mood by observing his or her face and listening to its vocalizations (Gaensbauer & Harman, 1976). Moreover, research on direct brain stimulation of subcortical areas of the brain resulting in "affective responses" indicates that affects are involuntary responses (Ekman, Friesen, & Ellsworth, 1972). This is important because it explains why, long before there is advanced development of neocortical associational capacity, infants seem to possess the full range of behavior associated with adult emotion.

Because the infant is born dependent on a continuing symbiotic relationship with the mother, it depends on her both to receive affective signals and to send a set of communications. If the parent is unable to send or receive affective communication development of the infant–mother relationship is seriously impaired. From this perspective, "proper mothering" involves creation of an atmosphere in which what happens to the baby relates to the signals sent to the mother (Emde et al., 1976). In questioning why there are so many instances in which neither timing, severity, nor multiplicity of insults can account for severe ego fragmentation observed among disturbed children, Mahler emphasizes the importance of signal communication as essential in understanding the nature of successes and failures in the relationship:

> I believe that the cardinal precipitory event in these cases of infantile psychoses is the breakdown of that highly subtle circular process to which Emmy Sylvester (1953) has called attention: the mutual reciprocal relationship which enables mother and infant to send out and receive each other's signals, a compatible predictable interaction . . . . If the infant's signals do not reach the mother because he is unable to send them, or if the infant's signals are not heard because the mother does not have the capacity to react to them, the mother–infant circular reaction takes on a dangerously discordant rhythm.*

Such observations regarding the impact of impaired signal communications among depressed mothers on the developing mother–child relationship raise a number of important questions regarding the impact on the child of this transmission of disturbance of affect from mother to child, including the following more specific questions to be addressed in the present study:

1. When do developmental deviations first become apparent in the child's behavior?
2. Why are some children more sensitive than others to childhood loss?
3. What factors can be associated with the diagnosis of observable depression of a young child?
4. When does this depression become crystallized into a recognizable syndrome?

|| Depression in Childhood

There is little consensus regarding the diagnosis of depression in childhood. While children unquestionably experience depressive affect of varying intensity in response to a variety of situations, such affect is not necessarily a sign of psychopathology (Jacobson, Lampl DeGroot, 1953; Schmale, 1964; Sperling, 1959; Toolan, 1962; Winnicott, 1954). If the child experiences a period of prolonged deprivation and object loss, including

*Reprinted with permission from Mahler, M. On sadness and grief in infancy. *Psychoanalytic Study of the Child,* 1961, *16,* 340.

"insufficient mothering," however, it may become difficult to reverse this depressive affect.

At the outset, it is important to distinguish depression as a reaction to such situations of loss and deprivation from depression as a particular psychological illness, just as it is important to distinguish between adult and childhood depressive disturbances.

|| *Diagnosis of Depression in Early Childhood*

Much of the literature on childhood depression considers the child's mood disturbance as a particular expression of affect, rather than as a disorder in the same manner that adult depression is considered to be a disorder (Abraham, 1924; Anthony, 1975a,b, 1976a; Bemporad & Wilson, 1978; Bibring, 1953; Gittelman-Klein, 1977; Klein, 1948; Malmquist, 1971, 1976, 1977; Rapaport, 1953; Raskin, 1977; Rie, 1966; Sandler & Joffee, 1965; Zetzel, 1961). As is frequently noted in the literature, this confusion regarding the nature of depression in childhood continues because little distinction is made between depression as a basic affective response in psychological experience and depressive illness as a regressive clinical syndrome. In the major systematic study to date of depressed parents and children with depressive disorders, Welner, Welner, McCrary, and Leonard (1977) and Welner (1978) report that 25 percent of the children of parents with an affective psychosis showed an affective disorder, as contrasted with none of the children of well parents. In making the decision as to whether to label a child depressed, Welner has equated symptoms of depression among adults with those among children. McKnew, Cytryn, Effron, Gershon, and Bunney (1979), studying the adjustment of a group of psychotic depressed parents, but without any control group, report that the boys of depressed parents are particularly likely to show sustained depressive symptoms over a 4-month period between interviews. Such findings are consistent with previous case reports that have suggested that depressed children are particularly likely to have depressed mothers (Schechtman, Gilpian, & Worland, 1976; Pozanski & Zrull, 1970). Once again such studies make the assumption that childhood and adult depression may be equated.

Psychoanalytic study of the origins of depression in childhood generally does not make this assumption of the equivalence of childhood and adult experience of depression: childhood depression may be understood as similar to, but not identical with, some forms of adult depression. Anthony (1975a,b) provides a tertiary model in which *primary manifestations of depression* (which include the core of the depressive disorder—characterized by ambivalence, loss of interest in the outside world, pessimism, joylessness, ego inhibition, diminished self-esteem, inhibition of function, and less than normal libidinal investment in self-representations—are shared by both child and adult depressive disorders, whereas *secondary manifestations*—which include clinging to people, searching for new objects, affect-equivalent psychosomatic states, and antisocial behavior—are characteristic primarily of childhood, and *tertiary manifestations*—which include a total involvement of the personality and a complete regression—are appropriate only to adult depression.

This model resolves the problem posed by structural theory in psychoanalysis, which suggests that, because a particular structuralized conflict is not possible in the "pre-oedipal child," childhood depression cannot be a meaningful concept. For example, Rochlin (1953) suggests that clinical depression is a superego phenomenon that involves aggression directed against the self with a certain directness and intensity that is not actually possible for the young child to experience. Rochlin's either–or view is based on a classic analytic view of depression. Although the childhood depressive reaction does not represent such a complex intrapsychic conflict, the child's reaction can still be a variant of the depressive reaction that is developmentally continuous with the adult clinical form.

Anthony's primary "manifestations of depression" closely resembles the diagnostic criteria developed by Joffe and Sandler (1965). The work of these authors is particularly important since their data are derived from a systematic review of 100 actual cases recorded in the Hampstead Index; much of the psychoanalytic literature on childhood depression remains purely theoretical. Nine aspects of depressive reactions were noted by these authors: (1) appearing sad, unhappy, or depressed; (2) showing a degree of withdrawal; (3) described as being discontented; (4) communicating a sense of feeling rejection or being unloved; (5) being unprepared to accept help or to conform; (6) tendency to regress to oral passivity; (7) insomnia; (8) autoerotic activities; (9) therapist having difficulty in maintaining sustained contact.

Psychoanalytic Formulations of Basis of Depression

Within psychoanalysis there have been two major theoretical approaches to the study of depression: (1) the classic view proposed by S. Freud (1917) and Abraham (1911, 1924) and (2) the ego-psychological view first described by Bibring (1953). The classic view is rooted in Freud's concept of primary narcissism, including that narcissistic injury suffered in childhood. Freud described a sequence that includes loss of the love object, attack on the internalized object with resulting self-reproach, and libidinal regression to the oral–cannibalistic stage. Abraham later noted the importance of considering simultaneous love and hate, repressed and projected sadism and its associated guilt, and inhibition and loss through oral expulsion.

Bibring's ego-psychological view restates this concept of loss in terms of the problem of frustrated ego development, in which the roles of orality and aggression inwardly directed at the self are given little emphasis. According to Bibring, in the depressed child, the early infant's experience, resulting from frequent frustrations of oral needs, consists first of anger and protest and, subsequently, as the "signals" are disregarded, of exhaustion and helplessness. Bibring maintains that depression is determined by tensions within the ego and defines depression as "everything that lowers or paralyzes the ego's self-esteem, without changing the narcissistically important aims." In Bibring's model, childhood depression involves a regression not of libido to oral fixation, but rather, ego regression to a primary infantile state characterized by inhibition, loss of self-esteem, and helplessness.

The concept of narcissism is considered in ego-psychological terms, related to level of psychosocial development and correlated with defensive need, precipitating factor, and central conflict. The issue of self-esteem is at the center of Bibring's theory; regulation of self-esteem is a critical issue in the life of the depressed child. The cycle described by Bibring, in which high aspirations (grandiosity) give rise to feelings of helplessness and hopelessness, and, finally, to depression, is more conceivable as a psychological event in the child's experience than the complex sequence portrayed by structural theory.

There is general agreement that structural views of depression have little bearing on the development of clinical depression during childhood. Indeed, Sandler and Joffee (1965, p. 88) "legitimately doubt whether theories which are heavily influenced by the study of melancholia in adults provide the most suitable starting point for the investigation of depression in children." They distinguish the "depressive reaction" from the "unhappy child" and these two states from the basic depressive response, a state in which there is a discrepancy between the ideal state of the self and the actual state of the self. The ideal state refers to a condition of satiation, security, and contentment [S. Freud's (1921) concept of primary narcissism], in contrast with chronic discomfort, unrelieved hunger, and frustration. Some persons later respond to such frustration with the attempt to recover this primary psychological state at any time in the life span when helplessness is experienced.

Melanie Klein (1948) postulated introjective–projective processes occurring from birth onward, connected with the loss accompanying weaning at 3–12 months. This is seen as an expectable developmental situation derived from an earlier "paranoid position." Superego structuralization during the first year is believed to be related to feelings of possessiveness and destructiveness toward the parental object. The "depressive position" develops as a consequence of moving from a part to a whole-object relationship.

Whereas Rapaport, Bibring, and Joffee and Sandler speak of depression as a usual reaction when the ego faces helplessness against overwhelming odds. Anthony maintains that:

> A basic depressive affect comparable to anxiety does appear to exist and that in many individuals it becomes the affect of choice which may, under some circumstances, consolidate into a periodic or persistent mood. As is the case with anxiety, depressive affect has a signal scanning function associated with the possibility of object loss, although more inner-directed and less object-related than anxiety. The child is no stranger to this affect, and certain children are more depression prone than others.†

However, there is no general agreement in the literature regarding how early in development it may be meaningful to talk about childhood depression. It is generally accepted that it is useful to distinguish depression as a basic affect from a specific clinical illness.

Depression and Development of Mother–Child Relationship

The concept of depression-proneness is central to the understanding of mental illness among both parents and children. Clinical reports in the literature suggest that parental depression is the most salient determinant of childhood depression (Anthony, 1975a,b; Posanski & Zrull, 1970; Schechtman et al., 1976), together with the early experience of object loss (Abraham, 1911, 1924; Bell, S., 1970; Bowlby, 1958, 1969). It should be noted that such object loss refers to more than an actual temporary or permanent loss. Rather, it refers to the child's subjective perception of a loss as having occurred.

A number of investigators have studied this phenomenon of object loss through demonstration of the impact of so-called "maternal deprivation" on young children (Bowlby, 1951). Levy (1937) reported on an 8-year-old child who was repeatedly placed in foster homes and later adopted and who continued to manifest an incapacity to form attachments; Goldfarb (1943) studied 30 children for 34–35 months and found the 15 children raised in institutions had lower IQs by 28 points; Spitz (1945, 1946) demonstrated that infants separated after 6 months experienced grief reactions only if the previous maternal relationship had been satisfactory. More recently, Michael Rutter (1972) has reported extensive empirical research regarding the influence of maternal deprivation on development in early childhood; however, he has not demonstrated a spe-

---

†Reprinted with permission from Anthony, E. J. Childhood depression. In E. J. Anthony & T. Benedek (Eds.), *Depression and human existence*. Boston: Little, Brown, 1975, p. 242.

cific link between maternal deprivation per se and the development of childhood depression.

Different kinds of deprivation—psychological, social, cognitive, and physical—must be specified in understanding the relationship of such early deprivation and the development of a depressive disorder. Bowlby (1958, 1969) maintains that proximity to the maternal figure is necessary for attachment behavior to develop. Attachment occurs as a result of certain behavioral systems activated for five discrete response patterns that are biologically determined: sucking, clinging, following, crying, and smiling. The problem with this approach is that studying attachment behavior, including the research reported by Ainsworth, Blehar, Waters, and Wall (1978), is that the study of such responses to strange situations is not the same as studying the internal psychological processes involved in attachment and object relations.

Prior research may have overemphasized the child's exclusive relationship to the mother and underemphasized both cognitive development and experiences with other family members (Kagan, Kearsley, and Zelazo, 1978; Lamb, 1976a,b). There has been a tacit assumption that a failure in the early mother–child relationship will inevitably lead to a particular deleterious outcome: however, depressive consequences can be subtle and need not necessarily appear as gross disturbances. Anna Freud (1936) has observed that maternal depression at any point during the first 2 years after birth may create a tendency to similar depressive mood in the child. Fusion with a depressed mother may, itself, induce a mood disturbance in the child (Anthony, 1971b, 1975a,b), especially among children who live "as if" their experiences are necessary for validation of parental needs, with consequent threat of abandonment if these experiences are not validating (Brodey, 1965). Serious and chronic parental preoccupations leave little room for the child's spontaneous curiosity and freedom to explore the immediate world. Parental pessimism induces feelings of failure in the child, together with a feeling of responsibility for the predicament of the parents. A depressed and worried parent limits the child's freedom to play and to test the environment. Similarly, parental expression of depressed mood, in the form of extreme and activity and periodic overstimulating play with a child, may also contribute to the child's depressive mood.

According to Mahler (1961, 1966), the depressive mood originates during the separation–individuation phase and is an expectable part of the developmental process. As toddlers gradually become aware of themselves and of the mother as a separate individual and observe that the mother does not minister automatically to their needs, they experience lower morale. The more understanding the mother actually is, the less upset the child becomes; when her mothering is experienced by the child as deficient, the child's self-esteem suffers and susceptibility to depressive moods increases. In a more recent formulation of this developmental process, Mahler, Pine and Bergman (1975) refer to the period during the first half of the second year of life as the practicing subphase. As a result of learning how to walk and to create physical separateness from the mother, the child experiences alternating periods of elation over accomplishments and sadness, or "low-keyedness," resulting from the mother's absence. Among children who are beginning to establish a symbiotic relationship with their mother, this variation mood is largely absent; whereas, among children developing a reciprocal social relationship with their mother, there are great variations in the expression of mood, with some children showing prolonged periods of crying, particularly after reunion with their mother.

In discussing this proneness to depression and its relation to narcissistic vulnerability in early childhood, Malmquist (1971, p. 189) observed that "Narcissistic vulnerability is not necessarily related to actual loss. What the vulnerability relates to are developmental lines leading to separation and individuation." When the baby leaves and returns, he or she is taking steps toward person constancy, relinquishing the fusion with the mother and reducing gradiose fantasies. As a result, the child experiences a mood disturbance that is a developmentally appropriate accompaniment of the development of psychic autonomy.

If "libidinal" object constancy is not successfully realized, there is marked ambivalence, precocious overidentification, pseudo self-sufficiency, and decreased spontaneity, which leads the child to develop a self-concept of being defective and unable to deal with the inner tensions resulting from experiences not dosed in developmentally appropriate ways (Bettelheim, 1967; Fraiberg, 1969; Kohut, 1975; Tolpin & Kohut, 1980). The child comes to feel unable to deal with these tensions or to resolve the reality experiences that evoke such tensions and as a result, feels depleted, unworthy, and even abandoned. The development of such a depreciated self-concept is a critical factor in the development of the "nucleus" of later depression during these early years of life.

It is believed that the psychotic mother, particularly the mother with a depressive psychosis, may provide the circumstances that lead to just this sense of a defective self, and accompanying depressive mood. Partially as a result of her disturbance, and partially as a result of multiple hospitalizations and disruptions in the family engendered by the disturbance and hospitalizations, the issues intrinsic to the separation–individuation phase cannot be resolved, and the child comes to feel overwhelmed and vulnerable to tensions that cannot be soothed, enhancing whatever sadness is learned by the child in identifying with the mother's feelings.

INTERVENTION WITHIN VULNERABLE FAMILIES: PERSPECTIVES ON TREATMENT AND PRIMARY PREVENTION

The traditional mode of intervention within families in which mothers had been hospitalized for mental illness, including psychotic depression during the early years in the family life cycle, when there were young children at home, was for the mother to remain in the hospital while her young children were placed with relatives or in foster homes. However, as Rice, Ekdahl, and Miller (1971) have noted, such multiple placement and resulting uncertainty regarding the child's care extract a heavy cost in terms of the child's psychological development. Multiple foster placements have much the same effect as the deprivation of mothering earlier described by Spitz, Bowlby, and others.

Beginning in 1959, a pioneering program was developed in Boston, as a result of which mothers were admitted to the wards of a university-affiliated state mental hospital together with their children. The mother–child dyad was viewed as the patient, rather than the mother herself, in this unique "joint-admission" program. Results of this innovative program were reported in a number of earlier papers and summarized in the volume by Grunebaum, Weiss, Cohler, Gallant, and Hartmann (1982), *Mentally ill mothers and their children.* When contrasted with young children of mentally ill mothers in traditional foster placements, such children participating in this joint-admission program showed an increment in developmental status, including overall developmental quotient (DQ), language and sensory-motor development, and object manipulation. Children admitted to the hospital with their mothers also showed a greater range of affect expression and a greater capacity to differentiate between mother and strangers than did the children in the traditional foster-care program.

The children of the mothers admitted to the hospital with their mothers still performed at a less satisfactory level of development than did children in the well control group, with differences most apparent in the area of interpersonal behavior. Examination of performance of well children and both groups of children of mentally ill mothers, at 12 months, with use of the Cattell schedule, revealed children of mentally ill mothers to show a preference for instrumental over interpersonal relationships as being intrinsically satisfying and to be more involved with things than with people. In contrast to the children not admitted to the hospital with their mother, when compared with their well counterparts, however, children of mentally ill mothers participating in the joint-admission program showed comparable stranger anxiety and ability to discriminate between mother and stranger. A follow-up study nearly a year later indicated that most of these findings regarding the relative advantage of the joint-admission program for children admitted to the hospital with their mothers were maintained over time.

Unfortunately, changing patterns of hospital admissions have made it difficult to continue joint-admission programs. Increasing hospital costs and changing patterns of hospital care have led to shortened periods of hospitalization. Since it usually requires many weeks to work out the details of the joint-admission program with nursing staff, the mother herself, and the family, it is difficult to prepare properly in a brief stay for a joint admission. In addition, this pattern of multiple brief admissions has much the same impact on the child as multiple foster care arrangements. The alternative has been to attempt to prevent rehospitalization and the attendant crisis generated within the family, by providing alternatives, including intensive nursing and social work support for home care, together with a variety of day-hospital or social rehabilitation programs that involve the mother in a support system for herself and her family.

In the first such alternative clinical trial of services provided for mentally ill mothers, there was only a partial success (Grunebaum, 1977). Contrasting rates of rehospitalization for mentally ill mothers using either intensive weekly aftercare, with lengthy visits to the home, or minimal contact by phone on a monthly basis, there was little difference in the nature of the mother–child relationship, the child's cognitive or social development, or the mother's own posthospital adjustment between the intensively and minimally treated groups of formerly hospitalized psychotic (schizophrenic and depressed) mothers. Indeed, although the average for rehospitalization for female psychotic patients is about 50 percent (Brown, Parkes, & Wing, 1961; Wessler & Iven, 1970), the average rehospitalization rate in the intensive nursing aftercare research was about 33 percent, a reduction in hospitalization possibly not of clinical interest considering the costs involved.

In more recent clinical research efforts at preventing rehospitalization and achieving stabilization of the mother's position within the family, the present authors have initiated a comprehensive intervention program at the Thresholds, a social rehabilitation center on Chicago's north side. The advantage of the Thresholds program is that it has a comprehensive intervention program with an explicit emphasis on the development of work skills, so that members who wish to do so will be able to obtain work. This work training program is supplemented by a variety of other kinds of intervention, including individual and group psychotherapy, activity groups, and explicit instruction in the use of psychiatric medication (including continual monitoring of medication compliance). Evening and weekend programs are available, as well as a series of graduated residential arrangements designed to foster independent living. This program is clearly ideal for intervention with mentally ill mothers and their young children who require such a supervised daily program. Work provides some alternative to remaining at home, and even part-time work provides the mother with a chance to get something for herself and to have time apart from her children.

Intervention Programs for Children of Mentally Ill Mothers

The Thresholds program offers an opportunity for the first time to intervene simultaneously with the mentally ill mother and her child. As a result of the intensive study over the past 15 years (Garmezy, 1972, 1974a, 1977, 1978), much more is known than before about areas of possible impairment in the cognitive and social development of the children of mentally ill mothers. At the preschool level, both the ideal program might include both cognitive skill training in such specific areas as attention, together with preventive remediation in the child's social development, and conjoint therapy of mother and child together. The few pilot programs proposed to date certainly point in the direction of this multifaceted approach to the intervention with the vulnerable child (Anthony, 1969, 1970a,b, 1972, 1973, 1974a,b, 1977; Heber, 1978).

Although there has been relatively little study of maternal diagnosis as related to the child's adjustment, it is almost certain that the nature and severity of the mother's illness is related to the quality of the child's subsequent adjustment (Cohler, Gallant, Grunebaum, Weiss, & Gamer, 1977). The child of a women with a thought disorder is likely to experience quite a set of problems different from those of the child whose mother is depressed or who alternates between euphoria and depression (Weissman & Paykel, 1974). The degree of the mother's disturbance also makes an important difference in the impact of her illness on her child. Frequent absence from the home due to rehospitalization, in itself, has a particularly disruptive effect (Rice, Ekdahl, Miller, 1971).

Even among the most profoundly disturbed women, not all children become disturbed. Indeed, only a small fraction of the children of mentally ill mothers (as opposed to the situation in which both parents are mentally ill) actually show a psychiatric disturbance. Indeed, studies reviewed by Kaufman, Grunebaum, Cohler, and Gamer (1979) show that some of the offspring, particularly those of schizophrenic mothers, appear to be more creative than the children of well mothers. Anthony (1974), Garmezy (1974a, 1977, 1978), and Kaufman, Grunebaum, Cohler, and Gamer (1979), stress the importance of studying those children of mentally ill mothers who remain competent and invulnerable to psychopathology. Of course, careful longitudinal study of children who do and do not succumb, together with increased understanding of the factors associated with the greater vulnerability, are among the most important contributions of clinical research projects where much data are collected on a relatively small group of mentally ill mothers and their children.

In those cases in which the child does ultimately succumb to psychopathology, it would appear that heredity and environment have combined to create a situation that is particularly hazardous for the child's development (Mednick & Schulsinger, 1968; Mednick et al., 1978). Rutter (1966), comparing disturbed and well children of psychiatrically ill parents, reports that ill children, who were most likely to have the mother rather than the father as the mentally ill parent and were found to have a greater intensity of anxiety and more obvious behavioral symptoms than the well children. Such children had more often been involved in a parental illness that had been of some duration. More chronically and seriously disturbed parents are more effective in bringing the child into the parental disturbance and appear to have a more deleterious impact on the child's own development.

This finding suggests that the factor that makes the single most important difference in the degree to which the child remains invulnerable to parental mental illness may be the nature of the mother–child relationship, including the degree of involvement that the child shows in the parental illness (Anthony, 1971b, 1975a,b, 1978a,b). Where the child has been helped to find alternate sources of emotional satisfaction, and where the mother's illness is less focused on the child, there is a greater chance that the child can maintain competence. Clearly, even with increased genetic risk, greater probability of perinatal risk, multiple or surrogate mothering during early childhood due to the mother's frequent absence, and adverse life circumstances such as economic deprivation, such factors can be overcome when the child is not directly involved in the mother's illness and is not taught disorganizing and maladaptive modes of transacting with others and focusing attention. Those children are likely to be more competent who have been able to form attachments to other family members or who have been less centrally involved in the mother's illness. Such competence can be enhanced by supportive intervention for the child in order to be able to better withstand the impact of severe maternal psychopathology, including frequent, unexpected separations due to rehospitalization.

Clearly, one major component of intervention with the children of mentally ill mothers is that aimed at preventing maternal rehospitalization, which leads to disorganization of the family and often requires placement of young children in foster care. Community-based intervention has an important impact not only on the mother's own rehabilitation, but also on her child's subsequent development. At the next level of intervention, assuming that the mother is able to remain in the community, specific rehabilitation measures can be employed to help both mother and child. Garmezy (1974a) advocates specific programs designed to foster particular areas of competence in the child that are believed to be adversely affected by having been raised by a mentally ill mother. For example, Anthony (1973, 1974a,b) emphasizes demystification and reality training for the children of mentally ill parents in which focused reality therapy may be used to counter the effects of parental reality distortions. Anthony's procedures are designed essentially for children of school age and beyond. For example, problems of separation and individuation are discussed with the adolescent offspring of mentally ill parents in an attempt to help the adolescent to be able to leave home. Similar sophisticated intervention efforts based on the belief that the child of a schizophrenic parent is impaired in the capacity to assume the role of the other have led Garmezy and Chandler to adapt Chandler's (Chandler, 1972, 1973, 1978; Chandler, Greenspan, & Barenboim, 1974) role-taking task, previously used with delinquent adolescents, in training school-aged and adolescent children of schizophrenic parents in role taking.

There has been less systematic work on the development of appropriate intervention programs for mentally ill mothers and their younger children, particularly within families in which the mother shows a psychotic depression. However, the model for such an intervention program could include elements of each of these prior programs: (1) Rice, Ekdahl and Miller's (1971) technique of creating day-care centers for the children of mentally ill mothers, with the goal of ensuring that the children of these chronically ill women were physically nourished; (2) Anthony's imaginative program for slightly older children; (3) Pavenstedt's (1967) specially designed day-care centers for children of disorganized lower-class families; (4) Rolf and Hasazi's (1977) day-care program for the children of mentally ill mothers; and (5) the therapeutic nursery school described by Katan and her colleagues in Cleveland (Furman & Katan, 1969). These programs all point to the need for a specially designed school-type setting with therapeutically trained staff who assist the child's cognitive (attentional) and emotional development, and simultaneously assist the mother in her attempt to gain better understanding of her child's development. Specific tasks would be designed to teach the child to attend more effectively and to foster cognitive development in the manner described by Heber (1978) in his work with retarded children. In addition, use of the group, together with the therapeutic relationship between teacher and child, would be employed in order to foster the child's social and emotional development. These techniques would be employed to prevent the later school failure and peer group conflict so often found among the children of mentally ill mothers.

|| *Description of the Thresholds Program*

As a result of a 5-year grant from the Mental Health Services Branch of NIMH and additional funding from a private foundation (The Joyce Foundation) in Chicago, it has been possible to develop a comprehensive program for mothers and children not possible in previous clinical research. Mothers of young children (birth to 5 years) are referred to the program if they have been hospitalized for schizophrenia or psychotic depression. Referrals have come from private and public psychiatric hospitals, mental health agencies, private practitioners, and self-referral. The cases are reviewed for validation of psychiatric classification using the New Haven Schizophrenic Index (Harrow, 1972) for schizophrenia and the Feighner Scale for Depression (Feighner, Robins, Guze, Woodruff, Winokur, and Munoz, 1972).

Mothers bring their children into the agency with them in the morning. For those mothers unable to drive or take public transportation, there is a special bus service with a van driven by a trained psychiatric worker who does whatever is required in order to organize the household and get both mother and child to the agency. Plans are under way to equip an entire apartment building for those multiproblem families unable to function in independent living arrangements. Mothers unable to live alone will take two- or three-bedroom apartments with their family. A trained psychiatric worker, either psychologist or social worker, will live in the building and will be available for assistance at times of crisis.

When the mother arrives at the agency each day, she brings her children to the nursery and settles into her own schedule of work, classes, and meetings. The mothers participate in a variety of activities with the agency. They spend half of their time in a vocationally oriented program (working on or completing unfinished degrees) or job training; the remainder of their time is spent in individual and group psychotherapy (with other mentally ill mothers) and in family therapy, discussing such issues as working and problems in reuniting with one's family after being hospitalized. Mothers also spend time in the nursery school, where specific problems between each mother and child are highlighted and the mother is helped to work on particular problems with her child, using videotaped examples of her interaction with her child. Opportunities for making observations (and interventions) among individual children and their mothers are quite frequent. Mothers and children are seen together during lunch; at transition times (when the mother brings the child to the agency in the morning and when she takes the child to the toilet and to lunch), during those mornings when the mother is specifically assigned to work in the nursery (with either her own child or another youngster), and during videotaping sessions. In addition, all the mothers, fathers, and children participate with the project staff and staff children in a summer camping trip, an experience promoting intimacy within the entire group and offering a chance to observe families over time.

The children are cared for by a teacher who has been trained in preschool education and has had extensive experience working with the children of mentally ill mothers and with mentally ill children themselves. She is assisted by a teacher who speaks Spanish and has lived in the Hispanic community for many years and who can help Spanish-surname mothers. The teachers provide instruction in the skills believed to assist reality testing and demystification (Anthony, 1974a,b), so that the children receive not only consistent and tender care, but also assistance in overcoming the possible effects of being raised by a psychotic parent deficient in the skills necessary to sponsor a good relation to reality. A psychiatrically trained pediatric nurse makes weekly visits and provides both routine pediatric care under the supervision of a pediatrician and also emergency treatment over evenings and weekends if one of the children in the program should become ill.

Special times are set aside each week for the mother to visit with her child in the nursery and to be observed interacting with her child by project staff. Special assistance is provided for the mother in helping her to learn how to determine and meet the child's needs and in realizing a more mutual relationship. As a result of observing the nursery school teachers and psychologists with the children, the mothers are exposed to the spirit of the tolerant approach to child care, as well as to specific ideas for the handling of their children. The nursery school provides a partial (trial) separation of mother and child. It offers the child an even, constant understanding environment where the child may form a stable relationship with accepting adults.‡

This work in the classroom is supplemented by regular videotaping of

---

‡The model of simultaneous treatment of mothers and children is influenced by the work done by Mahler and her colleagues, who discovered that very disturbed children were often exposed to "irreversible and catastrophic" experience when treatment of such children was interrupted by the parents. "Precisely such experiences . . . prompted Dr. Furer and myself to design a therapeutic approach in which the mother can be fully engaged in the treatment process and thus help to bind herself to her child for re-experiencing the mixed and distorted developmental phases (for both). Within their newly developed tripartite of therapeutic design, the therapist serves as the catalyst, the transfer agent, and the buffer between child and mother" (Mahler, 1968, p. 348). A second major influence in the design of a therapeutic nursery in which the mother serves as primary agent in the treatment of her child is the work of Anny Katan (1969, 1972).

the mother and child together. These videotapes, made when the mother begins the program and at regular intervals thereafter, are used as the subject of discussion with the mother regarding her relationship with her child. The advantage of the videotape over the classroom session is that the tape can be stopped so that the mother and her worker can talk together about the mother–child relationship. When this interaction becomes the focus of discussion between a mother and her worker, the mother's feelings about child care and the parental role acquire a sense of immediacy that is missing in the ordinary contact between a mother and her therapist in the consulting room.

| | *Evaluation of the Thresholds Program*

The design of the evaluation calls for three groups of mothers and their young children: (1) families involved in the Thresholds intervention program, (2) families participating in the home-visiting paradigm used in the intensive aftercare research, and (3) well mothers in the community participating with their children in a day-care home-focused Head Start program.

Mothers in this program are administered the same instruments used in the previous intervention studies of mentally ill mothers. In addition to these measures regarding maternal psychosocial functioning and child development, when both mother and grandmother live in the greater Chicago area, a more detailed evaluation is being made of their continuing relationship. Separate interviews are conducted with both mother and grandmother regarding the nature and extent of their contacts with each other.

The child's development is evaluated by using the same measures previously employed in the Boston research, which suggested that the young children of psychotic mothers tend to develop deviations in domains of behavior characterized as cognitive, interpersonal and affective. These children tend to exhibit unevenness in the acquisition of locomotor skills and discrepancies in the level and rate of development of different behavior domains (Grunebaum, Weiss, & Gallant, 1974).

Accordingly, they developed a set of rating scales to assess aspects of cognitive, interpersonal, affective, and symptomatic behavior. To supplement the information provided by the rating scale, measures of developmental level and variability were derived from the Bayley, Cattell, and Stanford Binet tests. The measure of development level was the DQ, an index analysis of the IQ. Two important additions are included in the present evaluation: a measure of the child's coping skill using the instrument designed by Burton White and his colleagues (White, B., 1978; White & Watts, 1973) to evaluate social competence in children, and a series of videotaped observations of the mother in a feeding situation, a separation situation (Ainsworth, 1973; Ainsworth, Bell, & Stayton, 1971), and a structured teaching situation comparable to that used in the intensive aftercare research.

To date, more than 20 mothers and their young children have participated in the Thresholds research, with additional groups of 20 mothers and children in the home visiting control group and the well group. The rehospitalization rate among mothers in the complete Thresholds program has been about 22 percent, less than the realized in the Boston research, but greater than the recidivism rate of about 10 percent for the agency overall. (Within the home visiting control group, nearly 40 percent of women had been rehospitalized across the first year of the study.) It is interesting to note that even this intensive social rehabilitation program is somewhat more effective among men than among women: overall, nearly 18 percent of women are rehospitalized, as contrasted with about 8 percent of men.

THE COURSE OF DEVELOPMENT: DEPRESSED MOTHERS AND THEIR CHILDREN

Initial observations at the Thresholds confirm findings from the previous Boston research with groups of somewhat older children (Cohler, Gallant, Grunebaum, Weiss, & Gamer, 1977; Grunebaum, Cohler, Kaufman, & Gallant, 1978): maternal depression appears to have a more deleterious impact on the course of the child's development than schizophrenia. There are few systematic empirical findings yet available from this intervention study; however, some support for these initial observations regarding the impact of maternal depression on the child's development emerges from review of two families in which the mother had been previously hospitalized for depression. In one family, the mother had been hospitalized 14 separate times since the child's birth (the child was 2 years old when she began the intervention program), in the other case (a mother of a 17-month-old boy) there was only one hospitalization, when the boy was about 3 months old.

Case 1

The data and initial formalization of this case are based on observations of Cathy and her parents during the first 2 weeks of their attendance at Thresholds. The project was contacted by a local day hospital where Francine (Cathy's mother) had been seen daily following a hospitalization for depression. Francine was 42, white, married, the youngest of three siblings, and a heavy-set woman of

European nationality who came to the United States in her twenties. She had five other children from a former marriage, all of whom were in foster care. The mother's first hospitalization was about 15 years prior to joining the project, when her child was 6 months old. Since that time she had been repeatedly hospitalized in most of the local private and public psychiatric hospitals and had a sister who had remained in a state mental institution. Since Cathy's birth there had been 14 hospitalizations.

During her mother's hospitalizations, Cathy had been cared for by her father—an unemployed man whose chief enterprise was attending meetings at Alcoholics Anonymous. At the time of referral, the couple were considering placing Cathy in foster care. Francine had had a total of 14 hospitalizations since Cathy's birth. An initial home visit revealed a child who was pale, looked frightened, and dressed in unkempt clothes. She seemed undifferentiated from both her mother and the examiner. She did not smile or play but rather sat and sucked aimlessly on her bottle. The mother did not make any efforts directed at involving Cathy in either conversation or play. There were no visible toys, although there was food in sight. Cathy was of average height and weight, but with poor facial color and distinctly poor personal hygiene.

|| *Developmental History*

Cathy was a full-term baby of average size. Both mother and father were 40 years old at the time. Cathy was bottle-fed from birth (her mother later revealed that she found breast-feeding disgusting) and from early infancy ate well and eagerly. She wanted her bottle available at all times. However, her mother was concerned that she was malnourished and constantly complained that "she doesn't eat right." The mother was incessantly ridiculed by her husband that she was feeding the child poorly and that it was laziness on her part that the child did not eat more. It was around these issues of feeding and eating that mother and daughter could be observed in direct battle. The mother was able to demonstrate interest in and concern for Cathy's eating, and her daughter responded by making meals lengthy and arduous battles, as if to prolong the period of time that her mother would remain involved and interested.

Cathy had always used her mother as a means of falling asleep. She coaxed her mother to stay with her while she fell asleep on the sofa and would remain asleep as long as her mother remained with her. However, she would awaken and refuse to go back to sleep when her mother attempted to move around or get into her own bed. Day after day, Cathy spent countless hours playing by herself while her mother remained halfawake. At the time of admission into the program, Cathy's night sleep schedule was approximately the same as that of her mother.

Psychological evaluation revealed that Cathy had above-average small and gross motor skills. At the time she began the program, she was able to walk up and down stairs, alternating her feet, and to jump and to walk on tiptoe. Cathy's motor development was significantly (18 points) more advanced than her cognitive functioning, where the evaluation showed a child of average intelligence who was able to complete nonverbal tasks efficiently (small puzzles and building a tower) but could not imitate the examiner (copying a horizontal or vertical line or mending a broken doll). Of particular significance, Cathy's *language* was that of a much younger child. This was striking because of her otherwise intact sensory and motor abilities. Cathy spontaneously produced a few single-word utterances; however, she did not use language to request the attendance of an adult, either for comfort or as a resource.

Cathy had learned a wide variety of techniques to obtain the attention of adults. She would climb into precarious places, blink her eyes in people's faces, refuse to comply with adult demands, and directly express hostility. However, she demonstrated little or no pride in her accomplishments and did not imitate adults in role play, statement, or action. She showed poor emotional rapport, little ability to communicate, and a poverty of affect. She also showed unreasonable obstinacy and negativism. Her expression was sad, miserable, and unhappy. She appeared to have a mild identification with her depressed mother and was markedly lacking in emotional response to the interviews ("seems difficult to get through to child, very little emotional involvement"). Her mood was generally moderately or, at times, markedly depressed, and she showed almost no spontaneous smiling. Cathy appeared to show little anxiety around strangers and was reported *never* to have reacted to them. She did not demonstrate any separation anxiety when left by her mother in a strange classroom with unknown children and teachers at the time of her entrance into the program.

The mother and father did not feel that there was any problem with Cathy's development, although her mother did complain that Cathy did not eat better and would not obey when told "No." According to Francine, "the baby" (as she was called for the first 3 months in the program) was spoiled and perhaps was not healthy because she did not "eat right," but that was the extent of her concerns. Cathy's father voiced his complaints about his wife by complaining about his daughter, saying that she should be "trained by now," and that "Fran was lazy." Neither mother nor father saw anything to be particularly concerned about.

|| *Initial Observation in the Nursery*

Cathy's mother sat, hat on, wrapped in a heavy sweater, while Cathy wandered about the nursery. Usually her mother's gaze did not follow her daughter. (Cathy was sick with bronchitis, a sore throat, and a virus infection almost every week. Her mother expressed interest and concern in these illnesses because she was afraid they were somehow caused by her poor mothering.) The most striking quality of the interaction between mother and daughter was the lack of enthusiasm. Cathy displayed no pride at all in any picture drawn or puzzle completed, and her mother made little effort to encourage her. Cathy said almost nothing and did not react when her mother left to smoke a cigarette or take a break. Usually another child could grab something from her with little reaction other than a sigh. Her mother did not intervene to help resolve the situation. Usually Cathy was compliant with the demands of her teacher and examiner, in contrast to her noncompliance when her mother asked something of her. Cathy moved around when her mother remained in one place appearing listless and miserable, but her expression was similar to that of her mother. Neither mother nor daughter made many noises, and neither initiated activities.

Cathy's reaction to her father and his reaction to her in the nursery were somewhat different from that with her mother and generally more like that with her teachers. Her father showed some obvious pleasure with what she did in the nursery, and Cathy was able to respond to him. In addition, father and daughter did not become involved in the same kind of compliance.

| | *Battles as Mother and Daughter*

Some of the areas of particular concern to the project staff after the first several observations of Cathy alone and with her mother included her depressed affect; her relationship with her mother, either nonrelated or "locked" in negative battles; her inhibition, shown in very limited exploration of materials; her lack of apparent pride in any accomplishment; her habit of walking on her toes, together with her nonspontaneous body activity; her short attention span; her nonresponsiveness to attention and affection from the staff; her very limited interaction with other children; her nonresponsiveness to attention and affection from the staff; her very limited interaction with other children; her nonresponsiveness to other children's needs; and her inappropriate nonresponsiveness to separation from her mother.

Observations at lunch. Francine usually carried Cathy to the dining room, which was unnecessary because Cathy was able to walk quite well. Rather, this action represented her mother's efforts at preventing "a fuss." Francine also chose to sit squeezed against the back wall in the dining room because she wanted to prevent Cathy from being able to run about. Cathy made it almost impossible for herself or for her mother to eat. She precipitated a loud tantrum every day, usually because of what or how much her mother wanted her to eat. During these episodes, Francine sat apathetic, appearing passive and hopeless, while her daughter flapped, yelled, and fussed. When Francine said anything, it was to complain that her child had not eaten enough of the right foods. Usually, Cathy succeeded in slipping under the table and would run up or down the center of the dining room, or out of the dining room altogether, in an attempt to force her mother's challenge, disturbing all the other mothers and children because of where she had positioned herself. Sometimes Cathy had managed to get into a dangerous situation (on a fire escape, out on the street). Francine would then reprimand her by saying she did not like that. However, the smile and expression on her face indicated some pleasure in her daughter's activity.

Later observations in the nursery. Cathy demonstrated a dramatic change within 2–4 weeks after beginning the program. She was "socialized" into the routine and demands of the school almost immediately. More importantly, when her mother was not in the room, she would ask teachers and peers questions and revert to her more isolated and negativistic behavior only when her mother was not in the room. Much of her self-preoccupied behavior ("gurgling" noises and blinking eyes) also vanished in the absence of her mother. She made the greatest strides in the area of social competence with peers. She held a dustpan for another child, requested a tissue for her runny nose, climbed upstairs *smiling,* and expressed the wish to participate in water play. She was able to form a relationship with one of the teachers and could ask her for help. The report on this child after 1 month read: "Cathy is curious—alert—interested in her environment. She *thrives* on attention, sustained and consistent adult presence, and is resourceful—asking adults (not mother) for help. Cathy shows some pride in accomplishments (learning words and using a fork) and is more resilient and persistent, appearing intelligent and independent."

|| Case 2

The data and observations on this family are based on the first 3 weeks of participation in the program. At the start of the program he was 1 year, 7 months old. Michael's mother had been hospitalized for a period of more than 6 weeks when he was 2½ months old but was not rehospitalized again prior to beginning our program, when Michael was 19 months old. (She was hospitalized a second time during participation in our program, when Michael was 28 months old.) The W.'s are second-generation Italian–Americans. His father is a city detective, while his mother, a high-school graduate with 9 years of work experience, has had several jobs as a bookkeeper. Prior to entering our program, the family was seen for over 1 year in family counseling.

The first contact with the family was when mother and son appeared for the evaluation session prior to beginning the program. Michael did not make any sounds at all when he sat on his mother's lap; his expression appeared blank and affectless. While they were dressing to leave, however, his mother zipped his snowsuit hood into the skin on his neck, causing it to bleed. At first Michael only stared in pain; he then screamed uncontrollably while the zipper was unzipped. His mother did not show any emotional response either to her son's cries or to her own action.

|| *Developmental History*

Michael was a full-term infant, born by cesarean section. (This was the second pregnancy for his mother; the first was a stillborn child born 3 months prematurely; Michael was born 14 months after the stillbirth.) His mother and father were both 27 years old at the time of his birth. Michael was breast-fed until age 2½ months, when he was abruptly weaned to the bottle after his mother's hospitalization. When he entered the program, Michael had a serious eating problem; his mother would stuff his mouth with baby food and a little liquid until he almost choked. He would then (somehow) swallow the food. Initially his mother refused to give him liquid from his bottle or a cup during feeding solids, nor did Michael reach for foods offered him by the staff (the mother didn't initially offer food, but stuffed it in his mouth). He did not initiate anything at the table either audibly or behaviorally.

On tests of motor development, Michael scored within the low–average range, significantly better than his cognitive and language development, which was in the retarded range. His motor skills at the time were close to age-appropriate (he could walk up and down stairs with help and could get up from a lying position without holding onto anything); however, the quality of his movement was undifferentiated. He frequently ran into things (people or objects indiscriminately) and fell off chairs without making any effort to brace himself. Michael's body activity was active and impulsive: he ran almost constantly from thing to thing, but in a nondirected fashion.

Because he made few responses to human voices, made no verbal utterances in direct response to contacts with people, and only grunted in an undifferentiated manner when attempting to gesture, Michael tested in the "retarded" range. His mother reported that he had spoken a few words at about 11–12 months, but that these words had vanished. Michael was tested at an audiology clinic for possible deafness but was found to have adequate responsiveness to nonhuman sounds. (Two months later he responded at an adequate level during audiology testing to human voices.) Of particular interest was the fact that Michael's maternal grandmother had poor hearing from "unknown causes," whereas his mother had poor hearing as a result of multiple ear infections, together with surgery to prevent the infections from recurring. In addition, because his father worked nights and slept during the day, Michael was expected to be very quiet around the house to avoid awakening his father; members of the family typically whispered at home during the day.

In addition to dramatic language delay, Michael showed seriously retarded development in nonlanguage cognitive tasks. For instance, he did not turn the pages of a book, imitate simple games, or build a tower out of two cubes. He was able to use gestures in order to make his wants known and showed a rudimentary ability to do simple small-motor puzzles. The most striking aspect of his performance on cognitive tasks was the scatter shown among his abilities. The range of functioning was at 12–17 months, with an average at about 13 months.

Michael was able to comply with some requests (putting things away) but more often was unresponsive. His teachers said that talking to him was "like reading a book to a wall." Responsiveness to adults and peers was random and undifferentiated. He treated other children as objects, banging them or bumping into them. Michael's relationship with his mother appeared almost nondifferentiated. He did not cling to her, nor was he especially comforted by her. Michael showed several psychoticlike symptoms, and although able to gesture effectively, demonstrated almost no ability to communicate by using sounds or words. He showed defective reality testing (running into walls and hurting himself when falling) and excessive daydreaming. He also showed a poverty of affect with a limited range of emotions, apparently an identification with his sick mother. His attention span was also poor, with excessive distractability, and it was rather difficult to gain or maintain rapport with the examiner. His observed mood level was moderately depressed; he smiled only very occasionally and made no spontaneous comments.

His parents reported that Michael was "developing beautifully" until about 10–12 months of age. He then was noticed to be making fewer and fewer sounds. However, neither parent was sure his mute state was anything to be particularly concerned about. They reported that he did not appear upset by his mother's hospitalization, at which time he was 10 weeks–4 months of age. It was not possible to make a direct assessment of Michael's reaction to strangers because of his primitive mode of relating to people in an undifferentiated manner. His motor activity did decrease somewhat when a stranger entered the room, which might have indicated some anxiety, but he did not cry or complain when his mother or father entered or left the room, and he was equally noncomplaining when strangers picked him up.

|| DISCUSSION AND CONCLUSION

A most striking observation provided by a comparison of these two cases is that any formula of the necessary correlation between frequency of separation of a child from the mother and inescapable trauma is unwarranted. Cathy should be more psychologically "damaged," showing greater permanent psychopathology as she had experienced 14 separations from her mother in 2 years, than Michael, whose mother was hospitalized only once. Moreover, the social history of each family would suggest greater difficulty for Cathy than for Michael. Her father was an alcoholic, and the previous history for five half-siblings was ominous since they had all been placed in foster homes. In addition, the history of constant maternal psychiatric hospitalizations prior to Cathy's birth, together with a family history of mental illness in which one maternal aunt had died in a mental hospital, would lead to the expectation that Cathy was a child at high risk for serious, perhaps irreversible, psychopathology. Finally, the timing of the separation for Michael (prior to 6 months of age) would lead to the expectation by some investigators that he would be less seriously damaged than Cathy, who had experienced separations both before and after the age at which she could be expected to be cognitively and emotionally aware of the loss of her mother as a separate and differentiated object.§

These observations of Michael and Cathy call into question the literature on "maternal deprivation" and early object loss. There has been an assumption that separations in early mother–child relationships must inevitably lead to certain outcomes. These assumptions have not taken sufficient account of either (1) mitigating factors in other relationships available to the child, (2) socializing and cognizing experiences, or (3) the possible beneficial aspects of certain separations. One plausible explanation for Cathy's relatively greater emotional strength would be the very expectable and frequent nature of the separations she experienced. In a sense, Cathy's "average expectable environment," to use Hartmann's

---

§The children's developmental gains appear to be continuing 1½ years into the program. Cathy's development has become more even, and her provocative behavior has largely disappeared; Michael's language development has shown enormous gains, and he is increasingly responsive to others. Although he still performs somewhat below the average for his age on measures of cognitive and social development, his performance is within the "normal" range.

(1939) term, was one of recurring separations. This may have become a predictable event and the traumatic nature of the experience thereby somewhat diluted.

Both children described in the present chapter show signs of depression in childhood, and each has a psychotic depressed mother. At the point at which we observe their development in greatest detail, each is dealing with the practicing subphase of development, and each shows a specific reaction in terms of instability of mood. Each child's response to this phase of separation–individuation, which is particularly important in the development of the capacity for modulated affectual response, however, is a function of the manner in which mother and child had negotiated prior phases in the development of psychic autonomy.

Michael was separated from his mother during the symbiotic phase of infant development (2½–4 months). Differentiation from the symbiotic orbit occurred at the peak of symbiosis, at about 4–5 months. Michael never adequately negotiated the first phase of individuation (differentiation) because he never fully "hatched" from the symbiosis with his mother, as shown in his lack of a specific social smile directed toward his mother, together with the absence of stranger reaction and the appearance of psychotic symptoms. When Michael's physical development made upright locomotion possible, he was not able to use periods of physical distance from his mother as first steps toward object constancy. Optimally, during this period (both differentiation and practicing) the mother remains physically available as a stable point to which the child can return for "emotional refueling" through physical contact (Mahler, et al., 1975). Michael's mother was physically absent for a prolonged critical period as he was attempting the initial task of differentiation and, then, later on, was emotionally absent while physically present, because of her serious depressive episodes. What remains in question, however, is the apparent serious regression in language use at about 10–12 months.

The paradigm of separation–individuation does not offer a completely satisfactory account of these cases because it does not focus on the meaning of the *child* for the *mother* during the differentiating period. To date, our observations of all the mother–child pairs in the program show that the psychotic mother is fairly able to care for her child up to the period of initial differentiation, when the child's first efforts at separation from the mother begin. These mothers perceive their children as narcissistic extensions, as part of their self–object orbit (Kohut, 1977). The child's efforts at independence, particularly those periods of crying when the child cannot be consoled or the angry cries of protest when the mother does not minister to the child's demands during the practicing subphase, are experienced by the mother as a fragmentation of the self and are often reacted to by total (although temporary) disavowal and disregard. What

Bibring (1953) referred to as "helplessness" and what Joffee and Sandler (1965) have called a "depressive self" is apparent in the mother's inability to regulate the infant's grandiosity because of her own narcissistic vulnerability. One of the most common reactions of these mothers is their pleasure with the baby, when the child is reactive, reflecting their own joy, and smiling when smiled at. When the child does not mirror the mother's moods or cannot stimulate his mother, however, the child becomes relatively irrelevant to the mother's emotional world.

A more traditional formulation of the development of dampened mood among the children of psychotic depressed mothers, based on the concept of identification, would suggest that these children had internalized their mothers' depression and developed an identification with this depression. An alternative formulation is suggested on the basis of observations such as those presented by the study of these two mother–child pairs, as well as other families in the present investigation, which is more inclusive than this explanation on the basis of developing identifications. Rather than understanding the child's depression as an identification with the mother's depression, this depressed mood appears to be a response to tensions perceived by the child as threatening fragmentation.

The continuing relationship between mother and child, including the nature of the communication between them, is of importance in understanding the child's feelings of fragmentation at a perilous point in the child's own early development. Observations of the relationship between these depressed mothers and their children suggests that maternal mood disturbance leads to an inability to provide what Marjorie Middlemore (1941) and Joyce Robertson (1962) have termed "ordinary devoting mothering," particularly the ability to respond empathically to the child's tension states. As a result, the child is left with unresolved tensions and has not internalized the mother's function in regulating such tensions. In the absence of such functions provided by the mother, and later internalized as a part of the child's own capacity for soothing, the child is forced to rely on "emergency" measures in order to achieve such inner regulation, the most effective of which appears to be pervasive "low-keyedness" or dampened affect. Excitement is contained, but at the cost of experiencing feelings of emptiness and of increasing lack of responsiveness to the environment.

Mahler refers to what she terms a "love affair with life," which is shown by the toddler who has successfully traversed the practicing subphase and is entering the rapprochment subphase with the mother. These children of seriously depressed mothers do not appear to demonstrate such joy in their accomplishments. Rather, they continue to show the abrupt and unmodulated variations in mood and predominant depressed affect that were first observed during the practicing subphase and that have continued as a tension-regulating mechanism, not specifically related to the realization of the possibility of increased distance from the mother that is experienced by many children as they develop increased psychic autonomy during this rapprochement phase. A depressed mood may be present; however, its origin is different from that of children whose mothers had earlier been able to respond empathically to the child's needs and to provide the function of tension regulation that the child has successfully internalized by the advent of the rapprochement subphase. Depression in these children of depressed psychotic mothers emerges as a final solution in the attempt to deal with the emergence of tension states in the absence of internalized controls and in the absence of communication with the mother characterized by empathy and support for the child's struggles in developing a cohesive self. In the absence of such empathy, the child develops a feeling of being unworthy because of the inability to elicit a maternal response in an attempt to develop such cohesion.

Studies of childhood depression among the children of mentally ill mothers highlight an important aspect of early development not often recognized. Separation–individuation and the process of achieving psychic autonomy involves not only children's ability to practice individuation and to take pride in their own accomplishments, but also the internalization of the mother's more or less empathic response to this process, which leads to the later ability of children to develop means for modulating their own moods, stimulated by both successes and failures in realizing their goals. Not just the ability to achieve an intimate relationship, characterized by appropriate closeness and distance, but also the ability to deal with affects engendered through experiences with others, in an important developmental gain realized at the conclusion of the practicing subphase, in the course of the child's psychological development across the second year of life.

10

Cognitive and Behavioral Treatments of Depressive Disorders: Interventions with Adults

Michael S. Greenberg and Marshall L. Silverstein

Of the psychological and psychiatric maladies, depressive states appear to be among the most widespread, ubiquitous, and complex. A variety of theories and models have been proposed to conceptualize the nature of depression; however, progress in this area has been impeded by considerable variation in the classification and diagnosis of the depressive disorders. This state of affairs has also tended to create some measure of confusion in treatment choice for depression, such that the recognition, understanding, and remediation of the wide variety of depressive conditions continues to remain an enigma in modern times. This chapter comprehensively examines and reviews one major conceptual strategy for the understanding and treatment of depression, the behavioral and cognitive approaches, with the goal of presenting a systematic description of these approaches and evaluating the efficacy of cognitive and behavioral methods as one contribution to the problem of depression.

Before beginning a consideration of the cognitive and behavioral approaches, it may be useful to briefly survey other major formulations of depressive phenomena. One of the earlier formulations of the nature of depression originates from classic psychoanalytic theory, which tended to consider depression as primarily arising from retroflected anger deflected from an ambivalently held lost object. This is the classic formulation proposed by S. Freud (1957) which was expanded by Bibring (1953) by use of an ego-psychological framework. Bibring's contribution, in the era of the structural theory in psychoanalysis, is the recognition that the ego is devitalized in depression on failing to meet goals and aspirations. This position views depression as essentially a deficit in the ego, rather than the classic drive-dominated viewpoint formulated prior to the articulation of the structural theory in psychoanalysis. Other ego psychologists such as E. Jacobson (1971), Spitz (1945, 1946), and Bowlby (1960) have called attention to the importance of separation and object loss as important conditions in early development predisposing to depressive states. More recently, Kohut (1971) has further expanded psychodynamic conceptualizations of depression in linking the experiences of self-esteem and cohesiveness of the self as important determinants of depression.

From a different perspective, biological approaches have played an important role in understanding the mechanisms of depression, based largely on controlled pharmacologic investigations. These have included biochemical mechanisms, particularly involving the neurotransmitters such as the catecholamines and the indoleamines (Schildkraut, 1965). The contributions of research in biological psychiatry, although plagued by inconsistent findings, have created a good deal of enthusiasm and renewed interest in the search for possible biological markers in depression, such as recent neuroendocrine investigations of dexamethasone suppression (Carroll, Feinberg, Greden, Tarika, Albala, Haskett, et al., 1981). Attempts at a synthesis of a variety of models of depression have also been proposed, such as the suggestion by Akiskal and McKinney (1975) implicating a feedback interaction at chemical, experiential, and behavioral levels intimately related to the reinforcement system in which diencephalic structures occupy an important role.

Epidemiologic (Tsuang & Wilson, 1977; Weissman & Klerman, 1977), family history-genetic (Winokur, Clayton, & Reich, 1969), and clinical investigations have also opened up a new era in the conceptualization of depressive conditions. Furthermore, the ubiquitous nature of depression in other disorders such as the postpsychotic depression in schizophrenia (Kayton, Beck, & Koh, 1976; McGlashan & Carpenter, 1976), as well as problems of differential diagnosis between depression and dementia (Wells, 1979) have also been noted where depression has been implicated as a link with other diagnostic conditions. Procci (1976) and Pope and Lipinski (1978) have discussed the problem of schizoaffective states and affective symptoms in schizophrenia, which has influenced the view that a number of nonaffective disorders as traditionally conceptualized may well be better regarded as variants of major affective disorders. A significant impact of these psychobiological, family history-genetic, epidemiologic, and clinical investigations has been in the area of nosology and classification strategies, which has culminated in the recent far-reaching diagnostic schemata exemplified by the DSM-III (APA, 1980).

An examination of the literature on syndrome characteristics, clinical course, and familial patterns has enlarged the scope of conceptualizing depression. The delineation of depressive disorders from other major affective states, particularly mania and hypomania, has contributed to an important body of literature on the unipolar–bipolar distinction (Depue & Monroe, 1978) that had led to the suggestion that finer distinctions may be required in classifying and comprehending depressive disorders. Pharmacotherapy and differential clinical response to tricyclics, monoamine oxidase (MAO) inhibitors, and lithium carbonate has also become important in the improved understanding of depressive conditions (Stern, Rush, & Mendels, 1980), as well as recent investigations of sleep studies in depression (Kupfer & Foster, 1973). Even formal thought disorder has not escaped examination as a characteristic feature of depression (Andreasen, 1979; Harrow & Quinlan, 1977; Ianzito, Cadoret, and Pugh, 1974).

Clinical and bilogical differences between unipolar and bipolar affective disorders, as well as within unipolar depression, have influenced the development of nosological schema with the goal of distinguishing relevant subgroups of depressive disorders. For example, several distinctive subtypes of major depressive disorder in the Research Diagnostic Criteria (Spitzer, Endicott, & Robins, 1978) include the primary–secondary, agitated–retarded, psychotic–nonpsychotic, endogenous, incapacitating, situational, and recurrent classifications. In addition, family history-genetic investigations have been influential in conceptualizing depression, notably in Winokur's (1971) distinction between pure depressive disease and depression spectrum disease.

Against this backdrop of historically significant formulations of depression, as well as recent strategies and approaches to understanding and reconceptualizing depressive states, the work described below is presented and evaluated as one major approach to understanding depression and its treatment. During the past decade there has been an upsurge of interest in cognitive and behavioral treatments of depression. Prior to this the efficacy of traditional psychotherapeutic interventions had been questioned in the treatment of depression (Akiskal & McKinney, 1975). Hollon and Beck (1979) concluded that as late as 1970 there were no existing studies demonstrating that psychotherapy was more effective than either no treatment or alternative treatments such as antidepressant medications and electroconvulsive shock therapy. The development of cognitive and behavioral approaches to depression led to an increasing number of reports, however, indicating that these treatments were more effective than traditional psychotherapy and standard psychiatric therapies. This chapter evaluates the progress that has been made in this exciting area and suggests some future directions for research.

The cognitive and behavioral treatments reviewed in this chapter are a diverse set of interventions, with each treatment designed to reduce depression by correcting a particular set of behavioral deficits. The behavioral treatments of depression have included strategies such as pleasant events scheduling, token economy and reinforcement paradigms, anxiety reduction therapies, assertiveness training, and social and communications skills treatments. The cognitive therapies have concentrated on correcting distorted and irrational cognitive processes by strategies such as self-control techniques and rational disputation of depressogenic cognitions. However, several of the cognitive therapies have included substantial behavioral components. In general, any classification scheme of cognitive and behavioral treatments of depression is arbitrary (Biglan & Dow, 1981), as particular treatments may contain cognitive and behavioral components, and specific treatment techniques may affect both cognitive and behavioral processes. Thus, regardless of the theoretical orientation of the developer of a particular therapy, the majority of treatments reviewed in this chapter can be broadly described as cognitive–behavioral approaches to depression.

BEHAVIORAL TREATMENTS OF DEPRESSION

Lewinsohn's Reinforcement Formulation

Although many recent psychological theories and treatments of depression have emphasized cognitive factors in the development and maintenance of depressive symptoms (Abramson, Seligman, & Teasdale, 1978; Beck, 1967; Beck, Rush, Shaw, & Emery, 1979; Hollon & Beck, 1979; Rehm, 1977; Rehm, Fuchs, Roth, Kornblith, & Romano, 1979), there have been several behavioral formulations of this disorder (Ferster, 1974; Lazarus, 1968). The behavioral approach that has generated the most research is Lewinsohn's (1974, 1975a) reinforcement treatment and theory of depression. Lewinsohn argued that depressed individuals receive less response-contingent positive reinforcement than nondepressed individuals. According to this formulation, there is an inverse relationship between the rate of contingent positive reinforcement received and the development of depressive symptoms, such as fatigue, dysphoric mood, somatic symptoms, and reduced levels of instrumental behaviors. Furthermore, the total amount of response-contingent reinforcement obtained by an individual is determined by the number of events and activities that are potentially reinforcing for that individual, the availability of reinforcers in the environment, and that individual's personal, social, and intellectual skills. In contrast to the cognitive theories of depression, Lewinsohn has argued that cognitive phenomena such as low self-esteem, pessimism, expressions of worthlessness, and hopelessness, are consequences of dysphoric and depressive moods. It is further argued that these affective responses are produced by low rates of response-contingent positive reinforcement. Thus Lewinsohn's theory maintains that depression is caused by reduced rates of response-contingent positive reinforcement, and improvement in the clinical picture is determined primarily by reestablishing an adequate level of reinforcement for the depressed individual.

The evidence presented in favor of this reinforcement theory is problematic, with most studies resting on correlations between self-rated mood inventories and various measures of daily activities for primary support. For example, Lewinsohn and Libet (1972) computed various correlational measures to determine whether activity levels on a given day predicted mood levels on the following day and whether mood ratings were able to predict activity levels on the following day. The results indicated that these correlational measures were not significantly different from zero. Similarly, Lewinsohn and Graf (1973) failed to confirm their prediction that depressed subjects would have a greater number of activities associated with mood levels than psychiatric and normal control groups.

In response to a treatment failure reported by Hammen and Glass (1975), Lewinsohn (1975b) argued that relationships between activity levels and mood levels would be expected to hold only for those patients in whom there is a significant association between the two factors. This statement represented a theoretical retreat by Lewinsohn, however, and indicated that this reinforcement interpretation of depression is essentially a tautology (Blaney, 1977; Hollon & Beck, 1979). The author is thus in agreement with Blaney's (1977) conclusion that Lewinsohn's "theory" should be treated as a characterization of depressed individuals rather than a cause–effect hypothesis of depression.

|| Pleasant Events Scheduling

The basic principle of Lewinsohn's (1975b) behavioral treatment of depression is to restore the depressed individual to an adequate schedule of response-contingent positive reinforcement. This treatment objective is usually accomplished by altering the level and range of activities and interpersonal interactions of the depressed individual. During treatment, depressed patients are presented with several psychometric scales (e.g., mood, symptom, and adjective checklists) to complete at the end of each day. One of these scales, the Pleasant Events Schedule, asks the subject to rate the frequency of engaging in a large number of daily activities and the subjective pleasure obtained from engaging in those activities. These daily ratings are then compared to the patient's daily assessments of mood levels. Lewinsohn has argued that this procedure is useful for focusing attention on specific activities and events that are potentially reinforcing for the patient and indicating various relationships between engagement in daily activities and self-rated mood levels.

Padfield (1976) reported a study where women of low socioeconomic status were given 12 weekly sessions of "pleasant events scheduling" (i.e., monitoring and increasing their engagement in pleasant events). A control group received the same number of nondirective therapy sessions. The results indicated that the pleasant events group showed improvement on only one of four psychometric scales, the Grinker Interview Checklist (Grinker, Miller, Sabashin, Nunn, & Nunnaly, 1961). Thus Padfield's study provided only marginal support for the efficacy of pleasant events scheduling. Similarly, Hammen and Glass (1975) failed to find increases in mood levels of depressed and nondepressed students following a course of pleasant events scheduling. Further, in a second experiment, a pleasant events group reported more depressive reactions than did various control groups not engaging in pleasant activities scheduling.

Several factors may mitigate the negative results for pleasant events scheduling reported by Hammen and Glass (1975). The subjects in this study were instructed that the events scheduling program was part of a research study, in contrast to a treatment for depression. The failure to provide subjects with a credible treatment rationale has been shown to weaken the therapeutic effects of other behavioral treatments (Bootzin, 1975); therefore, this effect is not particular to pleasant events scheduling. Rehm and Kornblith (1979) have suggested that the failure of the Hammen–Glass study may have been due to the instruction for the subjects to increase the frequency of any of 160 events, thereby making the task rather nonspecific. Furthermore, many of the events may not have been selected on the basis on an empirical correlation with depressive moods. In addition, Blaney (1981) has commented on several variables such as experimenter-selected versus subject-selected pleasant events that may interfere with the effectiveness of pleasant events scheduling. Thus an adequate and fair test of the pleasant events treatment for depression must consider some of these important treatment variables.

Lewinsohn (1976) instructed 10 depressed individuals to record their mood levels and engage in pleasant activities on a daily basis for 30 days. From this baseline information, 10 target activities that best correlated with "pleasant moods" were selected for each subject. The amount of therapy time received by the patients was dependent on the number of activities that they had previously completed. This procedure led to increases in the frequency of engaging in targeted activities for all subjects without corresponding increases in nonselected activities. Although the average level of depression as measured by self-report decreased, subjects were still characterized as mildly depressed by the end of treatment. Despite meeting an important requirement for an adequate test of pleasant events scheduling therapy (i.e., demonstrated correlations between specific activities and mood levels), therefore, this study provided only marginal support for the efficacy of this treatment of depression.

Barrera (1979) reported a study that evaluated the efficacy of a strategy designed to help depressed clients increase the frequency of engaging in pleasant events. Depressed volunteers were recruited through referrals and news media announcements and were screened according to cutoff scores on the Minnesota Multiphasic Personality Inventory (MMPI) and several other scales. Six men and four women were assigned to an immediate treatment group (IT), and four men and six women were assigned to a delayed treatment (DT) group. After pretreatment assessments, IT subjects received a self-instructional treatment manual describing techniques for increasing and recording pleasant activities and participated in 4 weeks of 2-hour group therapy sessions. After 4 weeks of this treatment, the IT subjects were simply required to self-monitor activity and mood levels for an additional 4 weeks. During the initial 4 weeks of treatment, the DT subjects were presented with only the treatment manual section describing self-monitoring and recording of activities and mood levels. At the end of the 4 weeks these subjects received the complete treatment manual and 4 weeks of group therapy. All subjects were assessed at five different times: at pretreatment, at the end of 4 weeks when the IT group completed treatment, at the end of 8 weeks when the DT group completed treatment, and at 1- and 7-month follow-up assessments.

The results indicated that at the 4-week assessment the IT subjects reported greater reductions in depression than did the DT subjects, although there were no significant group differences on any depression or activity measure. At the 8-week assessment the IT subjects reported no additional improvement, whereas the DT patients had significantly lower Beck Depression Inventory (Beck, Ward, Mendelson, Mock, & Erbaugh, 1961) scores than did IT patients and were engaging in a significantly greater number of daily activities. At 1- and 7-month follow-up assessments, the DT group had maintained their advantage over the IT subjects. The results of this study give some support for the effectiveness of increasing pleasant events as a strategy for treating depression. It is puzzling, however, that the DT subjects showed less depression at the end of 4 weeks of treatment than did the IT subjects, who, presumably, were receiving an active treatment package for 8 weeks. Barrera argued that as the DT subjects spent the initial 4 weeks self-monitoring, they were more sensitive to their own behavior and, therefore, more prepared for treatment than the IT subjects.

In a comparative study, Zeiss, Lewinsohn, and Muñoz (1979) examined the efficacy of three treatments for depression: one group was instructed to increase their participation in mood-related pleasant events, another group concentrated on increasing their assertiveness and social skills, and a cognitive therapy group focused on identification and correction of irrational beliefs and distorted thinking. The subjects in this study were given either immediate treatment with one of the three therapies or started treatment after a 1-month waiting period. All subjects were assessed at four different times during the course of the study on an extensive battery, which included several measures of interpersonal communications skills, the Pleasant Events Schedule, and the MMPI. The subjects were 66 depressed patients who were recruited through announcements in the surrounding university community. For inclusion in the study, subjects were required to meet predetermined MMPI Depression (D) and Grinker Scale cutoff scores.

The results indicated that subjects in the immediate treatment groups were less depressed at posttreatment assessment than subjects in the delay conditions. However, there were no group differences between immediate treatment groups in the level of depression at this assessment period. In general, there was an overall improvement for all treatment groups in social skills measures such as being more comfortable with others, experimenter-rated social skills, and peer ratings of social skills. However, the social skills group was not superior to any other group on these various measures of social skills. In addition, a similar pattern of results was found for various measures of pleasant events and cognitive processes.

The major findings of this study were that each treatment was relatively effective in reducing depressive symptomatology and there were minimal differences between treatment groups during posttreatment and follow-up assessments. In addition, this report recognized the need for multidimensional assessments of the depressive syndrome. With respect to the specific strategy of increasing pleasant events, this study has not shown that it is a more successful therapy than other behavioral and cognitive treatments of depression.

Grosscup and Lewinsohn (1980) investigated the relationship between pleasant and unpleasant events, depressive mood, and clinical improvement in depression. Ten females and 11 males were recruited through public announcements and from community agencies. Selection criteria included MMPI Depression (D) scores above 70 and scores above 1.0 on the Grinker Dysphoria Scale. The patient sample was described as moderately to severely depressed neurotic subjects. Treatment lasted 6 weeks with two sessions per week. The primary therapeutic goal was to assist the patients in increasing their engagement in pleasant events. The results of assessments on the Beck Depression Inventory indicated that the mean Beck score decreased from 25 at preassessment to 6 ("normal" range) at a 1-month follow-up assessment. Further, MMPI Depression (D) scale assessments indicated that the mean score decreased from 93 at pretreatment to 77 ("depressed" range) at follow-up. Although the data presented some support for the therapeutic strategy of helping clients to engage in pleasant events, the correlational relationship between pleasant events ratings and mood ratings and the lack of appropriate control or contrast groups limit the internal validity of this study (Cook & Campbell, 1979).

Turner, Ward, and Turner (1979) reported a study in which 56 university students were selected on the basis of self-reported depression and a Depression Adjective Checklist (Lubin, 1967) score above 70. These students were subsequently assigned to one of four treatment groups: an activities increase group, an expectancy control group given physical fitness training, a self-monitoring group that recorded their daily activities and moods, and a client-centered control group. The results indicated that the activities increase group showed the lowest level of depression as measured by the Depression Adjective Checklist. Furthermore, all groups showed decreases in depression levels, with no differences found among the three control groups. In addition, a greater proportion of subjects from the activities increase group fell into a "complete remission" category at posttreatment than did subjects from any of the other treatment groups. Despite therapeutic outcomes that were generally favorable to the activities increase model, it should be noted that this study was completed with one of the authors serving as therapist for all treatment groups, thus creating the possibility that the treatment groups were exposed to biased expectancy effects of the therapist.

In general, several studies of pleasant events scheduling have provided only marginal support for the effectiveness of this procedure (e.g., Lewinsohn, 1976; Padfield, 1976), whereas other studies have lacked adequate experimental designs (e.g., Grosscup & Lewinsohn, 1980) or have not shown that the treatment was more effective than other cognitive and behavioral approaches (Shaw, B., 1977; Zeiss et al., 1979). In addition, hospitalized, suicidal, and psychotic patients were usually excluded from these studies, indicating that the generalizability of these treatments to more severe forms of depression is, at present, not clearly understood. Future research might give more consideration to issues of diagnostic subtyping of depressed individuals, therefore, as many studies contain little or no diagnostic information.

Biglan and Dow (1981) have outlined some important problems in evaluating pleasant activities treatments of depression. For example, pleasant activities scheduling is often combined with other treatment strategies, thereby making attempts to determine the effective treatment processes extremely difficult. Another important issue that has been addressed by Biglan and Dow is the need to assess the effectiveness of activity programs on cognitive, behavioral, and affective behavior. An evaluation of pleasant events scheduling therapies has thus indicated that there are considerable treatment and assessment problems that have not been resolved. Commenting of pleasant events scheduling, Blaney (1981, p. 19) has concluded that "Indeed, one would be tempted to announce its funeral were it not for the fact that it was supported in one major study (Turner et al., 1979)."

Token Economies and Other Reinforcement Treatments

Hersen, Eisler, Alford, and Agras (1973) set up a token economy program designed to test the hypothesis that work behavior controlled by a token program was incompatible with the emission of depressive behaviors. This hypothesis was evaluated with an *ABA* reversal design with three neurotic depressive patients. The patients were awarded tokens on completion of occupational therapy, taking responsibility, maintaining personal hygiene, and various work details. The tokens were then exchanged for various hospital privileges. The results showed an *ABA* effect for the target behaviors that indicated that these behaviors had come under the control of the token program. In addition, nurses' assessments of activities such as smiling, talking, and motor activity indicated that these behaviors had also come under control of the token system. The program was eventually discontinued, however, with no mention made of strategies designed to aid in the generalization of treatment gains to extratherapeutic settings (e.g., fading of tokens). Hollon and Beck (1979) and Kovacs (1979) have pointed out that although this token program may have brought certain isolated signs and maladaptive behaviors under the control of the token program, it is not clear whether this treatment was effective in treating behaviors collectively known as the depressive syndrome. Thus it is necessary for outcome studies to include dependent measures that assess the patients' functioning on behavioral, emotional, and cognitive dimensions.

Hanaway and Barlow (1975) reported a token economy procedure with a recently blinded deaf mute suffering from a prolonged depressive reaction. The patient was rewarded for behaviors such as shaving, showering, having his shirt buttoned, and other selfcare behaviors. Although the response-contingent reinforcement was effective in bringing these behaviors under the control of the token system, the patient rapidly deteriorated after discharge. No mention was made of attempts to enlist this severely disabled patient's family in his postinstitutional care; therefore, it is not surprising that the treatment gains were short-lived.

Reisinger (1972) attempted to modify the depressive behaviors of a 22-year-old institutionalized female by rewarding low-frequency behaviors (e.g., smiling) while applying a response–cost contingency for the occurrence of high-frequency behaviors (e.g., crying). Reisinger employed a procedure in which the tokens and fines were "faded out" and social reinforcement was "faded in" for the smiling responses. The data indicated that the decreased crying behaviors and increased smiling behaviors were maintained within a 14-month follow-up period. Furthermore, the patient apparently was not referred back to treatment by any agency and, apparently, was functioning adequately in the community.

Most operant procedures employing a manipulation–extinction design (e.g., *ABA*) have not programmed generalization strategies into the treatment. Instead, they have usually terminated treatment after an extinction period or a manipulation phase (e.g., Hanaway & Barlow, 1975; Hersen et al., 1973; Robinson & Lewinsohn, 1973). Kovacs (1979, p. 504) has stated that "However, the success of reversal or extinction strategies also suggest the fragile and transient nature of the behavioral gains, *clinically* a very disturbing finding. Thus, generalization (Hanaway & Barlow, 1975) and behavior stabilization must be built into the treatment paradigms)."

Robinson and Lewinsohn (1973) employed the Premack principle of reinforcing low-frequency behaviors with high-frequency behaviors to change the verbalizations of depressed individuals. They argued that as depressed patients spend quite a bit of time engaging in "depressive talk" (e.g., complaining of unhappiness and misfortunes), these high-frequency behaviors are capable of reinforcing low-frequency behaviors that are likely to elicit positive reinforcement from others. Previously, Lewinsohn, Weinstein, and Shaw (1969) reported a procedure in which a client was permitted to engage in "depressive talk" if relevant career-related activities were discussed first. That is, the therapist listened to the client's self-accusations only to the degree that the goals of the particular therapy session were accomplished. In the Robinson and Lewinsohn (1973) study, four experimental groups were contrasted. In the Premack group, emission of nondepressive verbalizations led to the onset of a light signaling a time period in which depressive talk was permitted. A second condition consisted of a contingent control procedure where the onset of a light was contingent on the emission of low-frequency verbal behavior but signaled a period where another low-frequency behavior was permitted. This group was a control for the effects of contingent light onset. A third, deprivation, group was a control for high-rate behavioral "restriction," and light onset was presented on a random schedule. Finally, the fourth group was essentially a no-treatment control group.

The results indicated that the amount of increases in low-frequency "healthy talk" in the Premack group was greater than the no-treatment control and contingent control groups but did not differ from the deprivation control group. Although Robinson and Lewinsohn ruled out the possibility that behavioral change was due to the effects of having contingent light onset, the results did not reject a verbal behavior deprivation explanation. In addition, the rate of low-frequency verbal behaviors decreased over time for both the Premack group and the deprivation group. This indicated that the treatment gains were diminishing within the same experimental session, suggesting that this treatment would not have a lasting effect on depressive behaviors. Finally, Blaney (1981) has questioned the relevance of this study to the treatment of depression, in addition to pointing out that no depression-related dependent measure was monitored by Robinson and Lewinsohn.

|| Anxiety-Reduction Interventions

Biglan and Dow (1981) have argued that a large number of individuals suffering from depression also have problems with unmanageable anxiety. They suggested that severe anxiety reactions may play a role in increasing the level of depression in some depressed individuals. In a correlational study with 156 university students, Greenberg and Alloy (1980) found that the Beck Depression Inventory correlated higher (.60) with the Trait Anxiety Inventory (Spielberger, Gorsuch, & Lushene, 1970) than it did with the MMPI Depression (D) scale (.46). Furthermore, cross-tabulation analyses indicated that of 18 subjects scoring both above 9 on the Beck Depression Inventory and above 70 on the MMPI Depression (D) scale, none scored below the fiftieth percentile on the Trait Anxiety Inventory. Similarly, Biglan and Dow (1981) reported correlations of .60 between the Pt scale of the MMPI and the Beck Depression Inventory. Psychometric studies and reports by depressed patients have thus indicated that many depressed individuals have significant problems with anxiety.

Hannie and Adams (1974) randomly assigned 21 female patients suffering from agitated depression to either a flooding treatment, a supportive therapy control group, or a no-treatment control group. All subjects had at least nine therapy sessions over a 3-week period. During the flooding treatment, anxiety-eliciting stimuli were imagined by the subjects until the anxiety reactions had subsided. The results indicated that the flooding group showed the greatest treatment gains as measured by the Multiple Affect Adjective Checklist (Zuckerman & Lublin, 1965) and a mental status examination. Hannie and Adams interpreted the results as indicating that flooding was the most effective procedure for diminishing anxiety and depressive symptoms in the depressed patient. It is not clear, however, whether the flooding treatment was effective by reducing depression, anxiety, or both syndromes. In addition, there are few data bearing on whether this treatment would be effective for other subtypes of depression (Hollon & Beck, 1979).

Shapiro, Neufeld, and Post (1962) reported the treatment of a depressed inpatient with a combined program of systematic desensitization and rational-emotive therapy. However, the lack of appropriate experimental controls and clear-cut outcome data prevents a strong interpretation of this case study. In addition, Wanderer (1972), Ramsay (1976), Badri (1967), and Seitz (1971) have provided optimistic reports on the use of desensitization with depressed subjects, although the latter two studies have serious methodological problems. In view of the significant relationship between depression and anxiety, and the demonstrated effectiveness of systematic desensitization and other desensitization techniques, additional research is clearly indicated.

Maish (1972) compared a group of depressed subjects treated by relaxation training with an assertion skills procedure and a nonspecific control group. The results indicated no consistent pattern of improvement for the relaxation and nonspecific groups at posttreatment and follow-up assessments, although reductions in MMPI Depression (D) scores were reported for subjects treated with assertion training. On the other hand, McLean and Hakstain (1979) reported that depressed subjects given relaxation training improved as much as a group treated with the antidepressant drug amitriptyline. However, neither group did as well as subjects treated with a combined cognitive and behavioral intervention.

In general, there has been a short supply of studies investigating the efficacy of various anxiety-reduction techniques in the treatment of depression. Hollon (1981) sounded a pessimistic note by arguing that the existing evidence does not provide strong support for the efficacy and generalizability of the anxiety-reduction treatment interventions. Biglan and Dow (1981) stated that there are almost no existing studies on the efficacy of anxiety-reduction treatments on depressive problems such as social isolation, worry, dysphoria, and inactivity. Despite these pessimistic pronouncements, it is premature to offer any firm conclusions on the effectiveness of anxiety-reduction approaches in the treatment of depression. What is needed are well-planned, controlled experiments that contrast various anxiety-reduction treatments with control conditions and other cognitive and behavioral treatments of depression. It appears probable, however, that future research will find that anxiety-reduction interventions will be applicable only to particular subtypes of depression.

|| Assertiveness Training

Impersonal situations calling for assertive responses are often problematic for depressed individuals. Zeiss et al. (1979) have argued that depressed subjects are less socially skilled and are less comfortable in behaving assertively than are nondepressed individuals. Similarly, Lewinsohn, Golding, Johansson, and Stewart (1968) found that depressed individuals interacted with fewer people and had longer latencies in reacting to other people than did nondepressed individuals. Biglan and Dow (1981) reported that socially anxious women were significantly more depressed than nonanxious women on two psychometric measures. Coyne (1976) reported that depressed individuals often have a negative impact on individuals who interact with them. Thus several behavioral theorists have argued that social skills and assertiveness deficits are prominent aspects of the depressive syndrome.

Sanchez, Lewinsohn, and Larson (1980) investigated the effects of assertiveness training on depressed nonassertive patients. Thirty-two subjects seeking treatment at an outpatient clinic were selected for treatment on the basis of their meeting preestablished cutoff scores on the MMPI Depression (D) and Grinker scales. The patients were randomly assigned to either an assertiveness training group or to traditional (insight-oriented) group therapy. During treatment, the insight-oriented subjects were receiving medications whereas none of the assertiveness group subjects were being treated with drugs. The assertion treatment involved modeling, behavioral rehearsal, homework assignments, token feedback, coaching, and social reinforcement for several problematic situations calling for assertive responses. Treatment sessions were held twice a week for 5 weeks, with each session lasting 1½ hours. Posttreatment and 1-month follow-up assessments indicated that the assertiveness training group had lower scores on the MMPI Depression (D) scale and Beck Depression Inventory than did the insight-therapy group. In addition, the assertiveness training subjects were more assertive on an inventory asking subjects to indicate the subjective probability of engaging in selected assertive behaviors. Thus, despite the fact that the traditional psychotherapy subjects were receiving medications, the assertiveness training group was superior to the control group on measures of both depression and assertiveness.

Maish (1972) reported greater reductions on the MMPI Depression (D) scale for an assertiveness training group than for subjects treated with either an attention-placebo therapy or relaxation training. A follow-up assessment indicated that none of the five assertiveness training subjects sought additional treatment after 8 weeks of treatment, whereas 8 of 10 subjects in the relaxation and control groups had additional therapeutic contacts. Similarly, Lomont, Gilner, Spector, and Skinner (1969) reported greater improvement for depressed subjects treated with assertiveness training on the MMPI Depression (D) scale than for subjects receiving insight-oriented therapy. LaPointe (1976) compared assertiveness training with cognitive therapy and insight therapy with 33 women who were recruited through newspaper advertisements. Therapy sessions were conducted for 2 hours a week over a 6-week period. The results indicated that all groups improved on various measures of depression, assertiveness, and irrational beliefs, although there were minimal intergroup differences.

A review of studies that have contrasted assertiveness training with either insight-oriented treatment or attention-placebo control groups has thus shown assertiveness training to be at least as effective as these treatments in reducing depression and increasing assertiveness. Two studies in particular (Maish, 1972; Sanchez et al., 1980) have indicated a clear superiority for assertiveness training, with treatment differences being maintained at follow-up assessments.

In a comparative study, Rehm, Fuchs, Roth, Kornblith, and Romano (1979) assigned 14 depressed subjects to a self-control therapy program and 10 subjects to an assertiveness training treatment. The subjects were depressed women volunteers who met preestablished MMPI Depression (D) cutoff scores. The self-control program concentrated on self-monitoring of positive and negative events, self-evaluation and realistic goal-setting, and self-reinforcement for meeting various assertiveness-related situations such as refusing unreasonable requests and expressing criticism and disapproval. Training sessions also included group feedback, rehearsal, and modeling of assertive responses.

The results indicated that at posttherapy and follow-up assessments, both groups were significantly less depressed as measured by the Beck Depression Inventory. The greatest amount of improvement on the Beck Inventory was shown by the self-control subjects. On the MMPI Depression (D) scale, only the self-control group showed significant improvement in level of depression. In addition, the self-control group was found to be superior to the assertiveness group in the number of pleasant activities engaged in during the last 30 days of treatment and on several measures of depression derived from behavioral observations. However, assertiveness training subjects were found to be superior to the self-control group on a taped "situations test," in which the subjects were presented with an audiotape of eight situations that called for various assertive responses. The assertiveness skills training was thus most effective in improving assertiveness behavior but was clearly inferior to the self-control group on depression-related measures. This study is an example of the importance of including a wide variety of dependent measures in therapeutic outcome studies. If Rehm and coworkers had only included measures of assertiveness in their test battery, the results of this study would have simply shown that assertiveness training was the superior procedure for increasing targeted assertive behaviors. When a wide variety of measures assessing various aspects of the depressive syndrome were included in the test battery, however, the results of the study changed considerably.

Zeiss et al. (1979) randomly assigned subjects to immediate or delayed treatment with either cognitive therapy, activities increase therapy, or assertiveness training. The assertiveness training group concentrated on interpersonal styles of expression, social activity, and assertiveness and employed techniques such as rehearsal and feedback, goal setting, covert modeling, and therapist-modeled assertive behavior. The results indicated that all treatment groups were superior to the waiting-list control subjects on various measures of depression and social skills behaviors, although there were minimal differences between the treatment groups.

Similarly, Taylor and Marshall (1977) assigned depressed subjects to either cognitive therapy, behavioral–assertiveness therapy, a combined behavioral–cognitive treatment, or to a waiting-list control group. The results of posttest and follow-up assessments indicated that all treatment groups had significantly lower Beck Depression Inventory scores than did the waiting-list control group. There was no difference between the cognitive and behavioral groups, however, with both groups showing significantly less improvement than the combined treatment group. In addition, a similar pattern of results was found for measures of self-esteem, self-acceptance, and neuroticism.

Although there is some evidence that assertiveness training is superior to either an insight or attention-placebo control group, there is, at present, little evidence that assertiveness training is more effective than other cognitive and behavioral treatments. These conclusions, however, are quite tentative as there are an insufficient number of systematic investigations of the effects of assertiveness training to warrant firm conclusions [for a review of several unpublished studies of assertiveness training, see Blaney (1981)]. In view of the important role that deficits in assertive behavior plays in the development and maintenance of depression, additional research is clearly required.

|| Antidepressive Programs

Wadsworth and Barker (1976) described an "antidepressive program" for hospitalized patients in which depressive behaviors were punished by aversive work assignments. The work assignments were usually monotonous, repetitious, and of little value to either the patient or the hospital. The situations were structured so that assertive and aggressive responses by the patients, indicating that they had "had it" with the work assignments, resulted in the immediate termination of the work detail. After being released from the work details, the patients' assertive and aggressive responses were met with positive social reinforcement and more palatable work assignments. Treatment was thus conceptualized as helping the patient to behave assertively and express anger in a way that did not lead to punishment.

In this study, neurotic and psychotic subjects were assigned to either the antidepressive program or to a traditional psychotherapy group treated with group and supportive therapy. In addition, subjects in the traditional psychotherapy group were treated with antidepressant and antipsychotic medications, whereas subjects assigned to the antidepressive program received only antipsychotic medications. The results of assessments with a self-rated depression scale and a "Purpose in Life" scale indicated that both groups improved on the measures after 1 week of treatment. In addition, there was some evidence that the antidepressive program was more effective than the traditional therapy program for neurotic subjects, although the latter treatment appeared to be more effective with psychotic patients. Since the treatment groups differed in the types of medications received, however, interpretation of this study is problematic.

In general, the scattered reports of antidepressive programs have been promising; however, there is a dearth of studies with appropriate control and contrast conditions. For example, a study by Barnes (1977) is essentially uninterpretable as a consequence of several regression artifacts, lack of a proper control group, and failure to include dependent measures that adequately tested the author's hypotheses. In addition, although successful reports of the use of antidepressive programs have been reported by Taulbee and Wright (1971b) and Patterson, Taulbee, Golsom, Horner, and Wright (1968), each study has considerable methodological problems.

An important problem that has not been addressed in studies of antidepressive programs is the confounding effects of antidepressive behaviors with successful experience in mastering a problematic situation (Hollon, 1981; Hollon & Beck, 1979). Reductions in depressive behaviors may thus have been due to either increased "efficacy expectations" (Bandura, 1977) or the facilitating effects of successful performance on behavior (Klien & Seligman, 1976). Future research must attempt to determine whether the effectiveness of these programs is the result of the expression of anger and assertion or the consequence of other important treatment processes.

|| Social and Communication Skills Treatments

McLean, Ogston, and Grauer (1973) have argued that the reactive depressive syndrome is sometimes the result of the patient being punished by the spouse or a significant other. McLean and coworkers defined punishment as ignoring or criticizing another person's attempts at interpersonal communication. Furthermore, the patient and the significant other are often unaware of various aspects of their communicative behaviors that are irritating to the other party. The use of behavioral techniques focusing on discrimination and correction of faulty communication patterns can thus serve to break up a destructive pattern on interaction by providing the participants with information about the perceived appropriateness of their behaviors.

Lewinsohn, Weinstein, and Alper (1970) reported a behavioral–social skills approach to the group treatment of depression. The actions and reactions of all group members were coded into categories indicating the object, topic, content, and outcome of each verbal exchange. Following the recording period of this data, the therapist communicated the quantitative and qualitative aspects of the coded communications to the patients in the group setting. These data presumably served the function of providing a source of identification for specific behavior problems as well as a progress record for the patients. The subjects were four males and five females who participated in 3 months (18 sessions) of group therapy. The results indicated pretest-to-posttest decreases in MMPI Depression (D) scores and Grinker Checklist measures of dysphoria, material burden, anxiety, and introversion. However, pretest–posttest designs without control groups are quite risky in terms of the number of concomitant variables that might influence behavioral changes (Cook & Campbell, 1979). Despite the promising results of this study, therefore, the effects of the behavioral treatment cannot be separated from other processes such as spontaneous recovery, therapeutic relationship effects, and assessment effects.

Similarly, Lewinsohn and Shaffer (1971) described the use of home observations as part of the treatment of depression. The home observations were conducted around mealtime with two investigators recording the interactions between the patient and the patient's family. The family's interactions were coded into response categories by a scheme similar to that reported by Lewinsohn, Weinstein, and Alper (1970). Lewinsohn and Shaffer (1971) reported the use of this interpersonal recording feedback system with varying degrees of success with three depressed clients; however, the design was also a pretest–posttest paradigm with no control group and a small number of subjects. Once again, firm conclusions cannot be reached concerning the efficacy of this treatment.

McLean et al. (1973) employed a behavioral-social skills treatment where depressed patients and their spouses were treated together. The primary treatment modality involved the establishment of a "cue box" system that contained two buttons used to record incidents in which one partner felt that the spouse was being either supportive or destructive to a particular discussion. This procedure was designed to provide both patient and spouse with immediate feedback and discrimination information of problematic communication patterns, in addition to cues for subsequent discussion of the relevant issues. Subjects receiving this treatment were compared to a group of depressed subjects receiving a diverse set of psychological and pharmacologic interventions. The subjects were 20 nonpsychotic patients, ages 21–52, with 10 patients assigned to each treatment condition. The results indicated that there was a decrease in the number of negative communications from the beginning to the end of therapy for the behavioral group, as measured by the use of the cue box. In addition, self-reported depression (Depression Adjective Checklist) and reports by the patients' spouses indicated greater improvement for the behavioral group than for the comparison group; these differences were maintained at a 3-month follow-up assessment. It should be mentioned, however, that the differential improvement on the psychometric scale may have been the result of regression artifacts.

Similarly, Mclean and Hakstian (1979) compared the efficacy of short-term psychotherapy, behavioral–social skills therapy, amitriptyline treatment, and relaxation training (attention control group) with clinically depressed subjects. The clients were 196 depressed patients who were randomly assigned to the four treatment groups. To be admitted into therapy, the clients had to be depressed for at least 2 months and meet cutoff criteria on the MMPI Depression (D) scale, Beck Depression Inventory, and Depression Adjective Checklist. In the social skills training group, a hierarchy of treatment goals was developed for each patient, with employment of specific techniques such as graduated practice in social skills, modeling, communications and assertiveness training, problem-solving strategies, and decision-making exercises. The subjects receiving amitriptyline therapy started at a 75-mg dosage that was graduated to a daily dosage of 150 mg and then reduced at a rate of 25 mg/day. In the short-term psychotherapy group, treatment emphasized cognitive and symbolic distortions of experiences, with the overall treatment goal being the alleviation of symptomatic complaints. The relaxation training subjects received a course of progressive relaxation and muscle tension exercises.

The results indicated that at posttreatment assessment, the behavior therapy group had lower Beck Depression Inventory scores, fewer complaints, greater social interaction, improved mood ratings, and higher average satisfaction ratings than all other groups. On 6 of 10 measures, the psychotherapy group was inferior to the behavior therapy subjects. There were no significant differences between subjects receiving drug therapy and relaxation training. A 3-month follow-up assessment indicated that the behavioral group had greater levels of social activity and greater improvements in mood ratings than the psychotherapy group, with all other group comparisons reported as nonsignificant. McLean and Hakstian's study has indicated that a social skills training program is superior to relaxation training and traditional psychotherapy treatments. However, it is not clear whether this social skills treatment is really more effective than amitriptyline therapy as the dosage level prescribed was below the level typically given to subjects treated with amitriptyline (Hollon, 1981).

Shipley and Fazio (1973) reported a "functional problem solving" treatment with 28 depressed subjects. During treatment the patients' social reinforcement patterns were coded into categories such as "errors in discrimination" (e.g., emitting responses that fail to receive reinforcement) and "errors of responding" (e.g., failing to emit the appropriate response although the correct response is perceived). In addition, the clients and therapist worked on "functional problem solving alternatives" to various inappropriate responses that were then practiced between therapy sessions. The efficacy of this treatment was compared to a supportive psychotherapy treatment. The results indicated that only the functional problem-solving group improved from pretreatment assessment on the MPI Depression (D) scale. In addition, the effectiveness of the problem-solving treatment replicated an earlier report by Shipley and Fazio. Caution is warranted in evaluating this study, however, as only one therapist was employed (one of the authors), and the subjects were university students.

The results of social and communications skills treatment of depression suggest that these strategies may be quite useful in correcting a variety of deficits in depressed individuals, although most of the studies reviewed have important methodological problems. The studies reported by McLean and his colleagues (McClean et al., 1973; McLean & Hakstian, 1979) have provided some evidence that social skills treatments may be as effective as antidepressant medications in the treatment of depression. This conclusion is tentative, however, as the use of medications was, essentially, uncontrolled in the McLean et al. study and of questionable dosage level in the report presented by McLean and Hakstian.

|| COGNITIVE THERAPIES

|| Beck's Cognitive Theory of Depression

In recent years there has been increasing interest in the influence of cognitive processes in the development of depression. An important source of this upsurge in interest has been Beck's theory of depression

(Beck, 1967, 1976; Beck, Rush, Shaw, & Emery, 1979; Hollon & Beck, 1979). Beck's major premise is that affective responses are determined largely by a person's cognitive construction of his or her experiences. Furthermore, Beck has argued that depression-prone individuals have enduring and maladaptive cognitive organizations called "schemata" that contain negative beliefs about the self, the world, the future, and causality. According to Beck, depressive schemata become activated during periods of stress. In cases of severe depression, the schemata are automatically activated and may have an obsessional and intrusive quality to them. In addition, the depressive schemata often have elements of self-blame, personal deficiency, guilt, rejection, humiliation, and loneliness. Further, the idiosyncratic and irrational nature of these schemata may lead to systematic errors in logical thinking which Beck has labeled arbitrary inferences (drawing conclusions in the absence of data), selective abstractions (focusing on a detail taken out of context), personalizations and overgeneralizations of negative experiences, and minimizations of positive events.

Beck and his colleagues have stated that cognitive therapy techniques are designed to help the depressed patient identify, correct, and test the reality of irrational and distorted thinking processes. In addition, patients are taught to monitor negative automatic cognitions; recognize the connections between cognition, affect, and behavior; examine the evidence for and against the irrational automatic thoughts; and substitute more reality-oriented interpretations for negative cognitions and beliefs. Treatment usually consists of 15–20 weekly sessions of therapy, although severely depressed patients often receive 4–5 weeks of biweekly sessions. Other aspects of the treatment include daily logs of activities, scheduling of "mastery and pleasure activities," graded task assignments, and various homework exercises.

In a preliminary study, Rush, Khatami, and Beck (1975) reported the successful treatment of three cases of depression; however, this report was essentially a series of uncontrolled case studies and thus cannot be interpreted with confidence. B. Shaw (1977) reported a study in which the primary objective was to evaluate the cognitive approach described by Beck and a behavioral approach outlined by Lewinsohn. The behavioral treatment consisted of activity scheduling, verbal contracts, behavioral rehearsal, and instruction in communication and social reinforcement skills. In one control group, subjects were assigned to an assessment–attention treatment that included nondirective therapy, while another group of subjects was assigned to a waiting-list condition. Subjects were admitted into the study after meeting cutoff criteria on the Beck Depression Inventory and the Hamilton Rating Scale for Depression (Hamilton, 1960), and a measure of depression called the Visual Analogue Test. Therapy consisted of 2-hour sessions that were held for 4 weeks. The subjects were 32 depressed male and female individuals who were assigned in equal proportions to the four treatment conditions.

The results of an assessment conducted after 2 weeks of treatment indicated that on the Beck Inventory and Hamilton scales, the cognitive group had lower depression scores than did either the nondirective or waiting-list control groups. All other comparisons between treatment groups were nonsignificant. At posttreatment, the cognitive group reported significantly less depression on the Beck Inventory than did all other treatment groups. The behavioral group had lower Beck scores than did the waiting-list group but was not significantly different from the nondirective subjects. An analysis of the Hamilton Depression Scale indicated that the cognitive group showed less depression than did the nondirective and waiting list groups, although the differences between the cognitive and behavioral groups were not significant. A 1-month follow-up assessment indicated that there were no significant differences between the cognitive and behavioral groups, although the cognitive group had somewhat lower scores on the Beck Inventory.

In general, the cognitive therapy treatment resulted in significant reductions in depression and was superior to the behavioral, waiting-list, and assessment–attention control groups. However, the differences between the cognitive and behavioral groups were not as clear-cut as comparisons between cognitive and control groups.

In a preliminary study, Kovacs and Rush (1976) assigned chronically depressed subjects to either drug therapy with a tricyclic antidepressant (imipramine) or to cognitive therapy. The results of self-report data and clinical behavior ratings indicated that both treatments led to significant improvement from pretreatment assessments; however, there were fewer treatment drop-outs from the cognitive therapy group than from the imipramine group. In addition, a greater proportion of cognitive therapy subjects were classified as nondepressed at the end of treatment than were subjects receiving imipramine. Kovacs and Rush argued that cognitive therapy produced at least as much improvement as an established pharmacologic treatment.

Rush, Beck, Kovacs, and Hollon (1977) reported a study that tested the comparative efficacy of cognitive therapy and imipramine. Fifteen males and 26 females with prior depressive episodes participated in the study. Inclusion criteria for participation in the study consisted of Beck Depression scores of greater than 20, Hamilton Rating Scale for Depression scores of greater than 14, and symptoms that met the criteria for a diagnosis of depression. Therapy sessions consisted of a maximum of twenty 50-minute sessions over a 12-week period for the cognitive therapy group and a maximum of 12 pharmacotherapy sessions over 12 weeks. The pharmacotherapy treatment also included brief supportive therapy. Subjects who were treated with imipramine started on a daily dose of 75 mg, which was later raised successively to 150, 200, and 250 mg (if clinically indicated). During the last 2 weeks of treatment, the medication was tapered and eventually discontinued.

The results indicated that both treatments lead to significant reductions in depressive symptoms (Beck Inventory and Hamilton Rating Scale) and anxiety, with the cognitive therapy group showing the greatest reductions in overall symptomatology. In addition, a greater proportion of subjects in the imipramine group dropped out of treatment. A follow-up assessment at 3 months still showed their advantage to hold over the imipramine group.

Becker and Schuckit (1978) raised several important issues resulting from the study reported by Rush et al. (1977). These issues included questions of whether the medication type and dosage level of imipramine provided an optimal test of the efficacy of pharmacotherapy on depression. However, in a preliminary report, Hollon, Bedrosian, and Beck (1976) found that subjects treated with either cognitive therapy or a combination of cognitive therapy and up to 300 mg of amitriptyline per day were significantly less depressed at the end of treatment on the Beck Depression Inventory and the Hamilton Rating Scale for Depression. Furthermore, these groups did not differ from one another on the two measures of depression. The initial results of this study thus indicated that cognitive therapy was as effective as a dosage of antidepressant medication that was substantially greater than the amount reported by Rush et al. (1977). In addition, Hollon et al. (1976) suggested that the inclusion of antidepressant medication did not enhance the effectiveness of cognitive therapy.

Becker and Schuckit (1978) also commented on the fact that many of the patients in the Rush et al. (1977) study reported chronic difficulties with depression. They argued that past research has shown that antidepressants are relatively ineffective in treating chronic depression; thus the Rush et al. study may not have afforded an adequate test of the efficacy of the pharmacologic agent. In response to Becker and Schuckit (1978), Rush, Hollon, Beck, and Kovacs (1978) reported additional analyses of the original data indicating that the outcome of either treatment could not be predicted by patients' standing on the acute–chronic dimension. In addition, posttreatment assessments on the Beck Inventory and Hamilton Scale did not correlate significantly with the number of prior depressive episodes reported by the patients, the number of previous professionals contacted, or the number of previous hospitalizations. Thus Rush et al. (1978) appeared to have successfully countered an important criticism of the original study.

In a study reviewed in a previous section, Taylor and Marshall (1977) assigned depressed subjects to either cognitive therapy, behavioral assertiveness training, a combined treatment, or a waiting-list control group. Subjects in the cognitive therapy treatment were informed that faulty thinking and unrealistic self-evaluations were responsible for their depressive moods. Therapy consisted of the construction of alternative positive cognitions and self-statements and instructions for substitution of the new cognitions for habitual depressive thought patterns as early as possible in a cognitive chain of events. In addition, the subjects constructed a list of positive self-statements and read them silently several times per day. The results indicated that the cognitive and behavioral treatments were generally superior to the waiting-list control group on various measures of depression, self-esteem, and neuroticism, although both groups were inferior to the combined cognitive and behavioral treatment.

In an unpublished study, Schmickley (1976) reported a cognitive therapy treatment with 11 depressed (neurotic) female outpatients. The treatment consisted of four 1-hour sessions over a 2-week period. Therapy sessions emphasized the identification and correction of automatic depressive cognitions. In addition, the subjects developed a list of positive self-statements and were instructed to recite them silently prior to engaging in high frequency behavior. The results indicated that less than half of the subjects showed significant decreases in depression, and several of the subjects reporting improvement did not maintain the treatment gains. Although Schmickley's study indicated mixed results for the efficacy of cognitive therapy, it is possible that 2 weeks of therapy is simply an insufficient amount of time for cognitive therapy to be effective. According to the cognitive model, depressed patients have habitual and automatic depressogenic cognitions. If this premise is accepted, it is unlikely that significant cognitive restructuring can be accomplished in four therapy sessions (Beck and his colleagues recommend between 12 and 20 sessions).

In a study reviewed previously, Zeiss et al. (1979) compared the efficacy of cognitive therapy, activities increase therapy, and assertiveness training. The cognitive treatment consisted of self-monitoring and categorizing specific positive and negative thoughts, thought stopping, disputing irrational thoughts, and various role-playing exercises. The results indicated that all treatment groups were superior to a waiting-list control, although there were minimal differences among the treatments on a comprehensive assessment battery. Similarly, LaPointe (1976) found minimal differences between assertiveness training, cognitive therapy, and insight-oriented therapy, with all treatment groups showing significant improvement from pretreatment assessments.

In general, the studies that have been most favorable to cognitive therapy have been conducted by Beck and his colleagues. These studies have typically shown that cognitive therapy is superior to waiting-list control groups, behavioral treatments, nondirective therapy, and antidepressant medications. Studies conducted by other investigators (e.g., Schmickley, 1976; Zeiss et al., 1979), however, have not been as supportive of the superiority of cognitive therapy over other treatments of depression.

Blaney (1981) has commented on this conflicting picture by suggesting that therapies which have included substantial behavioral components (e.g., Rush et al., 1977; Taylor & Marshall, 1977) appear to be more effective than treatments which have relied primarily on cognitive techniques (e.g., La Pointe, 1976; Schmickley, 1976; Zeiss et al., 1979). Blaney's observation implies that studies reported by Beck and his colleagues, which have usually included activity scheduling and graded task assignments, can be more accurately described as cognitive–behavioral interventions. Perhaps the behavioral component of cognitive therapy has been underemphasized, because of the greater emphasis on cognitive theory and therapy techniques. For example, Hollon and Beck (1979) have stated that behavioral techniques are employed primarily as methods for challenging and correcting maladaptive cognitions, as opposed to merely increasing the client's activity level. Thus independent researchers attempting to investigate the efficacy of cognitive therapies may have neglected to include an important aspect of treatment into therapy.

On the other hand, Rehm and his colleagues (Rehm et al., 1979; Fuchs & Rehm, 1977) have presented a self-control treatment of depression that emphasized cognitive factors to a greater extent than Beck's cognitive therapy did. These studies have shown that self-control therapy is more effective than either a waiting-list control group or other behavioral treatments, thus complicating the picture even further. Another possibility, which occurs quite frequently in many fields, is initial support for a newly discovered technique, followed by less optimistic reports when attempts at independent replications are made.

Future research programs employing disassembly designs that sequentially introduce various cognitive and behavioral treatment components can serve to clarify the present situation. These studies must include assessments of important aspects of behavioral and cognitive functioning in order to determine the specific effects of cognitive and behavioral treatment components.

|| Self-Control Treatments

Fuchs and Rehm (1977) outlined a self-control treatment and theory of depression in which the disorder is conceptualized as resulting from cognitive deficits such as selective monitoring of negative events, selective monitoring of immediate as opposed to delayed consequences of behaviors, distorted attributions of responsibility, insufficient self-reward, excessive self-punishment, and rigid self-evaluative criteria. This theory is quite similar to Beck's cognitive model, although the latter theory probably emphasizes behavioral processes to a greater extent than does the self-control formulation [for discussions of theoretical problems of the self-control model, see Deutch (1978) and Hollon and Beck (1979)].

There are several independent reports of self-control therapies that can be fit into the conceptual framwork outlined by Fuchs and Rehm (1977). For example, B. Jackson (1972) described a case of depression that was successfully treated by a self-reinforcement procedure that focused on self-monitoring of problematic behavior, setting of realistic performance goals, selection of reinforcers for achieving treatment goals, and application of self-reinforcement when the treatment goals were accomplished. Similarly, Todd (1972) reported a *"coverant"* self-reinforcement treatment with several depressed outpatients. One procedure had the patients reinforce themselves with cigarettes after reading various positive self-statements. The patients apparently had made some significant improvement, although evaluation of the effective treatment components was difficult as the self-control treatment was embedded in a treatment package that included desensitization and assertiveness training. Although successful applications of self-control treatments have been reported by Johnson (1971), Mahoney (1971), and Hilford (1975), these reports did not approach the methodological sophistication and theoretical importance of subsequent studies reported by Rehm and his colleagues.

Fuchs and Rehm (1977) presented a three-phase treatment of depression emphasizing self-monitoring, self-evaluation, and self-reinforcement, with the entire procedure lasting approximately 6 weeks. The self-monitoring phase stressed accurate self-observations and monitoring of positive and negative events and activities. The self-evaluation phase focused on the importance of setting realistic and obtainable goals and accurate evaluation of self-performance. During this phase, a point system was introduced in which points could be earned for successfully completing various treatment goals. During the self-reinforcement phase, the subjects constructed "reward menus" of easily administered pleasurable activities and were instructed to engage in these activities after completing various treatment goals.

The self-control treatment of depression was contrasted with a nonspecific group therapy treatment and a waiting-list control group. The subjects were 36 women volunteers who were not suicidal, psychotic, or currently in treatment for psychological problems. The subjects were included in the study if their MMPI Depression (D) score was both above 70 and represented the highest elevation on the scale. The results of this study indicated that both self-control and nonspecific therapy groups had greater reductions on the Beck Depression Inventory than did the waiting-list control group, with the lowest scores shown by the self-control subjects. On the other hand, comparisons between the self-control and nonspecific groups were not significant at follow-up assessment. On the MMPI Depression (D) scale, a greater reduction in scores was shown by the self-control group, with this group maintaining its superiority at follow-up assessment. In addition, various measures of pleasant events, activity levels, and self-control behaviors indicated that the self-control group was more successful than the other treatments.

Rehm et al. (1979) compared the self-control treatment to an assertion training treatment with depressed women volunteers. The results indicated that the self-control group showed greater improvement than did the assertiveness group on the Beck Depression Inventory, the MMPI Depression (D) scale, pleasant activities measures, behavioral observations of overall depression, negative self-references, and negative references to others. This study thus represented a replication of Fuchs and Rehm's (1977) investigation and provided strong evidence that the self-control treatment was more effective in reducing depression than an alternative cognitive–behavioral treatment.

In an unpublished report, however, Rehm, Kornblith, O'Hara, Lamparski, Romano, and Volkin (1978) attempted to evaluate the major therapeutic elements in the self-control treatment of depression. In a disassembly design, a waiting-list control condition was compared to a self-monitoring treatment, a self-monitoring and self-evaluation group, self-monitoring and self-reinforcement treatment, and the full treatment package. The results indicated that any one of the therapy conditions was more effective in reducing depression than the waiting-list control group was. There was no clear-cut pattern of differences between the treatment conditions, however, with treatment effectiveness reported as inferior to the gains reported in the published studies.

Despite the problematic results reported by Rehm et al. (1978), the self-control program has shown considerable promise as an important treatment for depression. Future research must contrast the self-control treatment with other therapeutic interventions and investigate its effectiveness with various subtypes of depression. In addition, Kovacs (1979) has stated that the self-control studies reported by Rehm and his colleagues are notable for the systematic sequential application of treatment and the use of diverse outcome measures. Positive evaluations of the self-control treatment have also been reported by Hollon (1981) and Blaney (1981). However, future research will determine whether the initial enthusiasm generated by the self-control program is justified.

|| SUMMARY

With the exception of pleasant events scheduling, there is a dearth of research on the effectiveness of any specific cognitive or behavioral treatment of depression. An evaluation of the existing studies has indicated that many behavioral treatments of depression have considerable methodological and clinical shortcomings. Reports of pleasant events scheduling have provided weak support for the efficacy of this treatment of depression. In addition, the generality of this strategy to various subtypes of depression is unknown, as psychotic and suicidal patients are often excluded from participation in these studies. The few studies that contain acceptable experimental designs (e.g., Shaw, B., 1977; Zeiss et al., 1979), have shown that alternative cognitive and behavioral therapies were as effective as activities scheduling in the treatment of depression.

The studies that have employed token economies and other reinforcement therapies have indicated that without inclusion of significant generalization strategies, these paradigms have little chance of promoting lasting behavioral gains. This is particularly important as token programs have typically been employed with severely depressed and institutionalized patients. Furthermore, reinforcement programs employing the Premack principle and verbal reinforcement therapy suffer from the same problems, in addition to being of questionable relevance to the treatment of depression (Blaney, 1981).

The studies that have employed anxiety-reduction treatments have provided little evidence for evaluation of the efficacy of any one particular therapy. In addition, it is doubtful whether anxiety treatments and other affect-mediated approaches will prove to be applicable to a wide variety of depressive disorders. Evaluations of assertiveness training programs have indicated that this treatment is more effective than traditional psychotherapy and various attention-placebo control conditions in reducing depression and increasing assertiveness. Although one report suggested that assertion training was superior to pharmacological treatment (Sanchez et al., 1980), studies that have compared assertion training with cognitive and behavioral therapies have found it to be either inferior to or equally effective as the alternative treatments.

The scattered reports of antidepressive programs have been optimistic, although these studies have been conducted primarily with male inpatients; thus antidepressive programs may be applicable to only a circumscribed target population. Studies investigating social and communication skills treatments have indicated that these therapies may be quite useful in the treatment of depression; however, most of these studies contain a diverse set of treatment components such as assertion training, modeling, role playing, and social skills training. Future research is thus required for determination of the effective treatment components of these programs.

It appears that the cognitive therapies of depression have been the most effective treatments of this disorder, with several studies indicating that cognitive therapy is more effective than antidepressant medications and psychological treatments such as assertiveness training, mixed behavioral treatments, and psychotherapy. However, several studies have failed to indicate the superiority of cognitive therapies over alternative psychological treatments. There is an accumulating body of evidence implicating the important role of cognitive and perceptual distortions in depression (DeMondreun & Craighead, 1977; Nelson & Craighead, 1977). A therapeutic strategy that is directed toward correcting depressogenic cognitions may thus help the depressed patients to engage in a processing style in which nondepressive thinking becomes "automatic" and adaptive. The "automatizing" of nondepressive thinking would appear to promote longer-lasting treatment gains than any of the alternative treatments evaluated in this chapter.

|| CONCLUSIONS

Investigations of cognitive and behavioral treatments of depression have consistently failed to provide information pertaining to diagnostic subtypes of depressed subjects. This problem is not unique to depression, as behavioral researchers have traditionally minimized the role of diagnostic practices in personality functioning and psychopathology. How important is the issue of diagnostic subtypes in depression research?

Hollon (1981) has stated that affective disorders are quite heterogeneous with respect to symptomatology, course, prognosis, and response to treatment. This variation is manifested in diagnostic dimensions such as neurotic–psychotic, endogenous–reactive, unipolar–bipolar, and acute–chronic. Furthermore, DePue and Monroe (1978) have argued that it is impossible to speak of reactive depression as a unitary entity or to consider a single etiologic framework for the development of depression. Paykel (1971) has outlined four classes of reactive depression derived from cluster analyses of various depression scales: psychotic, anxious, hostile, and young depressives with personality disorders. In addition, statements concerning the problem of diagnostic subtypes and behavioral and cognitive treatments of depression have been presented by Rehm and Kornblith (1979), Blaney (1981), and Kovacs (1979). There is a strong consensus among these investigators that the efficacy of behavioral and cognitive treatments of depression with respect to various subtypes of depression is presently unknown.

Future research must, therefore, involve the specification of depressed subjects (particularly where nonclinical populations are studied) in order to establish more precisely the correspondence between clinical depression and rating scale classifications of depression. In this light, it is important for investigators of the comparative efficacy of cognitive–behavioral approaches to obtain independent diagnostic classifications, preferably by means of structured interview methods such as the Schedule for Affective Disorders and Schizophrenia (Spitzer & Endicott, 1975) or the Present State Examination (Wing, Cooper, & Sartorius, 1974), in order to establish whether treatment techniques and their therapeutic outcomes are effective in the actual clinical situation.

An important contribution would thus entail the effectiveness of one or another cognitive–behavioral method in situational and endogenous depression, for example, as well as the primary and secondary depression classifications. Not only would such demonstrations have practical importance, but such investigations would have great potential for contributing to knowledge about the nature of these various depression subtypes, toward the goal of a comprehensive integrated understanding and treatment plan for a variety of depressive states. Another area of promise, both theoretically and practically, might entail the effectiveness of a technique for the treatment of depression in conditions not typically regarded as primarily affective in nature, such as postpsychotic depression in schizophrenia and schizoaffective disorder. If it could be demonstrated that such conditions respond to cognitive–behavioral interventions, particularly in comparison to appropriate nondepressed control diagnostic groups, an important theoretical advance could be possible in conceptualizing the breadth of depression in conditions that at least traditionally have not been considered to be affective disorders.

An important area that also remains to be clarified concerns the place of cognitive–behavioral theories and techniques in a comprehensive integrated biopsychological understanding of depression. Within this framework, several key issues must be addressed. For example, many of the studies reported above selected depressed and nondepressed control subjects on the basis of self-report questionnaires such as the Beck and Hamilton inventories. Although these self-report scales tap many important clinical characteristics of depression, their correspondence with diagnosable depressive disorders is largely unknown. In particular, self-report inventories typically classify an individual on the basis of the number of depressive symptoms a given individual endorses, which may not automatically correspond to the clinician's assessment of depression, which is frequently nonadditive. The weighting of subjective depression, associated characteristics of depression, duration of illness, familial factors, and characteristics of onset of a depressive episode are germane to establishing a clinical diagnosis, whereas scales such as the Beck and Hamilton inventories are oriented primarily to the number of signs and symptoms of depression. To a certain extent, therefore, the self-report scales tap severity of disturbance. It is certainly plausible that many patients classified as depressed on these scales will include minor as well as major depressive episodes, as well as characterological depressive states, which may conceivably be disorders different from major depression.

Finally, it is important to continue long-term follow-up investigations of cognitive–behavioral techniques in depressed patients. In keeping with some of the suggestions raised earlier in regard to precise assessment of signs and symptoms of depression, it is becoming increasingly important to specify which particular features of depression are most responsive to cognitive–behavioral intervention techniques. Many therapeutic outcome investigations have failed to provide comprehensive assessments of depressed individuals' response to treatment. As depression consists of deficits in behavioral, cognitive, affective, and motivational processes, dependent measures that reflect the multidimensional nature of this disorder must be included in future therapeutic outcome studies. In this manner, it may be possible to develop a means for treatment planning where specific techniques are selected on the basis of their efficacy in depressed patients with a particular symptom or cluster of symptoms.

A number of techniques have been presented and evaluated that derive from cognitive–behavioral conceptualizations of the nature of depression. At this juncture, it would seem that several of these techniques have demonstrated efficacy and occupy an important place in the armamentarium of psychotherapeutic intervention strategies for depression. Several problems and directions for continued research have been presented, influenced largely by the position that the most advantageous approach for the future lies in the precise application of effective cognitive–behavioral techniques, guided by the realities of the clinical situation, and emerging psychobiological views of the etiology and understanding of the spectrum of depressive conditions.

11

Parental Depression and Child–Family Development: A Systems Approach

Alfred P. French

All the vital mechanisms, varied as they are, have only one object: that of preserving constant the conditions of life.

Claude Bernard

ADAPTATION

Adaptive behavior has been well described in Don Schlitz's award-winning song, "The Gambler": "You gotta know when to hold 'em, you gotta know when to fold 'em, you gotta know when to walk away and when to run . . . " (Schlitz, 1978). Adaptation is the use of all available means to ensure continued maintenance of the stable internal environment necessary for life and requires constant adjustment of the self–environment relationship. This is achieved through a *reference system* [e.g., the temperature at which a thermostat is set, a family's collective belief structure (Ferreira, 1963), or a country's constitution], *information* and a *central decision maker* that uses the information to determine whether the train is on or off the track defined by the reference system. If the train is off the track, the central decision maker may either take whatever measures are necessary to bring the train back on the track or may move the track under the train. These two fundamentally different types of maneuvers are defined as Type I maneuvers (getting the train back onto the track by moving the train, leaving the track alone) and Type II maneuvers (leaving the train alone and moving the track under the train).

The author wishes to express his appreciation to Doctors Ann Arvin, Tom Morrison, and Brian Schechmeister for invaluable discussion regarding earlier drafts of this chapter.

Table 11-1
Type I and Type II Maneuvers

Level	Problem	Type I Response	Type II Response
Cell	Insufficient energy supply	Increase production of energy-carrying molecules	Mutation of DNA of change engery requirements
Organ	Not enough contractile force	Increase contractile force, by whatever means	Shift body demands so that contractile force required is reduced
Organ system (cardiovascular)	Inadequate blood pressure	Increase blood pressure by both central and peripheral mechanisms	Reduce body requirements for tissue perfusion so that less blood pressure is required (e.g., hypothermia during surgery)
Individual (biological level)	Too weak to carry out required tasks	Increase strength	Change tasks
Individual (psychological level)	Inadequate skills	Learn	Change job aspirations according to existing skills
Family	Conflict between an individual's behavior and the family's collective self-image	Bring the deviant individual into line	Revise family collective self-image to include the previously deviant behavior
Social	Laws and mores discriminating against minorities	Keep minorities in line	Social reform

A central assumption of this chapter is that *any* process, function, or activity of any sort by any self-maintaining organism or social system of any size or composition may be understood as a Type I maneuver, a Type II maneuver, or a combination of the two. The appropriate smooth selection of a balanced combination of Type I and Type II maneuvers resulting ultimately in a healthy organism is adaptive behavior. This point is so important that we give examples in Table 11-1.

French and Steward (1975a) proposed that Type I processes are identical to both those of homeostasis, or maintenance of the steady state of the organism as proposed by Bernard (1927) as well as to assimilation as defined by Piaget (1970), and that Type II processes are identical with accommodation as defined by Piaget.

The addition of feelings dramatically expands the scope of this model. Feelings are the subjective, qualitatively specific signals that inform us of the adaptive value of our behavior. The model requires four distinct signals for adequate and inadequate Type I and Type II processes: pleasure for successful Type I, anxiety for unsuccessful Type I, satisfaction for adequate Type II, and grief for inadequate Type II processes. If we assume that Type I and Type II processes vary independently, we have the framework for the description of different adaptive processes and their associated feelings shown in Figure 11-1, which includes not only the four primary affective states proposed by the model, but those four that result from the combinations of the primary states (the "U" in Figure 11-1 is a formal, logical *and*).

The upper-right quadrant is optimal with adequacy in both Type I and Type II processes. Here homeostasis is maintained while the organism is able to carry on basic restructuring (i.e., DNA mutations, changes in family mythology, investments in the new manufacturing facilities, changes in the Constitution) at a rate adequate to permit the organism to explore the opportunities and meet the challenges of the current organism–environment relationship. The feeling, joy, is a combination of joy and satisfaction.

The upper-left quadrant represents an organism that is currently able to maintain homeostasis but is moving toward trouble since the rate of basic restructuring of its reference system (accommodation) is inadequate. Here we find the quadrant of the developmental arrest—the individual or institution that is an anachronism in its time and place and must depend on previously accumulated resources or the goodwill of others to survive. This is the quadrant of arrogant power.

The lower-right quadrant describes a high level of accommodation coupled with inadequate assimilation. The statement is: "Oh, don't think about me. I'll just fit in anywhere, and take whatever's left over."

The lower-left quadrant represents system failure on both axes: the

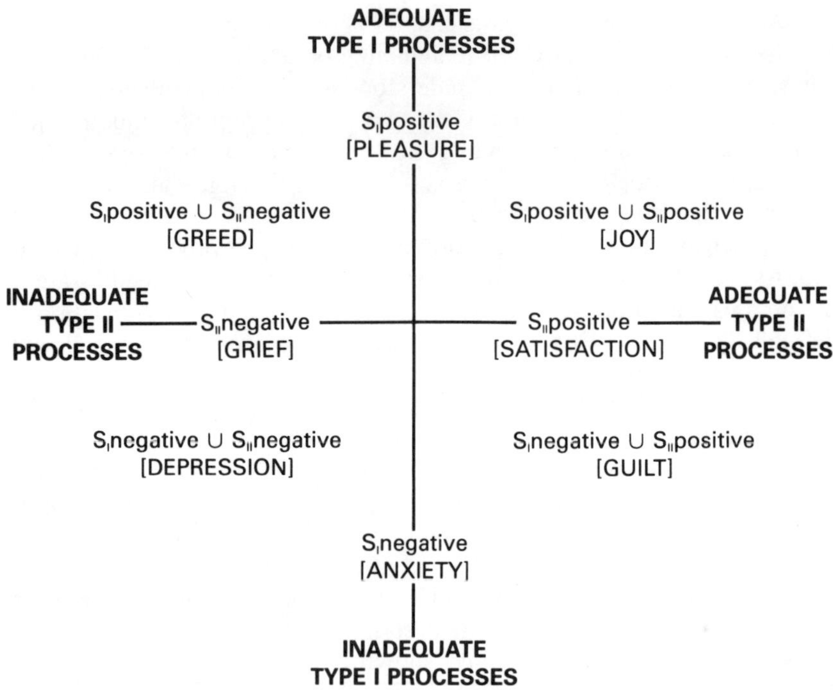

Figure 11-1. A structural scheme of adaptation.

system cannot maintain homeostasis *and* cannot reach a frame of reference with respect to which it could do so. Structurally, and "in feeling" terms, it is the opposite of the joyous upper-right-hand quadrant of good adaptation. The statement is "I cannot maintain my balance and am therefore anxious. And what's more, I can't find a frame of reference with respect to which I could do so." The feeling is *depression*.

A bit more discussion about "depression" is now in order. Building from the model of adaptation presented above, we propose depression to be a complex affect composed of both anxiety and grief that, in turn, arise from the perception of failure of Type I processes (anxiety) as well as of Type II processes (grief). The form of the self-environment relationship for which depression is appropriate is: "I cannot maintain my balance and I cannot find a reference system with respect to which I could." Since no organism will tolerate the pain of depression longer than necessary, the *affective* component of the response will change from time to time. The form of the response will be dependent on the individual's developmental level and mental mechanisms. Although we recognize the value of a rigorous definition of depression based on specified type of unconscious conflict in mature psyche, we are in agreement with Anthony (1975a), who argued forcefully for a broader concept of depression, applicable to all developmental stages:

> This ego psychology approach has a number of advantages that seem especially pertinent to the childhood situation. First of all, there is nothing in the theory that would preclude the consideration of clinical depression on the grounds of immaturity . . . all of the metapsychological difficulties associated with the operation of classic theory—oral fixation and incorporation, aggression against self—are here given merely a peripheral or complicating role *The child's depression can assimilate them later when he becomes an adult.**

Anthony's phrase "can assimilate" is particularly powerful, since it presents depression as an organizing factor that can assimilate subsequent experience on all developmental levels. This general concept of depression will be most valuable in examining the impact of parental depression in the child.

In two fine summary articles Akiskal and McKinney (1973, 1975) have pulled together the diverse literature on depression with remarkable clarity and, like Anthony (1975a), argued for the generality and indeed *universality* across species, of depression: "As a reduction or elimination of the tendency of any open system to seek relationship with the world, it represents *a behavioral state for which there is universal vulnerability.*"

These general summaries create broad base from which to consider "depression." We find the model of adaptation outlined above (French, 1977) and Piaget's (1970) and Nagera's (1966) discussions of development to be coherent with Anthony's (1975a), Akiskal and McKinney's (1973, 1975), and Lewis and Lewis's (1979) discussions of depression. "Depression" as an affect implies perceived failure of adaptation, which, in turn, implies the perception of a sufficiently severe trauma that Type I and Type II processes have failed. The clinical presentation and intrapsychic mechanisms involved will depend on the developmental level (Anthony, 1975a). Engel (1968) and Schmale (1964) have developed closely related concepts, emphasizing mastery of the self-environment relationship as a basis for good function and health an perceived failure of this mastery as a basis for illness. Similarly, Coopersmith (1968) has emphasized the importance of self-esteem.

Useful as discussions of depression are, however, the focus of this volume is the *interactional* aspects of the whole matter: the impact of parental depression on the child. Parental depression leads us in an entirely new direction since we are concerned with the impact of depression on a complex set of behaviors rather than with an individual's feelings, and the scope of this volume must include a wide variety of phenomena both acute and chronic, both mature and immature. We are only occasionally

---

*Reprinted with permission from Anthony, E. J. Childhood depression. In E. J. Anthony & T. Benedek (Eds.), *Depression and human existence*. Boston: Little, Brown, 1975, pp. 257–258.(a)

concerned with an obvious parental depression the impact of which on the child is clear. Since we are concerned with depression of parenting function rather than with depression of the parent, we use the term "depressed parenting" to refer to parenting that is distorted as a direct consequence of a failure in the parents' adaptation at some point in the parents' development. Operationally, this takes the form of a poor training program for the child that either under- or overstresses the child, as we outline in detail below by focusing our attention first on development and then by expanding our model to put the individual into a social context.

|| DEVELOPMENT

"Development" refers to all processes that contribute to the creation of structures that facilitate adaptation. It is thus a much more encompassing concept than "growth," which is simply "more of." Development, indeed, might mean less size, (e.g., in the treatment of obesity), but it always means creation of more effective structures. These structures develop on biological, psychological, family, and social levels through an interaction between the organism and the environment (Call, 1979; Erikson, 1945). For purposes of this chapter, we are keenly interested in events that challenge the organism's adaptive capacity. Because the right amount of exercise is crucial to the success or failure of any training program and thus to the success or failure of child development. Piaget (1970) has pointed out that an organism will respond to a block in normal development by detouring with as little fuss as possible or, failing this, will reroute to a course as parallel as possible to the original: "if an external influence causes the developing organism to deviate from one of its creodes (i.e., from one of its developmental sequences) there ensues a . . . reaction which tends channel it back to the normal sequence or, if this fails, switches it to a new creode as similar as possible to the original one."

Following a block to normal development, therefore, four different types of choice are available. The first choice is, of course, to simply remove the block all together, which we refer to as "path 0." (Usually this requires the assistance of someone else, as we outline below.) The next choice is, of course, the simplest possible rerouting around the block with maximum conservation of momentum and a return to the original track: path 1. Here there is no change of the essential internal structure of the organism. The train continues to run along on the same track after a minor bump. No type II changes are required. For example, a parent and child might have difficulty in organizing a Cub Scout pack but might rally and put together a successful group. Failing this option, as Piaget (1970) has pointed out, the organism with enough adaptive capacity will find 2: a developmental second path as parallel to the first as possible. For example, therefore, our family switches to a different activity such as Indian guides, conserving as much momentum as possible, yet with some Type II shift. The new track is parallel to the first but is, nevertheless, in some way a different track. Life, however, is not always so kind as to facilitate a smooth rerouting into the original path or into a nicely parallel path. Developmental disturbances, which Nagera (1966) defined as "Whatever disturbs the typical unfolding of development," may have a much greater effect than the simple rerouting described by Piaget. A true "pothole in the road of life" (PIRL) may force a more extensive restructuring, to which we refer as path 3. Here there is ultimately a reestablishment of homeostasis, but at the expense of a significant deviation from the original path and thus only after significant Type II processes have occurred. For example, some families may decide that parent–child activities are not a high priority, the children attend the Brownies or Cub Scouts with their aunts, uncles, and cousins, with neighbors, or not at all. If the children do not attend, however, path 3 requires that they find some track on which to run that part of their lives. Perhaps they develop a hobby on their own. If the children fail to retrack this part of their lives altogether, they move to path 4, in which the children give up that developmental line totally; therefore, if continued development of that area is critical, the organism dies. Indeed, the concept of "partial death" is useful.

We now relate this scheme to our prior model, for encounters with PIRL's give rise to feelings! The feeling experienced will, of course, be characteristic of the individual. In general, we expect to find painful feelings in the early stages of the rerouting and enjoyable ones as homeostasis once again establishes paths 1, 2, and 3 and a more complex sequence in path 4. Depression is the affect appropriate to path 4 since homeostasis is not maintained, *and* the organism cannot find a reference structure with respect to which homeostasis could be maintained. We would expect depression to occur transiently on the other paths as the organism reels from the trauma of the block as it has not yet reestablished balance. Although the detectable *affect* and *mood* of depression may not be apparent, we are concerned in this volume not only with clinically apparent and classically defined depression, but with damage to the development of self-confidence that may result from paths 2, 3, and 4. Here we refer again to the familiar relationship between the level of stress and the level of function: as stress increases, the level of function improves to a certain point; then, as the level of stress increases further, the level of function drops off. If we graph the level of function on a vertical axis and the level of stress on a horizontal axis, therefore, we find an inverted U-shaped curve. This inverted U-shaped curve is related to the four paths following PIRL in a very straightforward way: each individual's response to a PIRL will depend on the subjectively perceived level of stress *and* on that individual's particular inverted-U stress response curve. One Christmas morning, for example, twin girls came racing downstairs to find high piles of horse manure in the living room. The first of the two howled piteously, "Our parents hate us!" (path 4), while the other rushed forward shouting joyously "A pony!" (path 0). One might thus take path 1 or 2 and editorialize, "Well, I made it, good for me!" or "Well, I made it but that's only because it was an easy task, and I only choose easy tasks anyhow, which proves how crummy I am." And one might take path 3 and editorialize "I went through a big crisis and had to do extensive retracking and re-establish my homeostasis: Horray for me! I am an adaptive organism" or "I failed. I got knocked off the track. I never was able to stick with it. I am no good." In the case of path 4, we might have either a partial or total loss of life. The favorable editorial is "I have met obstacles with a good adaptive approach. The outcome is failure for me as an individual, and I experience this with dignity and self-respect," whereas the unfavorable counterpart is "I have lost, and therefore I am crummy."

In taking a developmental history, we are concerned not only with the specific content of the individual's and family's history, but with the extent to which certain events have facilitated or inhibited the development of self-confidence and self-esteem. Often, the specific PIRL may be forgotten and in fact a PIRL may be a pattern of relationships experienced over a period of time rather than a single, identifiable traumatic event. The PIRL may be recreated, however, in dreams, fantasies, symptoms, and maladaptive patterns of parenting in the unfortunate cases. Much of the intriguing detective work of clinical practice searches for an answer to "What was the developmental significance of a PIRL in your life? Which of the four paths did you take?" and "Did the whole thing lead to an increased or decreased sense of self confidence?" If optimal healing occurs, the anxiety, grief, and depression that are part of the rerouting process are resolved, and the resolution improves chances for healthy future development. Psychotherapy is always concerned, however, with the unfortunate outcome: painful feelings associated with the rerouting seem to spin off the great force like a tornado that is, itself, invisible and yet gathers material in its path into its own form, assimilating houses and barns into the tornado funnel. The depression associated with painful reroutings may persist for a lifetime and skip with impunity across generational boundaries, organizing experience into its own destructive form. As we interview a child or parent or occasionally members of two or three generations in the same family, we are looking for these organizing centers and their roots in PIRL-incurred trauma. For example, a woman traumatized as a child by her own mother's lack of interest in her activities may find difficulty in providing "free" emotional support for her daughter.

Obviously, the total number of PIRLs encountered in a given span of time is important. Far more important, and often accessible only to sensitive, careful interview, is the path followed after a PIRL. Healthy development, like the training of an athlete, must include a good mix of path 1, 2, 3 and 4 in an appropriate distribution. Furthermore, the family must do everything in its power to provide a developmental context such that the child traverses PIRL Paths in a way that increases self-esteem and self-confidence. Parenting thus requires a number of different functions, failure of any of which will impair the child's development. Families may be categorized operationally by the PIRL path distribution that they favor. Those families that identify "love" with "do what you can to reduce all PIRL paths to zero" will have a particular set of characteristics and will tend to identify all efforts to increase the average PIRL path waiting with mean, uncaring people. Parental maturity is required to discover and to carry out, throughout the development of the child–family system, the optimal distribution of PIRL paths.

It is thus necessary to explore the function of the social field within which an individual develops. *Information,* for example, may be invalidated by: "Well, they didn't really mean what they said," thereby interfering with Type I processes. The internal *reference system* itself may be questioned, as in "So what if you made your goal? That wasn't really the goal we had in mind anyhow so you go out there and try harder!" The decision-maker might be invalidated by: "Your ideas are never any good! You're just crazy!"

If the social field or a part of the social field that is in a position to interfere with adaptation stands to gain in some way from the organism's confused struggle to maintain adaptive posture in the face of this onslaught on its own basic functions, the organism is in serious trouble and will function at the service of the social field in apparent violation of its own basic rules of function! The argument of this chapter is that this is *precisely* the position in which depressed parents find themselves and that depression on the part of the parent tends to facilitate this situation. In terms of the PIRL path model, parental depression tends to shift the child's PIRL path distribution and cannot do so in a manner favorable to the child's development. Moreover, the child cannot assist the parent in correcting this situation, since the child by definition lacks maturity.

An expansion of the model of adaptation will clarify this point further by permitting a clearer description of the impact of the social field on the individual.

|| THE FAMILY AS A SYSTEM

Since the family contains at least two members who occupy significantly different roles within the family, a model adequate for analysis of family function must account for the capacity of the family to generate its own unique and complex internal structure: social power is used to decide who is and who is not "okay" and thus who will be a "scapegoat" (French, 1977). We may expand the two-dimensional model of Type I and Type II processes by adding the scapegoat role and power as further parameters, proposing that a family may be characterized by the distribution of its members in a four-dimensional space generated by (1) Type I processes—particularly, for clinical purposes, the extent to which failure of Type I processes is perceived (thus, we use "anxiety" as the first characteristic of a family), (2) Type II function, or the capacity to change, (3) the scapegoat role, and (4) power, or the ability to distribute other family members in the space generated by the first three axes.

For example, a high-power person will tend to decrease his or her own anxiety, minimize his or her own need to carry out fundamental internal restructuring, and minimize his or her identification as the person responsible for the whole mess. The person in power will tend to reduce his or her PIRL paths toward zero and to avoid trauma to self-esteem. This latter is often done by holding others responsible for the PIRL trauma.

To do otherwise requires great maturity: who can set up a rigorous training program and hold one's self to it faithfully, without outside structure of any kind? A child *cannot* do so. One of a child's basic rights, in this writer's opinion, is to experience loving and firm coaching that distributes the PIRL paths through an appropriate proportion of paths 1–4. Therefore, children have a basic right to *not* be given more power than they can handle. To violate tnis rule is to destroy the necessary rigor of the training program.

These four aspects of family function may be represented in a table (Table 11-2) and family members rank-ordered from low to high:

Table 11-2
Four Aspects of Family Function

	Low	High
Anxiety		
Capacity to change		
Symptom-carrier role		
Power		

Table 11-3
The Symptom-Carrier Role

Symptom-Carrier Role	Low	High
As seen by Ed	Ed	Jane
As seen by Jane	Jane	Ed

One further refinement is needed, however, since the designation of the symptom carrier, or a "person who is responsible for this whole mess," is often a contested matter of opinion and one of the most tender points of treatment. This is especially the case when the family is experiencing a significant shift and the person previously on the end of criticism is taking an unexpected turn on the "hot seat," and being criticized or questioned for the first time.

At such a junction it is important to further subdivide the third horizontal column, specifying the point of view (Table 11-3).

Here, both Jane and Ed hold the familiar position, "I am okay, but you are a turkey," with each seeing self as okay and the other as not okay. This is often a familiar presenting picture when couples comes in for help and will occur at high intensity when power shifts are occurring.

A complete rank-ordering of all family members on each of the four columns would not be possible. In practice, it is necessary only to pin down a few of the positions and the general form of the system soon becomes clear. Of particular value is the relationship between the first and fourth columns, for anxiety and power. Here we enunciate a principle that is probably already "somebody's law:" *If two individuals relate in such a way that, with respect to a particular issue, one is high in power and low in anxiety while the other is high in anxiety and low in power, the person who is high in poor and low in anxiety controls that area of the relationship*.

For example, if you have water and I have thirst, the water issue is a control point in our relationship and you are in control. This configuration, the "anxiety–power cross over," is essential in looking at the impact of parental depression on child development, as we soon outline. Consider, for example, a child who has a reading problem. The parents, however, are quite anxious about it. In this all-too-familiar situation, the parents receive the external information that the child's reading is inadequate. Acting adaptively, they seek to correct the problem. If the child were similarly motivated, the problem would be limited only by the reversibility of the block, given optimal use of all available interventions. Life tends not to be so simple, and this volume specifically concerns cases wherein family dynamics complicate the picture. In the cases with which we are particularly concerned, the child finds social power in the parents' concern, and as long as the child is willing to sacrifice reading progress for power in the family, bartering results: "I'll read if you will give me something." As parental self-confidence becomes increasingly involved in the problem, we may progress to "I'll tell you that you're okay if I get something I want." The parents are thrown into a situation that they cannot solve since their basic rules of function require that they get the train back on the track, that is, that they eliminate the discrepancy between their child's actual level of function and the level of function they would like to see. A Type I correction would leave the parental aspirations unchanged and would correct the child's problems. A Type II correction would require that the parents shift their expectations of the child (i.e., that they grieve the loss of their formerly desired level of function). To the extent that they are acting inappropriately in response to external information, a part of this process and, in fact, only a small part may be under their control. Basic homeostasis thus becomes very complex in the social field since the basic rule, "Keep the train on the track while moving the track as little as possible" is complicated to "You may consider your train to be on the track if and only another train stays on its track, but you are powerless to do anything about the second train." In other words, the child is in a very powerful position if parental self-esteem becomes contingent on the child's level of function. In terms of Table 11-2 given above, these asymmetries are anxiety–power crossovers. In terms of the PIRL-path-distribution description of development, anxiety–power crossovers within the family must have an impact on the child's development. A parent who is excessively high in an anxiety–power crossover with respect to the child will probably be insensitive and may jerk the child willy-nilly from path 0 to path 4 and back again, chastizing the child yet further for the child's complaints! In the opposite situation, children are high in power and, being immature by definition, will shift their own PIRL path distribution toward 0, to their short-term delight and much to their long-term detriment!

The real world tends to present us not with theoretical pure types, but with complex mixtures. This was most apparent in the treatment, by a young, eager, and naive therapist, of 11-year-old John, whom a psychiatric resident first met as he was consulting to a classroom for educationally handicapped children. The case history follows.

|| Case 1

The therapist observed a passive, quiet, withdrawn youngster who dawdled at his work, avoided other youngsters, and seemed to have no interest in anything. Through his contact with the school, the psychiatric resident was able to establish rapport with the parents, who were then willing to bring John to the clinic for treatment.

John offered no complaints and sat passively in the office. The initial individual interview with John was painfully boring and was more like a clumsy cross-examination of a dull-witted and recalcitrant witness than a psychiatric interview. John's parents complained that "He never does anything that we ask him to do." In particular, the parents were angry because John would not hold up his head and speak to them directly in response to their questions.

John had been adopted at the age of 2 years after a lengthy and unusual struggle. His adopting parents had known the biological parents and were concerned about their emotional and physical neglect of John as an infant. Their concern grew until they decided to do something definitive about this terrible problem: they would make John their own son. At length they were successful and formally adopted him. They were already pleased with their first son, a year older than John, and the basis of their interest in the second child of the same sex was not obvious. Nevertheless, their pursuit of John's adoption had been vigorous. John had been badly neglected as an infant and had been weak, sickly, and withdrawn for the first 2 years of his life. As nearly as can be determined, he met Spitz's (1964) description of a child with "anaclitic depression": "the weepiness subsided, and a stronger provocation became necessary to provoke it. A sort of frozen rigidity of expression appeared instead. These children would lie or sit with wide-open, expressionless eyes, frozen immobile face, and a faraway expression as if in a daze, apparently not perceiving what went on in their environment."

The father's developmental history seemed quite normal. He had one much younger brother, had been raised by normal parents in normal circumstances, and had experienced nothing unusual in life. The mother's childhood had been complicated by her parent's unusual attitude toward illness; one did not ask for medical attention unless and until one was near death, and John's mother had, as a child, nearly died as a consequence of this philosophy. She had a stomachache one evening but received the usual admonition from her mother not to complain. She became increasingly ill and at bedtime was in such pain that she was unable to tell her parents her usual "good night." Some time later, sensing difficulty, her father went to her room to find her curled up and moaning of pain. "That was the only time he went against mother's vote," she recalled. A trip to the doctor, much against the mother's wishes, resulted in the removal of a badly inflamed appendix. The biographical material did not emerge initially, however; they initially presented as the very picture of the healthy well-adjusted, Christian, American middle-class family with only one problem—John wouldn't cooperate.

John and his mother had immediately developed a close relationship as soon as he was successfully adopted from the family who had maltreated him through neglect in his infancy. She commented, "He never has to ask for anything. I always just knew what he wanted." Close and specific questioning revealed this to have been an unerring rule: John never had asked for so much as a drink of water, because his mother always knew what he wanted. Periodically, she tried to "break him" of this habit, but never with success. John would simply do without water or food rather than ask for it explicitly. As the years passed, the pattern became more and more ingrained. At length the mother gave up and decided that the matter was hopeless.

In weekly individual sessions, John was passive indeed, and after about 6 months of patient operant conditioning with the therapist's cooperation in setting up a board game acting as the reinforcer, he gradually advanced to the point where he entered the office with noticeable eagerness and actively set up the board game that he wished to play. John gradually became more assertive in play and gradually began to express some pleasure when he jumped his opponent's checkers. Meanwhile, however, he was as slow and passive as ever at school.

At this point the therapist advised the family to begin placing demands on John in order to reduce his now-ridiculous infantile dependence on his mother. The battleground was schoolwork, and all agreed that if his schoolwork were not completed he would lose TV-watching privileges. The following week, interestingly, the family reported that John was not doing his work and was watching TV, in violation of the agreement. We learned that John had indeed been sent to his room following the first infraction and had then stood at the door, peeking out at the television screen. His mother had held firm to the promise, but while she was at a neighbor's the father had permitted John to watch "just for a little," and on returning, the irate mother responded, "Well, if you're going to let him watch *I'm* not going to be the bad guy," and the battle was over. John had won back his TV-watching privileges, while his homework remained undone. He had successfully shifted from a path 2 or 3 to a path 0. This event led to a line of inquiry regarding John's use of his social network to circumnavigate rules. In years past when the family had sought to curtail him, John went to the neighbors, having first worked through a sequence of brother, then mother, and then father to gain his wishes. Failing this, this "shy, withdrawn, mentally retarded" boy rang the neighbors' doorbells and stood mournfully before the answerer. He has thus not only gained the object he wished (such as water or food), but the wrath of the neighbors against his parents as well; apparently, several of them were convinced that his parents were evil people who were neglecting him and were eager to support this unfortunate waif when and where they could, thereby recreating the original adoption scene! The parents were embarrassed and crestfallen by the whole matter, which stood in blatant contradiction to their self-image as helpful Christians. John had gained control of the family and had apparently used his power to keep his PIRL paths close to zero. Attempts by his parents to curtail him simply led to their being labeled as the "bad guys responsible for it all."

This first effort to impose reasonable expectations on John was thus unsuccessful. As we explored this phenomenon further, it became clear that not only the neighborhood, but he extended family was involved in these rescue processes: the sequence through the years had been: brother, mother, father, grandmother, and grandfather. John consistantly gained his objective while simultaneously avoiding the constraints initially imposed.

One side of the entire child–family system thus became clear: John, who initially presented as a pitifully woebegone, helpless, hopeless, and probably mentally retarded fellow, now appeared in an entirely different light: a highly effective organization man, master of the extended family and the neighborhood as well, who could throw into action a large network of people who would not

Table 11-4
The Family's Structure:
John Versus Mother

	Low	High
Anxiety	Mother	John
Capacity to change		
Symptom-carrier role	Mother	John
Power	John	Mother

only give him the material sustenance he wanted but *further extend* his social power as well, since the unfortunate individual who sought to deny John in any given instance was, ultimately, labeled a cruel and uncaring person who was being unkind to poor John.

In terms of Table 11-2, the very short-lived initial configuration would be, when John was denied TV by his mother, as shown in Table 11-4.

Here we have the parents determined to curtail John in some way and thus setting up a restriction, such as "no TV." John, however, through either a successful assault on parental guild and/or through mobilization of social forces, invariably managed to rearrange this to the pattern shown in Table 11-5.

The parents had accommodated, John had assimilated, the parents felt very badly about the whole thing, and were, further, blamed for the whole matter, whereas John clearly stood in a position of power.

A totally different side of the case emerged in the office at about the 6-month point, after John and his family had each been seen for 1 hour each week. At this point one of the original treatment goals had been reached: John was now able to raise his head, make eye contact with his mother, and answer a question directly in a clearly audible voice! The therapist was thrilled, and, with charming naiveté, anticipated that the parents would be similarly pleased. This was not the case. Initially, the parents did not notice John's long-sought improvement at all, and so the young and eager therapist pointed this out to them. They were not pleased. In fact, they were distinctly irritated. At this point, as John sat miserably in his chair

Table 11-5
The Family's Structure: John Versus
Parents, First Configuration

	Low	High
Anxiety	John	Parents
Capacity to change	John	Parents
Symptom-carrier role	John	Parents
Power	Parents	John

Table 11-6
The Family's Structure: John Versus Parents, Second Configuration

	Low	High
Anxiety	Parents	John
Capacity to change	John	
Symptom-carrier role	Parents	John
Power	John	Parents

apparently afraid to breath, the configuration of the family seemed to resemble that shown in Table 11-6.

"Well, that just proves how difficult he is," was the mother's comment. At this point she began to weep, and as great tears rolled across her cheeks, "That just *proves* how much he doesn't love us—he could have done that at home, all the time, if he wanted to—but he only does it here, in your office and just because you asked him to, and not because he really *wants* to, to show that he really loves us after all we've done for him." At this point the complexity of the case was

Table 11-7
Major Functional Categories

Adaptation	Failure in infancy: withdrawal
Depression	Apparently demonstrated findings of Spitz's "hospitalism" as an infant
Development	Once the relationship with the adopting mother was established, John followed path 0 or path 1: he developed social skills necessary to avoid all blocks
Parenting	The parents attempted to move John toward use of paths 1 or 2, but following confrontation wherein John's misery triggered familial pain, the family dropped the requirements down to those of path 0, thereby overall reenforcing the pattern
Parental Depression	No evidence for parental depression on any level or at any time in the father's life; maternal sadness, anger, and bitterness became clear as she described her own mother's cold and even cruelly life-threatening attitude
Depressed Parenting	The parents apparently assumed that John was incapable of adapting; path 0 was abruptly replaced by path 4 during one family session
Family Dynamics	Massive anxiety–power asymmetries in both directions were obvious

obvious while its structure was less obvious. The role of the underlying maternal depression was gradually emerging.

Here the demands seemed to be those of path 3 if not of path 4, in contrast to John's usual path 0 or path 1. As outlined above, the mother seemed to have invalidated the information that initially seemed to be so patently clear and obvious in the room, for all to see. But suddenly, by changing *information,* she had restructured the whole situation. What had previously appeared to be compliance (i.e., John's raising his head and looking at his parents) now was resistance ("He only does it because *you*"), and what had seemed to be the achievement of a goal for which reward was anticipated was now the basis for parental anger.

John made no attempt to defend himself, but simply sank into his chair with a hopeless air. He did not speak for the remainder of the hour.

As the months passed, the mother's depression became more clear. She was miserable and perceived herself as a failure in all areas of her life. Her husband's career, which was outwardly successful, she perceived to be an apparent success, but only because a hardworking colleague had made it so. Her own return to school had not met her expectations, and she found no satisfaction there despite a very good academic record. She had no satisfaction in her marriage, and her biological son's success (which were many) she attributed to his similarity to his father. John and John alone had been her great project in life, and she had dedicated herself to this objective. Herein lay her one hope for self-esteem. With each passing failure in John's life she thus had become more frantic and more vulnerable to his demands.

John continued to become more assertive on the checkerboard, and the parents continued to explore the power–support issues in their relationship with him. Again and again they vowed to hold to their promise to keep John accountable for some task or other, but again and again John successfully circumnavigated all blocks, finding at last someone who would rescue him and label the others cruel for their maltreatment of Poor John. Apparently the "wide-open expressionless eyes" of the anaclitically depressed infant had become John's greatest asset as he mobilized his social environment on his own behalf. With each such episode, the pattern seemed to deepen. At length the mother described her own pain at the points of confrontation as she looked into John's suffering eyes. With tears literally cascading down her cheeks and her body shaking with sobs, she blurted out: *"I absolutely can't stand to see him suffer! It hurts so much that I can't stand it! I can't stand it!"*

She reported a dream about her relationship with John: "I walked into John's room and he was reading that filthy pornographic literature. I was just so shocked. We've never exposed them to any such thing, and we're a Christian family. He has a Bible at his bedside, if he wants to read. But (weeping) he just looked at me, with that smirk that he gets on his face, and he just said, in the dream, 'Mom, I just do it because you hate it.' "

She was bewildered and utterly at a loss. This child, whom she had nurtured from a state below normal infancy, and to whom she had dedicated her life and best energy, had turned against her. Her tears subsided, and she sat quietly wringing her hands.

A summary of this case in terms of the major categories of this chapter is presented in Table 11-7.

At this juncture the role of long-standing maternal pain was clear. We learned of her childhood appendicitis and inferred that, if her mother demanded crisis-level pain before seeking medical help, she probably had a high threshold for other signals of distress as well. The mirroring into her adopted son's relationship with her is perfectly clear: she was ignored until she produced a distress signal so high that life itself was threatened. Her adopted son, on the other hand, enjoyed a milieu with precisely the opposite characteristics: he only needed to look at her and she "instinctively" knew what he needed, and got it for him. Interestingly, her own mother participated in this pattern and was one of the rescuers to whom John turned if anyone sought to change the pattern. It seems that John was, in short, her own treatment of her own hopelessness and helplessness in displaced form. All the problems of displacement were thus inherent, and the problem (imblance of the parent–child relationship in terms of the type of information required before the parent would join the child in making a corrective maneuver) continued, in a mirror-image form.

True treatment of this child–family system obviously required the mother to engage her own previously buried pain regarding the suffering child and insensitive parent. She did not do so, and John eventually moved to a residential treatment center where he soon polarized the staff into those who saw him as a manipulative youngster who needed a swift kick in the pants and those who saw him as Poor John who needed the love and understanding that had obviously been heretofore wanting. The old pattern was thus created again. This time, however, the staff were ready and recognized the need to avoid this polarization. As John was then unable to polarize the staff, he turned to acting out, which proved to be intolerable for that institution, and he was placed elsewhere. At last follow-up some 5 years following his last treatment under this writer's supervision, John was living in a board and care facility supported by public funds and, apparently, spending his time largely alone with no contact with his family. His mother's valiant attempt to heal her pain in displaced form ended as a limited success. John was not the pitiful basket case he had been at adoption. He was neither ill, psychotic, nor abusive to others. He stated to me that he liked his life and just wanted to be left alone.

In John's case there was not only the specific issue of illness, but the general distortion of child–family relationships. Careful exploration of almost any child–family problem will reveal the relevance of the parents' earlier disappointments and the resulting distortions of development.

|| Case 2

Susan presented with an unusual chief complaint: she refused to give up her favorite doll. Although this attachment in itself did not seem unusual, Susan was an otherwise apparently thriving 9-year-old at the time of evaluation. She was a solemn girl with thick glasses that obscured a mild lateral strabismus of one eye. She did not bring the doll to the office, and her mother reported that the doll was safe at home in her usual hiding place and that Susan would run to the doll immediately on her return home. Although Susan was reluctant to discuss her doll, she nodded in solemn agreement while her mother spoke. We learned that Susan absolutely insisted on carrying the doll with her at every moment while at home had finally agreed not to carry it to school during her kindergarten year, but seemed to experience true panic if the doll were washed. The mother had been advised that Susan would outgrow this but eventually sought a psychiatrist's opinion.

A background of early trauma was obviously to be sought, and the mother's own early experiences were obviously of great interest. Unfortunately from our investigative–teaching point of view, the mother, father, and grandparents all seemed to be disturbingly normal! The mother was a most pleasant and cooperative person who betrayed no trace of current depression and whose early experiences, as she recalled, seemed totally unimpaired by a lack of basic trust. She was happily married to a good fellow who took an active interest in his family. Yet Susan was a disturbed and disturbing child who presented gruesome scenes in the playroom ("And here's Charlie Brown, all cut up and bloody and lying in the middle of the road.") and who seemed totally unconcerned if her sisters fell and were hurt. On one occasion during the evaluation, she struck her mother forcefully in the face.

At length the role of her extremely poor vision became apparent. A more careful history revealed that, as a result of her extremely poor vision, she had lost nearly everything that was handed to her as an infant and small child. Only in toddlerhood when she began bumping onto things did her vision problem become apparent and only later was it correctable. The mother described how, in infancy, Susan lay passively in her crib while her bottle, only partly consumed, was ignored, just out of her reach. Initially, this first-child mother had interpreted this to mean contentment.

In this case, summarized below, parental depression and depressed parenting were red herrings, confidently expected but absent. An unusual PIRL in Susan's life seemed to be the entire issue, and her rapid progress in individual therapy confirmed the value of this point of view. The moral of the story is: if the child has accumulated sufficient trauma to account for observed symptoms, and if there are no links to parental PIRL's and if the family responds happily to improvement in the child, then work with the child individually.

Underlying parental pain may often be inferred from an unexpectedly vigorous parental response (see Table 11-8).

Parents may handle the re-creation of their own childhood pain in highly complex ways as did John's mother, in which case the parental depression was not immediately apparent, or more actively as in the case of *Jimmy,* a healthy 6-year-old boy.

|| Case 3

Jimmy was playing happily when his father came wearily home from work. Jimmy had set chairs and a mop to create an airplane that he was piloting. "I'm gonna be a pilot," he cheerfully greeted his father. The paternal response, in retro-

Table 11-8
Major Functional Categories: Susan

Adaptation	Failure in infancy to establish normal self-environment relationship due to impaired vision; passivity may have been due to temperamental factors as well as to depression–withdrawal
Depression	Must have been part of Susan's early experience as she reacted to numerous losses
Development	The mother did not know that her child's vision was severely impaired and thus inadvertently subjected the child to a large number of path 4s; unusual attachment to a favorite doll may have been a compensatory path 0
Parenting	Normal
Parental Depression	Absent: our conviction that there was a transgenerational failure in early development was a misleading assumption
Depressed Parenting	Absent
Family Dynamics	Normal: as Susan progressed in treatment, her parents were transiently guilty at not having recognized her problem earlier and yet did not, in any way, over compensate; they were thrilled at her progress in treatment and joyously established a healthy relationship with her

Table 11-9
Major Functional Categories: Jimmy

Adaptation	Although apparently normal in many ways, Jimmy's father seems in retrospect to have experienced substantial failure of adaptation
Development	The father's development had obviously been complicated by at least one memorable PIRL in his career development; he seems to have been motivated to train his son for a similar future event
Parental Depression	Never explored; readily inferred from his obvious anger
Depressed Parenting	The father transferred his son's experience abruptly from path 0 ("I'm gonna be a pilot") to path 4 ("*You* ain't *never* gonna be no God-damned *pilot*") in a context of hostility
Family Dynamics	Unknown

spect, may well have been a loving effort to protect his son from a PIRL later in life by sharing with his son his own painful experience: the chairs, mop, and Jimmy went flying in all directions. Jimmy found an angry father towering over him: "Look, Nigger, you get this once and get it right. When *you* pick up a mop, it's a *mop* and that's how you're gonna use it, a janitor all your life like your Dad, and *you* ain't *never* gonna be no God-dammed *pilot!*" Jimmy's teacher, years later, wondered why he was functioning "below his potential." In order to reach his academic potential, it might be necessary for Jimmy to alter his relationship with his father to the extent of extensive Type II maneuver. We may readily imagine and must empathize with the father's fear that Jimmy's education would take Jimmy away from him, leaving him a lonely old man (see Table 11-9).

Parental fear of loneliness and/or depression seems to be the underlying dynamic in a large group of disorders characterized by poor function in the identified patient (IP) and a close IP–family relationship with certain properties. Berne, 19, described "life games" between adults, such as alcoholism, wherein the "sickie" member of the pair is rescued when wet by the "wellie" member. Less apparent but equally important is the opposite maneuver: as the "sickie" member of the pair struggles to develop a good training schedule with which to develop the strength necessary for autonomy, the "wellie" member invariably recommends no such training program at all ("There, Dear, you just sit down and relax and let me take care of that") or disrupts progress at a critical point ("I don't know why in hell she did it, but I came home from work and all my school notes and papers was gone—I finally found them out in the trash all mixed up with the garbage—and *she* was the one all along who insisted I quit drinking and go to school").

The layers of adaptation failure and depression shown in Table 11-10 resemble the many layers of defense mechanisms encountered in intensive individual therapy. Therapy is less convenient, however, when many individuals and obnoxious symptoms are involved. Case examples of this "chronic depressive life style without overt depression syndrome" fill our jails and welfare case loads. Their resistant to change is well documented.

In a wonderfully optimistic report of families who broke the transgenerational cycle of child abuse, Hunter and Kilstrom (1979) emphasize the importance of "the apparent ability of the nonrepeating parents to come to an active resolution of their childhood experiences" and that families who successfully broke the child-abuse cycle were those most able to talk about their experiences "*and summon appropriate affects.*" Less severe but more prevalent is the dreary cycle of more subtle emotional neglect. This chapter closes with a brief description of a family who seemed to confirm Lewis and Lewis's grim prediction regarding the stability of life-long depression quoted earlier in this chapter.

Table 11-10
Major Functional Categories: Edward

Adaptation	Failure is usually grossly obvious; alcoholism, school phobia, and early pregnancy, for example, are common and often seen to occur in families as a clinical triad: the result of each of these is to bind the individual to a caretaker: the family holds, protects, and inhibits the school-phobia child or alcoholic adult while the too-young mother is forever bound to the parent (almost invariably her own mother) who becomes the developmental parent to the baby as the young mother seeks to return to the tasks and opportunities of early adulthood
Depression	Is not commonly identified as such, except in reaction to a crisis; underlying depression may become apparent only after years of therapy with these families and their obviously ill members who function as the IPs
Development	Is often plateaued at a surprisingly low level
Parenting	*Verbal* restraints (shifting the child from path 0 or 1 to path 2 or 3) are consistently contradicted by *behavioral* removal of such restraints: rules are inconsistently reenforced, thus requiring youngsters to behaviorally test the verbally promised limits; these patterns are built on variable-ratio reenforcement schedules and are thus very stable
Parental Depression	A global tone of depression seems apparent in the rounded shoulders, whining voices, wrinkled foreheads, and chronic anxiety of the "wellie" adults of these "wellie–sickie" pairs; clinically identifiable and treatable depression is uncommon, and it may be that these adults have moved through a sequence: adaptation failure, affective depression, biochemical changes, and recognition of the neurobiological state of depression as "normal", with subsequent resistance to any effort to change as described by Lewis and Lewis
Depressed Parenting	Continual admonitions not to engage in certain forbidden acts (in which the IP later engages, such as drinking or sexual activity), assaults on self-esteem (as in "You're no good") and disruption of

	normal development (e.g., as by moving frequently and/or forbidding children to have friends) create very confused developmental paths filled with rapid shifts from path 0 to path 4 and back again in an apparently random manner
Family Dynamics	Family members commonly describe themselves as constrained by someone else's needs, weaknesses, etc.; efforts to move away are unsuccessful or are maintained only with great effort, and anxiety–power crossovers are numerous and powerful

|| Case 4

The IP in this family was Edward, a small, awkward 8-year-old boy, the son of reformed amphetamine abusers. His mother had long hated her own father for abandoning the family when she was a child, and she had assumed major housekeeping responsibilities as an oldest child while her mother supported the family. Edward's parents separated and reunited frequently, with numerous noisy accusations of infidelity. Individually, Edward had very little to say and played quietly and cautiously in the playroom, refusing to permit the therapist to play with him. Edward's mother expressed an interest in both individual and group therapy. She attended faithfully and worked hard, and her life improved in many areas; she returned to school, where she did very well and began to observe her contribution to the marital discord. After a few months of successful functioning, she became quite worried that her mother would be injured or killed in an accident. One night she awoke abruptly from a dream in which her mother, extensively injured in a car wreck, leaped to her death from a hospital window. Edward's mother awoke from her dream panic-stricken, caller her mother, and begged her not to take an anticipated trip or to leave town at all. Months of marital discord followed. A theme of loss was evident in Edward's mother's dream, which apparently paradoxically had emerged in a context of increasing self-esteem and success. This dream makes sense, however, in light of the hypothesis that "success" and a "normal" life was abnormal for her and must thus be modified. She became anxious and marital strife increased. At length Edward's mother and grandmother established a good business and living arrangement that spelled the death-knell of the marriage but brought stability albeit in what appeared to be a developmentally regressed form, to Edward, his mother and grandmother.

And how will Edward develop self-esteem as he watches his lonely father struggle with alcoholism and marginal employment? This chapter is a success if the reader can use the conceptual tools presented to consider the impact of parental depression on Edward's development and treatment. A configuration for Edward is given in Table 11-10.

|| SUMMARY

Of all parental responsibilities, the most subtle is the design and use of a training program that exposes the child to an appropriate level of stress in a context that facilitates the development of healthy self-confidence regardless of the outcome of any particular adventure. The depressed parent is severely hampered in the ability to do so, and distortions in the child's development thus occur.

References

Abernethy, V. The abortion constellation: Early history and present relationships. *Archives of General Psychiatry,* 1973, *29*, 346–350.

Abernethy, V. Sexual knowledge, attitudes, and practices of young female psychiatric patients. *Archives of General Psychiatry,* 1974, *30*, 180–182.

Abernethy, V., & Grunebaum, H. Family planning in two psychiatric hospitals: A preliminary report. *Family Planning Perspectives,* 1973, *5*, 94–99.

Abernethy, V., Grunebaum, H., Hunt, B., & Groover, B. Family planning during psychiatric hospitalization. *American Journal of Orthopsychiatry,* 1976, *46*, 154–162.

Abernethy, V., Robbins, D., Abernethy, G., Grunebaum, H., & Weiss, J. Identification of women at risk for unwanted pregnancy. *The American Journal of Psychiatry,* 1975, *132*, 1027–1031.

Abraham, K. Notes on the psychoanalytic investigation and treatment of manic–depressive insanity and allied conditions (1911). In K. Abraham (Ed.), *Selected papers.* New York: Basic Books, 1960, pp. 137–156.

Abraham, K. A short study of the development of the libido viewed in the light of the mental disorders (1924). In K. Abraham (Ed.), *Selected papers.* New York: Basic Books, 1960, pp. 418–502.

Abrahams, M. J., & Whitlock, F. A. Childhood experience and depression. *British Journal of Psychiatry,* 1969, *115*(525), 883–888.

Abramson, L., Seligman, M. E. P., & Teasdale, J. Learned helplessness in humans: Critique and reformulation. *Journal of Abnormal Psychology,* 1978, *87*, 49–74.

Adam, K. S., Lohrenz, J. G., & Harper, D. Suicidal ideation and parental loss. A preliminary research report. *Canadian Psychiatric Association Journal,* 1973, *18*(2), 95–100.

Ainsworth, M. Object relations, dependency, and attachment. A theoretical review of the mother–infant relationship. *Child Development,* 1969, *40,* 969–1025.

Ainsworth, M. The development of infant–mother attachment. In B. Caldwell & H. Ricciuti (Ed.), *A Review of Research in Child Development,* Vol. 3. Chicago: The University of Chicago Press, 1973, pp. 1–94.

Ainsworth, M. Infant–mother attachment and social development: Socialization as a product of reciprocal responsiveness to signals. In M. Richards (Ed.), *The integration of the child into the social world.* Cambridge: Cambridge University Press, 1974.

Ainsworth, M., Bell, S., & Stayton, D. Individual differences in strange situation behavior of one-year olds. In H. Schaffer (Ed.), *The origins of human social relations*. London: Academic Press, 1971, pp. 17–52.

Ainsworth, M., Blehar, M., Waters, E., & Wall, S. Patterns of attachment. *A psychological study of the strange situation.* Hillsdale, N. J.: Lawrence Erlbaum, 1978.

Akiskal, H. S., and McKinney, W. T., Jr. Depressive disorders: Toward a unified hypothesis. *Science,* 1973, *182*, 20–29.

Akiskal, H. S., & McKinney, W. T., Jr. Overview of recent research in depression. Integration of ten conceptual models into a comprehensive clinical frame. *Archives of General Psychiatry,* 1975, *32*, 285–305.

Albee, G., & Joffe, J. (Eds.). *Primary prevention of psychopathology* (Vol. 1), *The issues*. Hanover, N. H.: University Press of New England, 1977.

American Psychiatric Association, *Diagnostic and statistical manual of mental disorders* (3rd ed.). Washington, D. C., 1980.

Amrith, M. V. Introjective and projective identification. *Samiksa,* 1975, *29*(1), 1–12.

Amsel, P. L., & Zaslow, S. The need to wean—As much for mother as for baby? A challenge, a response, and a plan. *Rural Nursing,* 1976, *46*, 8–14.

Anderegg, E. *Dietausend masken der resignation: Das antlitz der hoffnung*. Freiburg I. B., (W. Ger.): Herder, 1976.

Andrau, R., Cortial, C., L'ezine, I. Reflections on the mother–child relationship following premature or dysmature birth. *Psychiatric Infant,* 1973, *16*(1), 123–178.

Andreason, N. C. Thought, language and communication disorders. *Archives of General Psychiatry,* 1979, *36*, 1315–1321.

Angrist, S., Lefton, M., Dinitz, S., Pasamanick, B. *Woman after treatment*. New York: Appleton Century Crofts, 1968.

Anthony, E. J. The developmental precursors of adult schizophrenia. In D. Rosenthal & S. Kety (Eds.), *The transmission of schizophrenia*. New York: Pergamon Press, 1968, pp. 298–316.

Anthony, E. J. A clinical evaluation of children with psychotic parents. *American Journal of Psychiatry,* 1969, *126*, 177–184.

Anthony, E. J. The reactions of parents to the oedipal child. In E. J. Anthony & T. Benedek (Eds.), *Parenthood—Its psychology and psychopathology.* Boston: Little, Brown, 1970.(a)

Anthony, E. J. The reaction of parents to adolescents and their behavior. In E. Anthony & T. Benedek (Eds.), *Parenthood: Its psychology and psychopathology.* Boston: Little, Brown, 1970, pp. 307–324.(b)

Anthony, E. J. The reactions of adults to adolescents and their behavior. In G. Caplan & S. Lebovili (Ed.), *Adolescence*. New York: Basic Books, 1971, pp. 54–78.(a)

Anthony, E. J. Folie à deux: A developmental failure in the process of separation individuation. In J. McDevitt & C. Settlage (Eds.), *Separation–individuation: Essays in honor of Margaret S. Mahler.* New York: International Universities Press, 1971, pp. 253–273.(b)

Anthony, E. J. A clinical and experimental study of high-risk children and their schizophrenic parents. In A. R. Kaplan (Ed.), *Genetic factors in schizophrenia.* Springfield, Ill: Charles Thomas, 1972, pp. 380–406.

Anthony, E. J. Primary prevention with school children. In H. Basten & L. Bellak (Eds.), *Progress in community mental health* (Vol. 2). New York: Grune & Stratton, 1973, pp. 131–158.

Anthony, E. J. The syndrome of the psychologically invulnerable child. In E. J. Anthony & C. Koupernik (Eds.), *The child in his family: Children at psychiatric risk.* New York: Wiley, 1974, pp. 529–544.(a)

Anthony, E. J. A risk vulnerability intervention model for children of psychotic parents. In E. J. Anthony & C. Koupernik (Eds.), *The child in his family: Children at psychiatric risk.* New York: Wiley, 1974, pp. 99–122.(b)

Anthony, E. J. Childhood depression. In E. J. Anthony & T. Benedek (Ed.), *Depression and human existence.* Boston: Little, Brown, 1975, pp. 231–278.(a)

Anthony, E. J. The influence of a manic–depressive environment on the developing child. In E. J. Anthony & T. Benedek (Eds.), *Depression and human existence.* Boston: Little, Brown, 1975, pp. 279–315.(b)

Anthony, E. J. How children cope in families with a psychotic patient. In E. Rexford (Ed.), *Infant psychiatry.* New Haven: Yale University Press, 1976, pp. 239–247.(a)

Anthony, E. J. The genesis of childhood depression. In E. J. Anthony & D. Gilpin (Eds.), *Three clinical faces of childhood.* New York: Wiley, 1976, pp. 165–172.(b)

Anthony, E. J. Preventive measures for children and adolescents at high risk for schizophrenia. In G. Albee & J. Joffe (Eds.), *Primary prevention of psychopathology* (Vol. 1), *The issues.* Hanover, N. H.: The University of New England, 1977, pp. 164–174.

Anthony, E. J. From birth to breakdown: A prospective study of vulnerability. In E. J. Anthony (Ed.), *The child in his family* (Vol. 4), *Vulnerable children.* New York: Wiley-Interscience, 1978, pp. 273–291.(a)

Anthony, E. J. Piagetian egocentrism, empathy, and affect discrimination in children at high risk for psychosis. In E. J. Anthony (Ed.), *The child in his family* (Vol. 4), *Vulnerable children.* New York: Wiley-Interscience, 1978, pp. 359–380. (b)

Antonov, V. V. The role of maternal contact in the psychological development of a child. *Zhurnal Nevropatology Psikhiatri,* 1975, *75*(10), 1568–1572.

Apperson, L. B., & Stinnett, P. W. Parental factors as reported by patient groups. *Journal of Clinical Psychology,* 1975, *31*(3), 419–425.

Arieti, S. Psychoanalysis of severe depression: Theory and therapy. *Journal of American Academy of Psychoanalysis,* 1975, *4*(3), 327–345.

Arieti, S., & Bemporad, J. *Severe and Mild Depression: The therapeutic approach.* New York: Basic Books, 1978.

Arnold, L. E., & Smeltzer, D. J. Behavior checklist factor analysis for children and adolescents. *Archives of General Psychiatry,* 1975, *30*(6), 799–804.

Asarnow, R., Steffy, R., MacCrimmon, D., & Cleghorn, J. An attentional assessment of foster children at risk for schizophrenia. *Journal of Abnormal Psychology,* 1977, *86*, 267–275.

Bach-y-Rita, G., & Veno, A. Habitual violence: A profile of sixty two men. *American Journal of Psychiatry,* 1974, *131*(9), 1015–1017.

Badri, M. A new technique for the systematic desensitization of pervasive anxiety and phobic reactions. *Journal of Psychology,* 1967, *65*, 201–208.

Bandura, A. Self-efficacy: Toward a unifying theory of behavioral change. *Psychological Review,* 1977, *84*, 191–215.

Barnes, M. R. Effects of antidepressive program on verbal behavior. *Journal of Clinical Psychology,* 1977, *33*, 545–549.

Barnett, J. On aggression in the obsessional neuroses. *Contemporary Psychoanalysis,* 1969, *6*(1), 48–57.

Barrera, M. An evaluation of a brief group therapy for depression. *Journal of Consulting and Clinical Psychology,* 1979, *47*, 413–415.

Bart, P. B. Depression in middle aged women. In V. Gornick & B. K. Moran (Eds.), *Women in sexist society,* Springfield: C. C. Thomas, 1971.

Bartak, L., & Rutter, M. Differences between mentally retarded and normally intelligent autistic children. *Journal of Autism and Childhood Schizophrenia,* 1976, 6:109–121.

Basch, M. The concept of affect: A reexamination. *Journal of the American Psychoanalytic Association,* 1976, *24*, 759–778.

Battle, C. U. Symposium on behavioral pediatrics: Chronic physical disease: Behavioral aspects. *Pediatric Clinics North America,* 1975, *22*(3), 525–531.

Beck, A. *Depression: Clinical experimental and theoretical aspects.* New York: Harper & Row, 1967.

Beck, A. The development of depression. In R. Friedman & M. Katz (Eds.), *The psychology of depression: Contemporary theory and research.* Washington, D. C.: Winston, 1974, pp. 3–20.

Beck, A. T. *Cognitive therapy and the emotional disorders.* New York: International Universities Press, 1976.

Beck, A. T., Rush, A., Shaw, B., & Emery, G. *Cognitive therapy of depression.* New York: Guilford, 1979.

Beck, A. T., Ward, C., Mendelson, M., Mock, J., & Erbaugh, A. An inventory for measuring depression. *Archives of General Psychiatry,* 1961, *4*, 561–571.

Becker, J. *Affective disorders.* Morristown, N. J.: General Learning Press, 1977.

Becker, J., & Schuckit, M. A. The comparative efficacy of cognitive therapy and pharmacotherapy in the treatment of depression. *Cognitive Therapy and Research,* 1970, *2*, 192–197.

Becker, J. M., Kaveggia, E. G., Pendleton, E., & Opitz, J. M. A biologic and genetic study of 40 cases of severe mental retardation. *European Journal Pediatrics,* 1977, *124*, 231–256.

Bee, H., Van Egeren, L., Streissguth, A., et al. Social class differences in maternal teaching strategies and speech patterns. *Developmental Psychology,* 1969, 726–734.

Beisser, A., Glasser, N., & Grant, M. Psychosocial adjustment in children of schizophrenic mothers. *The Journal of Nervous and Mental Disease,* 1967, *145,* 429–440.

Bell, G. Parents who abuse their children. *Canadian Psychiatric Association,* 1973, *18*(3), 223–228.

Bell, R. Q. Convergence: An accelerated longitudinal approach. *Child Development,* 1953, *24,* 145–152.

Bell, S. The development of the concept of the object as related to infant–mother attachment. *Child Development,* 1970, *41*, 291–311.

Bemporad, J., & Wilson, A. A developmental approach to depression in childhood and adolescence. *Journal of the American Academy of Psychoanalysis,* 1978, *6*, 325–352.

Bender, L. Schizophrenic spectrum disorders in the families of schizophrenic children. In R. Fieve, D. Rosenthal, & H. Brill (Eds.), *Genetic Research in Psychiatry,* Baltimore: John Hopkins Press, 1972, pp. 126–145.

Benedek, T. Toward the biology of the depressive constellation. *Journal American Psychoanalytic Association,* 1956, *4*, 389.

Benedek, T. Parenthood as a developmental phase: A contribution to the libido theory. *Journal of the American Psychoanalytic Association,* 1959, *7*, 389–417.

Benedek, T., & Anthony, E. *Depression and human existence.* Boston: Little, Brown, 1975.

Benjamin, L. S. A reconsideration of the Kety and associates study of genetic factors in the transmission of schizophrenia. *American Journal of Psychiatry,* 1976, *133*, 1129–1133.

Bergsma, D., & Lowry, R. B. (Eds.). Numerical taxonomy of birth defects and polygenic disorders. *Birth defects: Original Article Series XIII,* 1977 (3A), 1–68.

Berlin, I. N. Some models for reversing the myth of child treatment in community mental health centers. *Journal of the American Academy of Child Psychiatry,* 1975, *14*(1), 76–94.

Bernard, C. *An introduction to experimental medicine* (Henry Copley Greene, trans.). New York: Henry Schuman, 1927.

Berns, B., & Golden, M. Prediction of intellectual performance at 3 years from infant test and personality measures. *Merrill-Palmer,* 1972, *18,* 53–58.

Bernstein, B. B. A sociolinguistic approach to socialization. In J. Gumperz & D. Hynes (Eds.), *Direction in psycholinguistics.* New York: Holt, Rinehart & Winston, 1942.

Beskow, B. Psychic trauma in children of insane parents. *Nordisk-Medicin,* 1955, *53*, S233. (Abstract)

Bettelheim, B. *The empty fortress.* New York: Free Press, 1967.

Bibring, E. The mechanism of depression. In P. Greenacre (Ed.), *Affective disorders.* New York: International Universities Press, 1953, pp. 13–48.

Bieber, I. Pathogenicity of parental preference. *Journal of the American Academy of Psychoanalysis,* 1977, *10*:846–861.

Biglan, A., & Dow, M. Toward a second-generational model: A problem specific approach. In L. Rehm (Ed.), *Behavior therapy for depression: Present status and future directions*. New York: Academic Press, 1981.

Birtchnell, J. The relationship between attempted suicide, depression and parent death. *British Journal of Psychiatry,* 1970, *116*(532), 307–313.

Birtchnell, J. Psychiatric breakdown following recent parent death. *British Journal Medical Psychology,* 1975, 48(4), 379–390.

Bishop, B. A guide to assessing parenting capabilities. *American Journal of Nursing,* 1976, *76*(11), 1784–1787.

Black, D. Pain and parenting. *Midwife Health Visit Community Nurse,* 1975, *11*(8), 263–266.

Blaney, P. Contemporary theories of depression: Critique and comparison. *Journal of Abnormal Psychology,* 1977, *86*, 203–223.

Blaney, P. The effectiveness of cognitive and behavioral therapies. In L. Rehm (Ed.), *Behavior therapy for depression: Present status and future directions*. New York: Academic Press, 1981.

Blatt, S. J. Levels of object representation in anaclitic and introjective depression. *Psychoanalytic Study of the Child,* 1974, *29*, 107–157.

Bleuler, M. The long-term course of the schizophrenic psychoses. *Psychological Medicine,* 1974, *4*, 244.

Block, J., & Block, J. *Ego development and the provenance of thought: A longitudinal study of ego and cognitive development in young children*. NIMH, Washington, D. C.: National Institute of Mental Health, 1973.

Blok, F., Bearle, K., & Caspar, B. From the correspondence of a melancholic. In F. F. Blok (Ed.), *Assen Van Gorcum,* 1976.

Bloom, K., & Esposito, A. Social conditioning and its proper control procedures. *Journal Experimental Child Psychology,* 1975, *19*, 209–222.

Blos, P. On adolescence: *A psychoanalytic interpretation*. New York: The Free Press, 1962.

Blos, P. The second individuation process of adolescence. *Psychoanalytic Study of the Child.* 1967, *22*, 162–186.

Bloschl, L. Psychosoziale Aspekte der Depression. Ein lerntheoretisch–verhaltenstherapeutischer ansatz. Bern: Huber, 1978.

Blum, H. P. The borderline childhood of the wolf man. *Journal of American Psychoanalytic Association,* 1974, *22*(4), 721–742.

Blumenthal, I. S. *Research and the ulcer problem*. Rand Corporation, 1959.

Bolman, W. M. Aggression and violence in children. *Current Problems Pediatrics,* 1974, *4*(9), 1–32.

Bootzin, R. R. *Behavior modification and therapy: An introduction*. Cambridge, Mass.: Winthrop, 1975.

Bowlby, J. *Maternal care and mental health*. New York: Columbia University Press, 1951.

Bowlby, J. The nature of a child's tie to his mother. *International Journal of Psychoanalysis,* 1958, *39*, 350–373.

Bowlby, J. Grief and mourning in infancy and early childhood. *Psychoanalytic Study of the Child,* 1960, *15*, 9–52.

Bowlby, J. Processes of mourning. *International Journal of Psychoanalysis,* 1961, *42*, 317–340.

Bowlby, J. Effects on behavior of disruption of an affectional bond. *Eugenics Social Symptom,* 1968, *4*, 94–108.
Bowlby, J. *Attachment and loss* (Vol. 1), *Attachment.* New York: Basic Books, 1969.
Bowlby, J. Disruption of affectional bonds and its effects on behavior. *Journal of Contemporary Psychotherapy,* 1970, *2*(2), 75–86.
Bowlby, J. *Attachment and loss* (Vol. 2), *Separation: Anxiety and anger.* New York: Basic Books, 1973.
Bowlby, J. The making and breaking of affectional bonds. II. Some principles of psychotherapy. *British Journal of Psychiatry,* 1977, *130*, 421–431.
Bowlby, J. *Attachment and loss* (Vol 3), *Loss, sadness and depression.* New York: Basic Books, 1980.
Brand, M., Escher, M., & Menzl, A. Interdisziplin ares forschungszentrum f'ur die Gesundheit Hochschule St. Gallen fur Wirtschafts-und Sozialwissenschaften. Institut f'ur Betriebswirtschaft *Kosten-Nutzen-Analyse Antidepressiva.* Berlin: Springer-Verlag, 1975.
Brazelton, T. B. *Infants and mothers: Differences in development.* New York: Delacorts Press, 1969.
Brenner, C. Depression, anxiety and affect. *International Journal of Psychoanalysis,* 1974, *55*, 25–32.(a)
Brenner, C. On the nature and development of affects: A unified theory. *Psychoanalytic Quarterly,* 1974, *43*, 532–566. (b)
Brian, V. A. Postnatal depression. *Nursing Mirror,* 1975, *140*(18), 68.
Bridges, P. K., Goktepe, E. O., & Maratos, J. A comparative review of patients with obsessional neurosis and with depression treated by psychosurgery. *British Journal of Psychiatry,* 1973, *123*(577), 663–674.
Brierley, M. Affects in theory and practice. *International Journal of Psychoanalysis,* 1937, *18*, 256–268.
Brock, H. Untersuchungen Uber die entwicklung der kinder nervenkranker mutter. *Acta Paedopsychiatrica,* 1962, *29*, 116–123.
Brodey, W. On the dynamics of narcissism: Externalization and early ego development. *Psychoanalytic Study of the Child,* 1965, *20*, 165–193.
Brodey, W., & Axelrod, S. Anxiety, socialization and ego formation in infancy. *International Journal Psychoanalysis,* 1966, *47*, 218–229.
Brown, C. Baby blues. *Nursing Mirror,* 1975, *141*(12), 61–62.
Brown, G., & Harris, T. Social origins of depression: A study of psychiatric disorder in women. London: Tavistock Publications, 1978.
Brown, G., Parkes, C., & Wing, J. Admissions and readmissions to three London mental hospitals. *Journal of Medical Science,* 1961, *107*, 1070–1077.
Brubakken, D. M., Derouin, J. A., & Morrison, H. L. *Contemporary issues in the treatment of psychotic and neurologically impaired children: A systems approach.* New York: Van Nostrand Reinhold, 1980.
Brumback, R. A., & Weinberg, W. A. Relationship of hyperactivity and depression in children. *Perceptual and Motor Skills,* 1977, *45*(1), 247–251.
Bruner, J. Organization of early skilled action. *Child Development,* 1973, *44,* 1–11.
Burland, J. A., Andrews, R. G., & Headsten, S. J. Child abuse: One tree in the forest. *Child Welfare,* 1973, *52*(9), 585–592.

Burrows, G. (Ed.) *Handbook of studies on depression.* Amsterdam: Excerpta Medica (distributed in the United States by Elsevier-North Holland, New York), 1977.

Burton, R. Validity of retrospective reports assessed by the multitrait–multimethod analysis. *Developmental Psychology Monograph,* 1970, *3*(3, Pt. 2), 15.

Call, J. D. *Introduction in basic handbook of child psychiatry* (Vol. 1). New York: Basic Books, 1979.

Cammer, L. Schizophrenic children of manic–depressive parents. *Diseases of the Nervous System,* 1970, *31*, 177–180.

Campbell, A., Converse, P., & Rodgers, W. *The quality of American life: Perceptions, evaluations, and satisfactions.* New York: Russell-Sage, 1976.

Campbell, B., Dyer, F., & Boersma, F. Field dependency and picture recognition ability. *Perceptive Motor Skills,* 1967, *25*, 713–716.

Cantwell, D. P., & Carey, W. B. Prevalence of psychiatric disorder in a pediatric clinic for military dependent children. *Journal of Pediatrics,* 1974, *85*(5), 711–716.

Caplan, G., & Grunebaum, H. Perspectives on primary prevention: A review. *Archives of General Psychiatry,* 1967, *17*, 331–346.

Carroll, B. J., Feinberg, M., Greden, J. F., Tarika, J., Albala, A., Haskett, R., James, Kronfol, Lohr, Steiner, deVigne, & Yang. A specific laboratory test for the diagnosis of melancholia. *Archives of General Psychiatry,* 1981, *38*, 15–22.

Castets, B. *La'faille: Essai sur l'é*tat d'epressif. Toulouse: Privat, 1975.

Cath, S., Gurwitt, A., Ross, J. M. (Eds.). *Father and child: Developmental and clinical perspectives.* Boston: Little-Brown, 1982.

Chandler, M. Egocentrism in normal and pathological childhood development. In F. Monks, W. Hartup, & J. DeWit (Eds.), *Determinants of behavioral development.* New York: Academic Press, 1972, pp. 569–576.

Chandler, M. Egocentrism and antisocial behavior: The assessment and training of social perspective-taking skills. *Developmental Psychology,* 1973, *9*, 326–332.

Chandler, M. Role taking, referential communication, and egocentric intrusions in mother–child interactions of children vulnerable to risk of parental psychosis. In E. J. Anthony (Ed.), *The child in his family* (Vol. 4), *Vulnerable children.* New York: Wiley, 1978, pp. 347–358.

Chandler, M., Greenspan, S., & Barenboim, C. Assessment and training of role-taking and referential communication skills in institutionalized emotionally disturbed children. *Developmental Psychology,* 1974, *10*, 546–553.

Chiland, C. Some paradoxes connected with risk and vulnerability. In E. J. Anthony and C. Koupernik (Eds.), *The child in his family: Children at psychiatric risk.* New York: Wiley, 1974, pp. 23–31.

Chodorow, N. *The reproduction of mothering.* Berkley: The University of California Press, 1978.

Clark, D. *Children of women with affective disorders.* Unpublished manuscript, 1979. (Available from the author, Department of Psychiatry, Rush Presbyterian–St. Luke's Hospital, 1753 West Congress, Chicago, Illinois 60612)

Clausen, J. *Marital role, life stage and response to mental illness*. Paper presented at Annual Meetings, The American Sociological Association, Toronto, Canada, August 1981.

Clausen, J. A fifteen to twenty year follow-up of married psychiatric patients. In L. Erlenmeyer-Kimling, N. Miller, and B. Dohrenwend (Eds.), *Life-span prediction of psychopathology*. New York: Columbia University Press, in press.

Clausen, J., Yarrow, M. The impact of mental illness on the family. *Journal of Social Issues,* 1955, *9*.

Climent, C. E., Plutchik, R., Ervin, F. R., & Rolling, A. Parental loss, depression and violence. III. Epidemiological studies of female prisoners. *Acta Psychiatrica Scandanavia,* 1977, *55*(4), 261–268.

Coates, S. Sex differences in field independence among preschool children. In R. Friedman, Z. Richart, & R. Van De Weik (Eds.), *Sex differences in behavior.* New York: Wiley, 1974.(a)

Coates, S. Sex difference in field dependence–independence between the ages of 3 and 6. *Perceptive Motor Skills,* 1974, *39*, 1307–1310.(b)

Cohen, D. J. Competence and biology: Methodology in studies of infants, twins, psychosomatic disease, and psychosis. In E. J. Anthony & C. Koupernik (Eds.), *Dakar, Senegal Conference on children at psychiatric risk,* (1973), 1974, 361–394.

Cohen, M. M., Jr. Dysmorphic syndromes with craniofacial manifestations. In R. E. Stewart & G. H. Prescott (Eds.), *Oral facial genetics*. St. Louis: Mosby, 1976, pp. 500–662.

Cohen, R., & Balikov, H. On the impact of adolescence upon parents. In S. Feinstein & P. Giovacchini (Eds.), *Adolescent psychiatry* (Vol. 3). New York: Basic Books, 1974, pp. 217–235.

Cohler, B. J. Character, mental illness and mothering. In H. Grunebaum, J. Weiss, B. J. Cohler, C. Hartman, D. Gallant (Eds.), *Mentally ill mothers and their children*. Chicago: The University of Chicago Press, 1974, pp. 132–234.

Cohler, B. J. *Parenthood, socialization, and mental health*. Unpublished review, 1977.

Cohler, B. J. Developmental research on the second half of life. *Career Directions,* 1978, *5*, 19–35.(a)

Cohler, B. J. Personal communication. (Re: The Thresholds project.) Chicago, 1978.(b)

Cohler, B. J., Gallant, D., Grunebaum, H., & Weiss, J. Pregnancy and birth complications among mentally ill and well mothers and their children. *Social Biology,* 1976, *22*, 269–278.

Cohler, B. J., Gallant, D., Grunebaum, H., Weiss, & Gamer. Attention dysfunction and child-care attitudes among mentally ill and well mothers and their young children. In J. C. Glidewell (Ed.), *The social context of learning and development*. New York: Gardner-Wiley, 1977, 133–162.(a)

Cohler, B., J., Gallant, D., Grunebaum, H., et al. Disturbance of attention among schizophrenic, depressed and well mothers and their five year old children. *Journal of Child Psychology and Psychiatry,* 1977, 115–136.(b)

Cohler, B. J., Grunebaum, H., *Mothers, grandmothers, and daughters: Personality and childcare in three generation families.* New York: John Wiley, 1981.

Cohler, B. J., Grunebaum, H., Weiss, J., Robbins, D., Shader, R., Gallant, D., & Hartman, C. Social role performance and psychopathology among recently hospitalized and nonhospitalized mothers. II: Correlated with stress and self-reported psychopathology. *Journal of Nervous and Mental Disease,* 1974, *159*, 81–90.

Cohler, B. J., Grunebaum, H., Weiss, J., Hartmann, C., & Gallant, D. Life stress and psychopathology among mothers of young children. *American Journal of Orthopsychiatry,* 1975, *45*, 58–73.

Cohler, B., & Grunebaum, H. Afterward, 1982. In H. Grunebaum, J. Weiss, B. Cohler, C. Hartman, & D. Gallant (Eds.), *Mentally ill mothers and their children*. Chicago: University of Chicago Press, 1975/1982, pp. 341–384.

Cohler, B. J., Grunebaum, H., Weiss, J., Gamer, E., & Gallant, D. Disturbance of attention among schizophrenic, depressed and well mothers and their children. *Journal Child Psychology and Psychiatry,* 1977, *18*, 115–135.

Cohler, B. J., Robbins, D., Hartman, C., Shader, R., Grunebaum, H., Weiss, J., & Gallant, D. Social adjustment and psychopathology among formerly hospitalized and nonhospitalized mothers. I: The development of the social role adjustment instrument. *Journal of Psychiatric Research,* 1975, *12,* 1–18.

Cohler, B. J., Weiss, J., & Grunebaum, H. Childcare attitudes and emotional disturbance among mothers of young children. *Genetic Psychology Monographs,* 1970, *82,* 3–47.

Cole, J. *Depression: biology, psychodynamics and treatment*. New York: Plenum Press, 1978.

Coleman, R., Kris, E., & Provence, S. The study of variations of early parental attitudes. A preliminary report. In *Psychoanalytic study of the child,* Vol. VIII, 1953, pp. 20–47.

Connell, H. M. Psychiatric emergencies in childhood. *Australian Family Physician Supplement,* 1977, *5–9*.

Cook, T., & Campbell, D. T. *Quasi-experimentation: Design and analysis for field settings*. Chicago: Rand-McNally, 1979.

Cooper, S. F., Leach, C., Storer, D., & Tonge, W. L. The children of psychiatric patients: Clinical findings. *British Journal Psychiatry,* 1977, *131*, 514–522.

Coopersmith, S. Studies in self-esteem. *Scientific American,* 1968, *230*, 96–106.

Corominas, R., & Ralla, J. Delayed consequences of early parental loss (statistical study of an ambulatory psychiatric population). *Review Clinical Esperencia* 1973, 129(4), 369–380.

Costello, C. *Anxiety and depression: The adaptive emotions*. Montreal: McGill-Queen's University Press, 1976.

Cowen, E., Pederson, A., & Babigian, H. Long term follow-up of early detected vulnerable children. *Journal of Clinical and Consulting Psychology,* 1973, *41*, 438–446.

Cowenthal, M., & Cheriboga, D. Transition to the empty nest crisis, challenge or relief? *Archives of General Psychiatry,* 1972, *26*, 8–14.

Coyne, J. Depression and the response of others. *Journal of Abnormal Psychology,* 1976, *85*, 186–193.

Craighead, W. E. Issues resulting from treatment studies. In L. Rehm (Ed.), *Behavior therapy for depression: Present status and future directions.* New York: Academic Press, 1981.

Cramer, B. Problems in prevention of mental disorders in preschool children. *Soz Praeventivmed,* 1977, *22*(1–2), 16–22.

Crisp, A. H., Harding, B., & McGuiness, B. Anorexia nervosa. Psychoneurotic characteristics of parents: relationship to prognosis. A quantitative study. *Journal of Psychosometric Research,* 1974, *18*(3), 167–173.

Crnic, K. A. Maternal sensitivity to children in problem situations. *American Journal of Orthopsychiatry,* 1978, *48*, 291–299.

Crook, T., & Raskin, A. Association of childhood parental loss with attempted suicide and depression. *Journal of Consulting Clinical Psychology,* 1975, *43* (2), 277.

Crook, T., Raskin, A., & Davis, D. Factors associated with attempted suicide among hospitalized depressed patients. *Psychological Medicine,* 1975, *5*(4), 381–388.

Crumley, F. E., & Blumenthal, R. S. Children's reactions to temporary loss of the father. *American Journal of Psychiatry,* 1973, *130*(7), 778–782.

Cummings, S., & Hess, R. *Family influences on children's ego development: A reader.* Working Outline, 1965.

Cytrynbaum, S., Patrick, R., Stein, J., & Wilk, C. *Gender and adult midlife development: Critical appraisal.* Paper presented at the meeting of the American Psychological Association, Toronto, May 1978.

Dabrowski, R. *La'd'epression dite nerveuse.* Paris: Laffont, 1975.

David, C. A. The use of the confrontation technique in the battered child syndrome. *American Journal Psychotherapy,* 1974, *28*,(4), 543–552.

Davidson, L. *Personal communication.* September, 1977.

Davidson, P. Banff International Conference on Behavior Modification (7th), 1975. *The behavioral management of anxiety, depression, and pain.* New York: Brunner/Mazel, 1976.

Davis, W. M., Waters, I. W., Hatoum, H. T. Triphasic dose lethality relationships for amphetamine and certain ring-substituted amphetamines in isolated or aggregated mice. *Research Communication Chemists Pathology Pharmacology,* 1977 *17*(4), 575–582.

Deasy, L., & Quinn, O. The wife of the mental patient and the hospital psychiatrist. *Journal of Social Issues,* 1955, *11*, 49–60.

Debry, G., Bleyer, R., & Martin, J. Nutrition of the elderly. *Journal of Human Nutrition,* 1977, *31*(3), 195–203.

Decaux, F., Rodriguez, T., & Zlotowicz, M. Difficult situations for adolescents: Analysis of content, vocabulary and affectivity themes. *Enfance,* 1970, *3*(5), 365–396.

d'Elia, G., von Knorring, L., & Perris, C. Non-psychotic depressive disorders: A ten year follow-up. *Acta Psychiatrica Scandanavia Supplement,* 1974 (255), 173–186.

de Graff, T. Pathological patterns of identification in families of survivors of the Holocaust. *Israel Annual Psychiatry,* 1975, *13*(4), 335–363.

DeMondreun, B., & Craighead, W. E. Distortion of perception and recall of positive and neutral feedback in depression. *Cognitive Therapy and Research,* 1977, *14*, 211–229.

Dempster, R. Depression, depth of relatedness, and early experience. *Dissertation Abstracts International,* 1972, *33*(5-B), 2341.

DePue, R., & Monroe, S. Learned helplessness in the perspective of the depressive disorders: Conceptual and definitional issues. *Journal of Abnormal Psychology,* 1978, *87*, 3–20.

DeRosis, H., & Pellegrino, V. *Women and happiness*. New York: Macmillan, 1976.

Despert, J. *Children of divorce*. Garden City, New York: Doubleday, 1962.

Desseigne, F., & Carr'ere, J. Mothers who kill their children. *Annals Medical Psychology,* 1974, (Paris) 2(1), 238–248.

Deutch, A. Self control and depression: An appraisal. *Behavior Therapy,* 1978, *9*, 410–414.

Developmental and longitudinal study of a constitutional complex discussion. *Journal of American Psychoanalytic Association,* 1977, *25*, 529–538.

Dominian, J. *Depression*. Glasgow: Fontana/Collins, 1976.

Dorner, S. Sexual interest and activity in adolescents with spina bifida. *Journal of Child Psychological Psychiatry,* 1977, *18*(3), 229–237.

Dreyer, A., Nebelkopf, E., & Dreyer, C. Note concerning stability of cognitive style measures in young children. *Perceptive Motor Skills,* 1969, *28,* 933–934.

Dugas, M., Gu'eriot, C., & Jullien, P. Depressive periods in mental anorexia. *Annual Medica Interne* (Paris), 1973, *124*(8), 637–640.

Dumont, C. *Neuropsychopharmacology*. New York: Pergamon Press, 1979.

Dunham, H. W. Schizophrenia: The impact of sociocultural factors. *Hospital Practice,* 1977, *12*(8), 61–68.

Dunkas, N., & Nikelly, G. The persephone syndrome: A study of conflict in the adaptive process of married Greek female immigrants in the U.S.A. *Social Psychiatry,* 1972, *7*(4), 211–216.

Dupont, R., Ryder, R., & Grunebaum, H. An unexpected result of psychosis in marriage, *American Journal of Psychiatry,* 1971, *128, 735–739.*

Durkin-Stamm, M. V. Personal communication, 1978.

Dyk, R., & Witkin, H. Family experiences related to the development of differentiation in children. *Child Development,* 1965, *36*, 21–55.

Editorial: Neurological foundations of infantile autism. *The Lancet,* 1976, 668–669.

Ekman, P., Friesen, W., & Ellsworth, P. *Emotion in the human face: Guidelines for research and an integration of findings*. Elmsford, N.Y.: Pergamon Press, 1972.

Emde, R., Gaensbauer, T., & Harman, R. Emotional expression in infancy: A biobehavioral study. *Psychological Issues Monograph,* 1976, 37.

Emery, A. *Methodology in medical genetics*. Edinburgh: Churchill Livingstone, 1976.

Engel, G. Anxiety and depression—withdrawal: The primary affects of unpleasure. *International Journal of Psychoanalysis,* 1962, *43*, 89–97.

Engel, G. A life setting conducive to illness: The giving-up–given-up complex. *Annals of Internal Medicine,* 1968, *69*, 293–300.

Engel, G. The need for a new medical model: A challenge for biomedicine. *Science,* 1977, *196,* 129–136.

Engel, G., & Schmale, A. Conservation–withdrawal: A primary regulatory process for organismic homeostasis. In *Physiology, emotion and psychosomatic illness,* Ciba Foundation Symposium 8. Amsterdam: Elsevier, 1972.

Erikson, E. H. Childhood and tradition in two American Indian tribes: A comparative abstract with conclusions. *Psychoanalytic Study of the Child,* 1945, *2,* 319–350.

Erikson, E. H. Ego development and historical change. *Psychoanalytic Study of the Child,* 1946, *2,* 359.

Erikson, E. H. *Childhood and society.* New York: Norton, 1950.

Erikson, E. H. *Identity, youth, and crisis.* New York: Norton, 1968.

Erlenmeyer-Kimling, L. A prospective study of children at risk for schizophrenia: Methodological consideration and some preliminary findings. In R. Writh, G. Winokur, & M. Roff (Eds.), *Life history research in psychopathology* (Vol. 4), Minneapolis: University of Minnesota Press, 1975, pp. 23–46.

Erlenmeyer-Kimling, L. Issues pertaining to prevention and intervention of genetic disorders affecting human behavior. In G. Albee and J. Joffe (Eds.), *Primary prevention of psychopathology* (Vol. I), *The Issues.* Hanover, N. H.: The University Press of New England, 1977, pp. 68–91.

Erlenmeyer-Kimling, L., Rainer, J. D., & Kallmann, F. J. Current reproductive trends in schizophrenia. In P. H. Hoch & J. Zubin (Eds.), *Psychopathology of schizophrenia.* New York: Grune & Stratton, 1966.

Ernst, P. A., Badash, D. Psychiatric problems of the aged a new approach more useful for both patient and doctor. *Israel Annals Psychiatry,* 1977, *15*(1), 12–15.

Escalona, S. Emotional development in the first year of life. In M. Senn (Ed.), *Problems of infancy and childhood.* New York: Josiah Macy Foundation Publication, 1953.

Escalona, S. Patterns of infantile experience and the developmental process. *Psychoanalytic Study of the Child,* 1962, *18,* 197–244.

Escalona, S. *The roots of individuality.* Chicago: Aldine, 1968.

Escalona, S., & Helder, G. Prediction and outcome: A study in child development. *Menninger Clinic Monograph Series* (Vol. 14). New York: Basic Books, 1959.

Evans, J. Depression in adolescents. *Proceedings Royal Society Medicine,* 1975, *68*(9), 565–566.

Fann, W. *Phenomenology and treatment of depression: Symposium on the phenomenology and treatment of depression.* New York: Spectrum Publications, 1977.

Feighner, J., Robins, E., Guze, S., Woodruff, R., Winokur, G., & Munoz, R. Diagnostic criteria for use in psychiatric research. *Archives of General Psychiatry,* 1972, *26,* 57–63.

Feldmann-Bange, G. Psychological examination of depressively structured children. *Prax Kinderpsychology Kinderpsychiatry,* 1973, *22*(6), 208–209.

Felner, R. D., Stolberg, A., Cowen, E. L. Crisis events and school mental health referral patterns of young children. *Journal of Consultation Clinical Psychology, 36,* 1975.

Ferreira, A. J. Family myth and homeostasis. *Archives of General Psychiatry,* 1963, *9*, 457–463.

Ferster, C. Behavioral approaches to depression. In R. Friedman and M. Katz (Eds.), *The psychology of depression: contemporary theory and research.* Washington, D. C.: Winston-Wiley, 1974.

Fish, B. The maturation of arousal and attention in the first months of life: A study of variations in ego development. *Journal of the American Academy of Child Psychiatry,* 1963, *2*, 253–270.

Fish, B. An approach to prevention in infants at risk for schizophrenia: Developmental variations from birth to ten years, *Journal of the American Academy of Child Psychiatry,* 1976, *15*, 62–82.

Fish, B., & Alpert, M. Abnormal states of consciousness and muscle tone in infants born to schizophrenic mothers. *American Journal of Psychiatry,* 1962, *119*, 439–445.

Fish, B., & Alpert, M. Patterns of neurological development in infants born to schizophrenic mothers. In J. Wortis (Ed.), *Recent advances in biological psychiatry* (Vol. 6). New York: Plenum Press, 1963, pp. 24–27.

Fish, B., & Hagin, R. Visual–motor disorders in infants at risk for schizophrenia. *Archives of General Psychiatry,* 1973, *28,* 900–904.

Fisher, L. Child competence and psychiatric risk: I. Model and method. *Journal of Nervous and Mental Disease,* 1980, *168,* 323–321.

Fisher, L., Harder, D., & Kokes, R. Child competence and psychiatric risk: III. Comparisons based on diagnosis of hospitalized parent. *Journal of Nervous and Mental Disease,* 1980, *168*, 338–342.

Fisher, L., & Jones, F. Planning for the next generation of risk studies. *Schizophrenia Bulletin,* 1978, *4*, 223–235.

Fisher, L., & Jones, J. Child competence and psychiatric risk: II. Areas of relationship between child and family functioning. *Journal of Nervous and Mental Disease,* 1980, *168,* 332–337.

Fisher, L., Kokes, R., Harder, D., & Jones, J. Child competence and psychiatric risk: VI. Summary and integration of findings. *Journal of Nervous and Mental Disease,* 1980, *168*, 353–355.

Fisher, R. A. *The genetical theory of natural selection* (2nd rev. ed.). New York: Dover Publications, 1958, pp. 52–76.

Flach, F., & Draghi, S. *The nature and treatment of depression.* New York: Wiley, 1975.

Fraiberg, S. Libidinal object constance and mental representation. *Psychoanalytic Study of the Child,* 1969, *24*, 9–47.

Fraiberg, S. *Every child's birthright: Clinical studies in infant mental health: The first year of life.* New York: Basic Books, 1980.

Frazier, S. Murder—single and multiple. *Research Public Association Research in Nervous and Mental Disease,* 1974, *52*, 304–312.

French, A. *Disturbed children and their families.* New York: Human Sciences Press, 1977.

French, A., & Steward, M. Adaptation and affect: Toward a synthesis of diagetian and psychoanalytic psychologies. *Perspectives in Biology and Medicine,* 1975, *18*, 464–474.(a)

French, A., & Steward, M. Family dynamics, childhood depression, and attempted suicide in a 7-year old boy: A case study. *Suicide,* 1975, *5*(1), 29–37.(b)

Freud, A. *The ego and the mechanisms of defence*. London: Hogarth Press, 1936.

Freud, A. Indications for child analysis. *Psychoanalytic Study of the Child,* 1945, *1*, 127.

Freud, A. Adolescence. *The Psychoanalytic Study of the Child.* New York: International Universities Press, 1958, *13*, 255–278.

Freud, A. Discussion of Dr. Bowlby's paper. *Psychoanalytic Study of the Child,* 1960, *15*, 53–62.

Freud, A. *Normality and pathology in childhood.* London: The Hogart Press, 1966.

Freud, A., & Burlingham, D. *War and children.* New York: International Universities Press, 1943.

Freud, A., & Burlingham, D. *Infants without families.* New York: International Universities Press, 1944.

Freud, S. Project for a scientific psychology (1895). In S. Freud, *Standard Edition* (Vol. 1). London: Hogarth Press, 1950, pp. 283–397.

Freud, S. Group psychology and the analysis of the ego (1921). *Standard Edition* (Vol. 8). London: Hogarth Press, 1955, pp. 69–144.

Freud, S. The analysis of a phobia in a five-year old boy (1909). *Standard Edition* (Vol. 10). London: Hogarth Press, 1955, pp. 5–152.(a)

Freud, S. Beyond the pleasure principle (1920). *Standard Edition* (Vol. 18). London: The Hogarth Press, 1955.(b)

Freud, S. Recommendations to physicians practicing psychoanalysis (1921). In S. Freud, *Standard Edition* (Vol. II). London: Hogarth Press, 1957, pp. 109–120.

Freud, S. Formulations on the two principles of mental functioning (1911). In S. Freud, *Standard Edition* (Vol. 12). London: Hogarth Press, 1958, pp. 218–226.

Freud, S. Mourning and melancholia (1915, 1917). *Standard Edition* (Vol. 14). London: Hogarth Press, 1957, pp. 243–258.

Freud, S. Formulations on the two principles of mental functioning (1911). *Standard Edition* (Vol. 12). London: Hogarth Press, 1958, pp. 218–226.

Freud, S. Inhibitions, symptoms and anxiety (1926). In S. Freud, *Standard Edition* (Vol. 20). London: Hogarth Press, 1959, pp. 77–178.

Freud, S. The ego and the Id. (1923). In S. Freud, *Standard Edition* (Vol. 19). London: Hogarth Press, 1961, pp. 3–68.

Freud, S. New introductory lectures on psychoanalysis: Lecture 32 (1933). In S. Freud, *Standard Edition* (Vol. 22). London: Hogarth Press, 19xx, pp. 3–182.

Freudenberger, H., & Overby, A. Patients from an emotionally deprived environment. *Psychoanalytic Review,* 1969, *56*(2), 299–312.

Friedman, R. MMPI characteristics of mothers of pre-school children who are emotionally disturbed or have behavior problems. *Psychological Reports, 1974,* 34(3, Pt. 2), 1159–1162.

Fries, M. Longitudinal study: Prenatal period to parenthood. *Journal of the American Psychoanalytical Association,* 1977, *25*(1), 115–132.

Frommer, E., & O'Shea, G. Antenatal identification of women liable to have problems in managing their infants. *British Journal of Psychiatry,* 1973, *123*(573), 149–156.(a)

Frommer, E., and O'Shea, G. The importance of childhood experience in relation to problems of marriage and family-building. *British Journal Psychiatry,* 1973, *123*(573), 157–160. (b)

Fuchs, C., & Rehm, L. A self control behavior therapy program for depression. *Journal of Consulting and Clinical Psychology,* 1977, *45*, 206–215.

Furman, E., & Katan, A. *The therapeutic nursery school.* New York: International Universities Press, 1969.

Gale, A., & Lynn, R. A developmental study of attention. *British Journal of Education Psychology,* 1972, *42*, 260–266.

Gallant, D. *Selective and sustained attention in young children of psychotic mothers.* Unpublished doctoral dissertation. Boston University, 1972.(a)

Gallant, D. *Attention deficit in young children of psychotic mothers.* Paper presented at the 80th Annual Convention, American Psychological Association, 1972.(b)

Gallant, D. Children of mentally ill mothers. In H. Grunebaum, J. Weiss, B. Cohler (Eds.) *Mentally ill mothers and their children.* Chicago: The University of Chicago Press, 1975, pp. 177–233.

Gallant, D. & Simpson, M. Depression: Behavioral, biochemical, diagnostic and treatment concepts. In D. Gallant & M. Simpson (Eds.), *Symposium on depression: Behavioral, biochemical, diagnostic and treatment concepts.* New York: Spectrum Publications, 1976.

Gamer, E., Gallant, D., & Grunebaum, H. Children of psychotic mothers: An evaluation of 1-year-olds on a test of object permanence. *Archives of General Psychiatry,* 1976, *33*, 311–317.

Garattini, S. *Depressive disorders symposium on depressive disorders: Symposium, Rome, May 9–11th, 1977.* New York: Schattauer Verlag, 1978.

Garber, H., & Heber, R. *The Milwaukee project: Early intervention as a technique to prevent mental retardation.* Paper presented at the National Leadership Institute: Teacher Education/Early Childhood, University of Connecticut at Storrs, 1973.

Garcia, Reinoso. *Depresi'on, man'ia y melancol'ia: Un estudio psicoanal'itico.* Buenos Aires: Ediciones Nueva Visi'on, 1975.

Gardiner, S. The effects of social contact on hypertension induced by short-term isolation in the rat (proceedings). *Journal Physiological,* 1977, *269*(1), 62–63.

Gardner, L. A survey of the attitudes and activities of fathers. *Journal of Genetic Psychology,* 1943, *63*, 15–53.

Gardner, R., Holzman, P., Klein, G., Linton, H., & Spence, D. S. Cognitive controls: A study of individual consistencies in cognitive behavior. *Psychological Issues,* 1959, I, monograph 4.

Garmezy, N. Models of etiology for the study of children at risk for schizophrenia. In M. Roff, L. Robbins & M. Pollack (Eds.), *Life history research in psychopathology* (Vol. 2). Minneapolis: The University of Minnesota Press, 1972, pp. 9–34.

Garmezy, N. Children at risk: The search for antecedents of schizophrenia. Part I: Conceptual models and research methods. *Schizophrenia Bulletin,* 1974, Spring, 14–90.(a)

Garmezy, N. Children at risk: The search for the antecedents of schizophrenia. Part II: Ongoing research programs, issues, and interventions. *Schizophrenia Bulletin,* 1974, *9*, 55–125.(b)

Garmezy, N. Competence and adaptation in adult schizophrenic patients and children at risk. In S. Dean (Ed.), *Prize lectures in schizophrenia: the first ten Dean Awards.* New York: MSS Publications, 1974.(c)

Garmezy, N. The study of competence in children at risk for severe psychopathology. In E. J. Anthony and C. Koupernik (Eds.), *The child in his family: Children at psychiatric risk. Bled Conference on Genetic–Constitutional and Early Childhood Factors in Risk:* New York: Wiley, 1974, 77–98.(d)

Garmezy, N. Observations on research with children at risk for child and adult psychopathology. In M. McMillan & S. Henao (Eds.), *Child psychiatry: Treatment and research.* New York: Brunner/Mazel, 1977, 51–70.

Garmezy, N. Attentional processes in adult schizophrenia and in children at risk. *Journal of Psychiatric Research,* 1978, *14,* 3–34.(a)

Garmezy, N. Observations on high-risk research and pre-morbid development in schizophrenia. In L. Wynne, D. Cromwell, & S. Matthysee (Eds.), *The nature of schizophrenia.* New York: Wiley, 1978, pp. 460–472.(b)

Garmezy, N. Current status of a sample of other high-risk research programs. In L. Wynne, D. Cromwell, & S. Matthysee (Eds.), *The nature of schizophrenia.* New York: Wiley, 1978, pp. 473–480.(c)

Garmezy, N., & Devine, V. Longitudinal vs. cross-sectional research in the study of children at risk for psychopathology. In J. Strauss, H. Babigan, & M. Roff (Eds.), *The origins and course of psychopathology.* New York: Plenum Press, 1977, pp. 193–222.

Gartner, D., & Goldstein, H. Some characteristics of mothers of severely disturbed children in a therapeutic nursery. *Psychological Reports,* 1972, *30*(3), 900–902.

Gath, A. The impact of an abnormal child upon the parents. *British Journal of Psychiatry,* 1977, *130*, 405–410.

Gauthier, Y. Depression: Introduction and comments on depression in children. *Union Medical Canada,* 1977, *106*(6), 799–800.

Gayle, A., & Lynn, R. A developmental study of attention. *British Journal of Educational Psychology,* 1972, *42*, 260–266.

Geller, J. Developmental symbiosis. *Perspective Psychiatric Care,* 1975, *13*(1), 10–12.

Gellman, C. *Comment comprendre sa d'epression.* Paris: Le Hameau, 1976.

Gershon, E. S. Genetics of the affective disorders. *Hospital Practice,* 1979, *14*, 117–122.

Gittelman-Klein, R. Definitional and methodological issues concerning depressive illnesses in children. In J. Schulterbrandt & A. Raskin (Eds.), *Depression in children: Diagnosis, treatment and conceptual issues.* New York: Raven Press, 1977, pp. 69–80.

Glidewell, J., Kantor, M., Smith, L., & Stringer, L. Socialization and social structure in the classroom. In M. Hoffman & L. Hoffman (Eds.), *Review of research in child development* (Vol. 2). New York: Russell-Sage, 1966, pp. 221–256.

G'oktepe, E., Young, L., & Bridges, P. A further review of the results of sterotactic subcaudate tractotomy. *British Journal of Psychiatry,* 1975, *126*, 270–280.

Goldberg, B., & Soper, H. Childhood psychosis or mental retardation—a diagnostic dilemma—I. Psychiatric and psychological aspects. *Canadian Medical Association Journal,* 1963, *89*, 1015–1019.

Goldfarb, W. Infant rearing and problem behavior. *American Journal of Orthopsychiatry,* 1943, *13*, 249–265.

Goodenough, D., & Eagle, C. A modification of the embedded-figures test for use with young children. *Journal Genetic Psychology,* 1964, *103*, 67–74.

Gottesman, I., & Shields, J. *Schizophrenia and genetics: A twin study vantage point*. New York: Academic Press, 1972.

Gottsegen, M. Management of mourning of a dead or dying parent. *American Journal Psychotherapy,* 1977, *31*(1), 36–42.

Gray, W., Duhl, F., & Rizzo, N. (Eds.). *General systems theory in psychiatry.* Boston: Little, Brown, 1969.

Green, A. Conceptions of affect. *International Journal of Psychoanalysis,* 1977, *58*, 129–156.

Green, M. A developmental approach to symptoms based on age groups. *Pediatric Clinical North America,* 1975, *22*(3), 571–581.

Green, M. Anticipation, hope, and despair. *Journal American Academy Psychoanalysis,* 1977, *5*(2), 215–232.

Greenberg, M., & Alloy, L. *Psychometric analyses of depression and anxiety inventories*. Unpublished manuscript, Department of Psychology, Northwestern University, 1980.

Grimm, V., & Samuel, D. The effects of dark isolation on the performance of a white–black discrimination task in the rat. *International Journal Neurosciences,* 1976, *7*(1), 1–7.

Grinker, R., Miller, J., Sabashin, M., Nunn, R., & Nunnaly, G. *The phenomena of depression*. New York: Hoeber, 1961.

Grosscup, S., & Lewinsohn, P. Unpleasant and pleasant events, and mood. *Journal of Clinical Psychology,* 1980, *36*, 252–259.

Grossman, M. Early child development in the context of mothering experiences. *Child Psychiatry Human Development,* 1975, *5*(4), 216–223.

Grunebaum, H. Children at risk for psychosis and their families: approaches to prevention. In M. McMilland and S. Henao (Eds.), *Child Psychiatry: research and treatment*. New York: Brunner/Mazel, 1977, pp. 172–189.

Grunebaum, H., Gamer, E., & Cohler, B. *The spouse in depressed families*. American Psychiatric Association annual meeting, Atlanta, 1978.

Grunebaum, H., & Abernethy, V. Ethnical issues in family planning for hospitalized psychiatric patients. *American Journal of Psychiatry,* 1975, *132*, 236–240.

Grunebaum, H., Abernethy, V., Clough, L., & Groover, B. Staff attitudes toward a family planning service in mental hospitals, *Community Mental Health Journal,* 1975, *11*, 280–285.

Grunebaum, H., Abernethy, V., Rofman, S., & Weiss, J. The family planning attitudes, practices and motivations of mental patients. *American Journal of Psychiatry,* 1971, *128*, 740–744.

Grunebaum, H., Cohler, B., Kaufman, D., & Gallant, D. Children of depressed and schizophrenic mothers. *Child Psychiatry and Human Development,* 1978, *8*, 219–228.

Grunebaum, H., Weiss, J., Cohler, B., Gallant, D., & Hartmann, H. *Mentally ill mothers and their children* (2nd ed.). Chicago: The University of Chicago Press, 1982.

Grunebaum, H., Weiss, J., Gallant, D., & Cohler, B. Attention in young children of psychotic mothers. *American Journal Psychiatry,* 1974, *131*, 887–891.

Gutmann, D. Individual adaptation in the middle years: Developmental issues in the masculine midlife crisis. *Journal of Geriatric Psychiatry,* 1976, *9*, 41–59.

Gunderson, J., Autry, J., & Mosher, L. Special report: Schizophrenia, 1973. *Schizophrenia Bulletin,* 1974, 15–54.

Gurland, B. The comparative frequency of depression in various adult age groups. *Journal of Gerontology,* 1958, *31*, 273–278.

Gutmann, D. Parenthood: A comparative key to the life-cycle. In N. Datan & L. Ginsburg (Eds.), *Life-span development psychology: Normative crises.* New York: Academic Press, 1975, pp. 167–184.

Haase, H. *Depressionen: Entstehung, erscheinung, behandlung.* Stuttgart; New York: Schattauer, 1976.

Haka-Ikse, K. Child development as an index of maternal mental illness. *Pediatrics,* 1975, *55*(3), 310–312.

Hamburg, D. A., Hamburg, B. A., & Barchas, J. D. Anger and depression in perspective of behavioral biology. In L. Levi (Ed.), *Emotions: Their parameters and measurement.* New York: Raven Press, 1975.

Hamilton, M. A rating scale for depression. *Journal of Neurology Neurosurgery, and Psychiatry,* 1960, *23*, 56–62.

Hammen, C., & Glass, D. Depression, activity, and evaluation of reinforcement. *Journal of Abnormal Psychology,* 1975, *84*, 718–721.

Hampton, R. *The far side of despair: A personal account of depression.* Chicago: Nelson-Hall, 1975.

Hanaway, T. P., & Barlow, D. H. Prolonged depressive behaviors in a recently blinded deaf mute: A behavioral treatment. *Journal of Behavior Therapy and Experimental Psychiatry,* 1975, *6*, 43–48.

Hannie, T., & Adams, H. Modification of agitated depression by flooding: A preliminary study. *Journal of Behavior Therapy and Experimental Psychiatry,* 1974, *5*, 161–166.

Hanson, D., Gottesman, I., & Heston, L. Some possible childhood indicators of adult schizophrenia inferred from children of schizophrenics. *British Journal of Psychiatry,* 1976, *129*, 142–154.

Hanson, D., Gottesman, I., & Meehl, P. Genetic theories and the validation of psychiatric diagnoses: Implications for the study of children of schizophrenics, *Journal of Abnormal Psychology,* 1977, *86*, 575–588.

Harder, D. W., Kokes, R. F., Fisher, L., & Strauss, J. S. Child competence and psychiatric risk: IV. Relationships of parent diagnostic classification and parent psychopathology severity to child functioning. *Journal of Nervous and Mental Disease,* 1980, *168,* 343–347.

Harrow, M. Checklist for the diagnosis of schizophrenia. *The British Journal of Psychiatry,* 1972, *121,* 529–539.

Harrow, M., & Quinlan, D. Is disordered thinking unique to schzophrenia? *Archives of General Psychiatry,* 1977, *24*, 15–21.

Hartmann, H. The development of ego concept in Freud's work. *International Journal of Psychoanalysis,* 1956, *27*, 425–438.

Hartmann, H. *Ego psychology and the problem of adaptation* (1939) (D. Rapaport, trans.). New York: International Universities Press, 1959.

Hartmann, H. The mutual influences in the development of ego and id (1952). In Hartmann, H., *Essays on ego psychology*. New York: International Universities Press, 1964, 155–182.(a)

Hartmann, H. Problems of the infantile neurosis. In H. Hartmann, *Essays on ego psychology*. New York: International Universities Press, 1964, 207–214.(b)

Hauck, P. *The national management of children* (2nd ed.). New York: Libra, 1972.

Heber, R. Sociocultural mental retardation: A longitudinal study. In D. Forgays (Ed.), *Primary prevention of psychopathology* (Vol. 2), *Environmental issues*. Hanover, N. H.: University Press of New England, 1978, pp. 39–62.

Heider, G. Vulnerability in infants and young children. *Genetic psychology monographs,* 1966, 73.

Heilbrunn, G. Comments on adolescent drug users. *Northwest Medical Journal,* 1967, *66*(5), 457–460.

Heimann, P. A discussion of the paper by C. Brenner on depression, anxiety and affect theory. *International Journal of Psychoanalysis,* 1974, *55*(0), 33–36.

Heinicke, C. Parental deprivation in early childhood: a predisposition to later depression. In Scott, J., & Senay, E. (Eds.), *Separation and depression: Clinical and research aspects* (Vol. 8). Washington, D. C.: American Association for thc Advancement of Science, 1973, 256.

Heitler, K. Postpartum depression: A multi-dimensional study. *Dissertation Abstracts International,* 1976, *36*(11-B), 5792–5793.

Henning, M. Adverse reactions to antihypertensive drug therapy: Central nervous system. *Acta Medical Scandinavia,* 1979, *628,* 33–37.

Herjanic, B., Reich, W. Development of a structured psychiatric interview for children: Agreement between child and parent on individual symptoms. *Journal of Abnormal Child Psychology,* 1982, *10*, 307–324.

Herman, J., Mirsky, A., Ricks, N., & Gallant, D. Behavioral and electrographic measures of attention in children at risk for schizophrenia. *Journal of Abnormal Psychology,* 1977, *86,* 27–33.

Hersen, M., Eisler, D., Alford, G., & Agras, W. Effects of token economy on neurotic depression: An experimental analysis. *Behavior Therapy,* 1973, *4*, 392–397.

Hess, R., & Shipman, V. Early experience and the socialization of cognitive modes in children. *Child Development,* 1965, *36,* 869–886.

Heston, L. Psychiatric disorders in foster home reared children of schizophrenic mothers. *British Journal of Psychiatry,* 1966, *112*, 819–825.

Hetherington, E., Cox, M., & Cox, R. Divorced fathers. *The family coordinator.* 1976, *25*(4), 417–428.

Higgins, J. Effects of child-rearing by schizophrenic mothers. *Journal of Psychiatric Research,* 1966, *4*, 153–167.

Higgins, J. Effects of child rearing by schizophrenic mothers: A follow-up. *Journal of Psychiatric Research,* 1976, *13*, 1–9.

Hilford, N. Self initiated behavior change by depressed women following verbal behavior therapy. *Behavior Therapy,* 1975, *6*, 703.

Himwich, H. *Biochemistry, schizophrenias, and affective illnesses*. Huntington, N.Y.: Krieger, 1977.

Hinton, G. Childhood psychosis or mental retardation—a diagnostic dilemma—II. Pediatric and neurological aspects. *Canadian Medical Association Journal,* 1963, *89*, 1020–1024.

Hirai, T. Kigyo wa hito o dame ni suru; shigoto kara nogarerarenai otoko no yuutsu. (Enterprise ruins man; depression is unavoidable). Tokyo: Daiyamondosha, Showa, 1975.

Hirschfeld, R., Klerman, G., Chodoff, P. Dependency self-esteem clinical depression. *Journal American Academy Psychoanalysis,* 1976, *4*(3), 373–388.

Hoechst Aktiengesellschaft. Medizinische abteilung *Aliva (Nomifensin): Symposium "uber ergebnisse der experimentellen und klinischen Pr"ufung, Berlin, 1 und 2,* 1976. Stuttgart: Schattauer, 1977.

Hoffbrand, B., & Birdwood, G. *Biological aspects of clomipramine: Proceedings of a symposium held at Marbella, Spain* In B. Hoffbrand & G. Birdwood (Eds.), London: Fellowship of Postgraduate Medicine, 1976.

Hollingshead, A. Two factor index of social position. In J. Myers & Y. Beau (Eds.), *A follow-up of social class and mental illness.* New York: Wiley, 1968.

Hollister, L. Tricyclic antidepressants. *New England Journal of Medicine,* 1978, *299*, 1106–1109.

Hollon, S. Comparisons and combinations with alternative approaches In L. Rehm (Ed.), *Behavior therapy for depression: Present status and future directions.* New York: Academic Press, 1981.

Hollon, S., & Beck, A. Cognitive therapy of depression. In P. Kendall & S. Hollon (Eds.), *Cognitive behavioral interventions: Theory, research and procedures.* New York: Academic Press, 1979.

Hollon, S., Bedrosian, R., & Beck, A. J. *Combined cognitive-pharmacotherapy versus cognitive therapy in the treatment of depression.* Paper presented at the annual meeting of the Society for Psychotherapy Research, Oxford, England, July 1976.

Hopkins, I., Psychiatric illness following childbirth: Are husbands an etiological factor? *Social Science and Medicine,* 1980, *14A*, 621–626.

Horn, R. Psychosexual problems of the middle years. *Clinical Obstetrics and Gynecology,* 1970, *13*, 746–755.

Horner, J., & Althea, J. Oscillatory patterns of object relations and the borderline patient. *International Review of Psychoanalysis,* 1976, *3*(4), 479–482.

Horowitz, J., & Perdue, B. Single-parent families. *Nursing Clinical North America,* 1977, *12*(3), 503–511.

Houillon, P. Place of psychosocial factors in the appearance and course of an atypical depressive state. *Annual Medical Psychology Paris,* 1975, *2*(1), 189–197.

Howell, S. Psychiatric aspects of habilitation. *Pediatric Clinics of North America,* 1973, *20*(1), 203–219.

Hudgens, R. W. Personal catastrophe and depression. In B. S. Dohrenwend and B. P. Dohrenwend (Eds.), *Stressful life events: Their nature and effects.* New York: Wiley, 1974.

Hunter, R., & Kilstrom, N. Breaking the cycle in abusive families. *Journal of the American Psychiatric Association,* 1979, *136*, 1320–1322.

Ianzito, B. M., Cadoret, R. J., & Pugh, D. Thought disorder in depression. *American Journal of Psychiatry,* 1974, *131,* 703–707.

Ilfield, F. W., Jr. Methodological issues in relating, psychiatric symptoms to social stressors. *Psychology Report,* 1976, *39* (3 Pt. 2), 1251–1258.

Ilfield, F. W., Jr. Current social stressors and symptoms of depression. *American Journal of Psychiatry,* 1977, *134*(2), 161–166.

Illick, J. E. John Quincy Adams: The maternal influence. *Journal of Psychohistory,* 1976, *4*(2), 185–195.

Inhelder, B., & Piaget, J. *The growth of logical thinking from childhood to adolescence.* New York: Basic Books, 1958.

Izard, C., & Thompkins, S. Affect and behavior: Anxiety as a negative affect. In C. D. Speilberger (Ed.), *Anxiety and behavior,* New York: Academic Press, 1966.

Jackson, B. Treatment of depression by self reinforcement. *Behavior Therapy,* 1972, *3,* 298–307.

Jackson, D. D. A critique cf the literature on the genetics of schizophrenia. In D. D. Jackson (Ed.), *The etiology of schizophrenia.* New York: Basic Books, 1960.

Jacobson, E. The affects and their pleasure–unpleasure qualities in relation to the psychic discharge processes. In R. M. Lowenstein (Ed.), *Drives, affects, behavior* (Vol. 1). New York: International Universities Press, 1953.

Jacobson, E. Adolescent moods and the remodeling of psychic structures in adolescence. *The psychoanalytic study of the child.* New York: International Universities Press, 1961, *16,* 164–183.

Jacobson, E. *The self and the object world.* New York: International Universities Press, 1964.

Jacobson, E. *Depression: Comparative studies of normal, neurotic and psychotic conditions.* New York: International Universities Press, 1971.

Jacobson, L., Kaij, L., & Nilsson, A. Post-partum mental disorders in an unselected sample: Frequency of symptoms and predisposing factors. *British Medical Journal,* 1965, *1,* 1640–1643.

Jacobson, S., Fasman, J., & DiMascio, A. Deprivation in the childhood of depressed women. *Journal Nervous Mental Diseases,* 1975, *160*(1), 5–14.

Jacques, E. Death and the midlife crisis. *International Journal of Psychoanalysis,* 1965, *46,* 502–514.

James, W. *The principles of psychology.* New York: Henry Holt and Co., 1890.

Jenkins, R. L., & Boyer, A. Effects of inadequate mothering and inadequate fathering on children. *International Journal of Social Psychiatry,* 1969 (1), 16.

Jensen, G. D. Reaction of monkey mothers to long-term separation from their infants. *Psychonomic Science,* 1968, *11*(5), 171–172.

Jessner, L., Weigert, E. & Foy, J. L. The development of parental attitudes during pregnancy. In E. J. Anthony & T. Benedek (Eds.), *Parenthood: Its psychology and psychopathology.* Boston: Little Brown & Sons, 1970.

Joffee, W., & Sandler, J. Notes on pain, depression, and individuation. *Psychoanalytic Study of the Child,* 1965, *20,* 394–424.

Joffee, W., & Sandler, J. Comments on the psychoanalytic psychology of adaptation, with special reference to the role of affects and the representational world. *International Journal of Psychoanalysis,* 1968, *49,* 445–454.

Johnson, G., & Kamara, J. L. Growing up and growing old: The politics of age exclusion. *International Journal on Aging and Human Development,* 1977–1978, *8*(2), 99–110.

Johnson, W. Some applications of Homme's coverant control therapy: Two case reports. *Behavior Therapy,* 1971, *2,* 240–248.

Jones, F. The Rochester adaptive behavior inventory: A parallel series of instruments for assessing social competence during early and middle childhood and adolescence. In J. Strauss, H. Babigian, & M. Roff (Eds.), *The origins and course of psychopathology: Methods of longitudinal research.* New York: Plenum Press, 1978, 249–281.

Jung, C. G. The stages of life. *Structure and dynamics of the psyche.* Princeton, N. J.: Princeton University Press, 1969.

Kagan, J. Attention and psychological change in the young child. *Science,* 1970, *170,* 826–832.

Kagan, J. Personality development in behavioral science. In N. Talbot, J. Kagan, & L. Eisenberg (Eds.), *Pediatric Medicine.* Philadelphia: Saunders, 1971, pp. 283–349.

Kagan, J., Kearsley, R., & Zelazo, P. *Infancy: Its place in human development.* Cambridge, MA: Harvard University Press, 1978.

Kagan, J., & Kogan, J. Individual variation in cognitive processes. In Mussen, P. L. (Ed.), *Carmichael's manual of child psychology* (3rd ed.). New York: Wiley, 1970.

Kanner, L. Autistic disturbances of affective contact. *Nervous Child,* 1943, *2,* 217–250.

Kaplan, E. B. Manifestations of aggression in latency and preadolescent girls. *Psychoanalytical Study of Children,* 1976, *39,* 243–261.

Kaplan, E. B., & Blackman, L. The husband's role in psychiatric illness association with childbearing. *The Psychiatric Quarterly,* 1969, *43,* 396–409.

Karp, S. Field dependence and overcoming embeddedness. *Journal of Consulting Psychology,* 1963, *27,* 294–302.

Katan, A. *The therapeutic nursery school.* New York: International Universities Press, 1969.

Katan, A. The infant's first reaction to strangers: Distress or anxiety? *International Journal Psychoanalysis,* 1972, *53,* 501–503.

Katz, J. Depression in children. *Medical Journal Australia,* 1977, *1*(16), 592–594.

Kaufman, C., Grunebaum, H., Cohler, B., & Gamer, E. Superkids: Competent children of schizophrenic mothers. *American Journal of Psychiatry,* 1979, *136,* 1398–1402.

Kaufman, I. C., & Rosenblum, L. A. The reaction to separation in infant monkeys: Anaclitic depression and conservation–withdrawal. *Psychosomatic Medicine,* 1967, *29*(6), 648–675.

Kayton, L., Beck, J., & Koh, S. D. Post-psychotic state, convalescent environment, and therapeutic relationship in schizophrenic outcome. *American Journal of Psychiatry,* 1976, *133,* 1260–1274.

Kelly, J. B., & Wallerstein, J. S. Brief interventions with children in divorcing families. *American Journal Orthopsychiatry,* 1977, *47*(1), 23–39.

Kempster, S., Weiss, R., & Weiss, C. *How to end mental depression.* New York: Arco Publishing Company, 1977.

Kety, S. Disorders of the human brain. *Scientific American,* 1979, *241,* 202–214.

Kinsman, R. A., & Hood, J. Some behavioral effects of ascorbic acid deficiency. *American Journal of Clinical Nutrition,* 1971, *24,* 455–464.

Klein, M. A contribution to the psychogenesis of manic–depressive states. In Klein, M., *Contributions to psychoanalysis.* London: Hogarth Press, 1948, pp. 282–310.

Klien, D., & Seligman, M. Reversal of performance deficits and perceptual deficits in learned helplessness and depression. *Journal of Abnormal Psychology,* 1976, *85,* 11–26.

Knoblach, D. Psychogenetic aspects of bronchial asthma: A case report. *Zeitschrift fur klinische psychologie und psychotherapie,* 1971, *19*(2), 163–177.

Knobloch, H., & Passamanick, B. Some etiologic and prognostic factors in early infantile autism and psychosis. *Pediatrics,* 1975, *55,* 182–191.

Kohut, H. *The analysis of the self.* New York: International Universities Press, 1971.

Kohut, H. *The restoration of the self.* New York: International Universities Press, 1977.

Kokes, R., Harder, D., Fisher, L., & Strauss, J. Child competence and psychiatric risk: V. Sex of patient parent and dimensions of psychopathology. *Journal of Nervous and Mental Disease,* 1980, *168,* 348–352.

Kosky, R. Severe depression in young adolescents. A report of five cases. *Medical Journal Australia,* 1975, *53*(2), 191–193.

Kostowski, W., Czlonkowski, A., Rewerski, W., & Piechocki, T. Morphine action in grouped and isolated rats and mice. *Psychopharmacology,* 1977, *53*(2), 191–193.

Kovacs, M. Treating depressive disorders: The efficacy of behavior and cognitive therapies. *Behavior Modification,* 1979, *3,* 496–515.

Kovacs, M., & Rush, J. Cognitive–behavior psychotherapy vs. antidepressant medication in the treatment of depression. In A. T. Beck (Ed.), *Current developments in the psychotherapy of depression.* Symposium at the meeting of the Eastern Psychological Association, New York, 1976.

Kreindler, S. Psychiatric treatment for the abusing parent and the abused child. Some problems and possible solutions. *Canadian Psychiatric Association Journal,* 1976, *21*(5), 275–280.

Kreitman, N. The patient's spouse. *British Journal of Psychiatry,* 1964, *110,* 159–173.

Kupfer, D., & Foster, F. Sleep and activity in a psychotic depression. *Journal of Nervous and Mental Disease,* 1973, *156,* 341–348.

Lamb, D. *Psychotherapy with adolescent girls.* San Francisco: Jossey Bass, 1978.

Lamb, M. (Ed.), *The role of the father in child development* (2nd Ed.). New York: Wiley, 1981.(a)

Lamb, M. The role of the father: An overview. In M. Lamb (Ed.), *The role of the father in child development.* New York: Wiley, 1976, pp. 1–63. (b)

Lamont, A. M. Bereavement. *Central African Journal Medicine,* 1977, *23*(8), 167–170.

Lamont, J., & Fischoff, S. Recall of parental behaviors in female neurotic depressives. *Journal Clinical Psychology,* 1976, *32*(4), 762–765.

Lamont, J., & Gottlieb, H. Convergent recall of parental behaviors in depressed students of different racial groups. *Journal of Clinical Psychology,* 1975, *31*(1), 9–11.

Lampl-DeGroot, J. Depression and aggression. In Lowenstein, R. (Ed.), *Drives, affects and behavior.* New York: International Universities Press, 1953, pp. 153–168.

Langner, T., Gersten, J., McCarthy, E., et al. A screening inventory for assessing psychiatric impairment in children 6 to 18. *Journal Consultor Clinical Psychology,* 1976, *44*(2), 286–296.

LaPointe, K. *Cognitive therapy vs. assertive training in the treatment of depression.* Unpublished doctoral dissertation, Southern Illinois University, 1976. *Dissertation abstracts international,* 1977, *37,* 4689B. (University Microfilms No. 77-6232)

Lawrence, H., & Sundel, M. Behavior modification in adult groups. *Social Work,* 1972, *17*(2), 34–43.

Lax, R. F. The role of internalization in the development of certain aspects of female masochism: Ego psychological considerations. *International Journal of Psychoanalysis,* 1977 *58*(3), 289–300.

Lazarus, A. Learning theory and the treatment of depression. *Behavior Research and Therapy,* 1968, *6,* 83–89.

Lebovici, M. *Living with a psychotic parent.* Doctoral thesis, 1973. [Cited in C. Chiland (1974), op. cit.]

Lebovici, S., & Kiatkine, R. Normality as a concept of limited usefulness in the assessment of psychiatric risk. In E. J. Anthony & C. Koupernik (Eds.), *The child in his family: Children at psychiatric risk.* New York: Wiley, 1974, pp. 11–21.

Legatis, G. *Education of the elderly.* Deutsch Krankenpflegez, 1977, *30*(8), 432–435.

Leiderman, P. Mothers at risk: A potential consequence of the hospital care of the premature infant. From the Bled Conference on Genetic–Constitutional and Early Childhood Factor in Risk (1972). In E. J. Anthony & C. Koupernik, (Eds.), *The child in his family: Children at psychiatric risk.* New York: Wiley, 1974, pp. 149–156.

Lesse, S. Psychotherapy in combination with antidepressant drugs in patients with severe masked depressions. *American Journal of Psychotherapy,* 1977, *31*(2), 185–203.

Letter: Tranquilizers causing aggression. *British Medical Journal,* 1975, *1,*(5952), 266.

Levi, D., Stierlin, H., & Savard, R. Fathers and sons: The interlocking crisis of integrity and identity. *Psychiatry,* 1972, *35*(1), 48–56.

Levinson, D. J., Darrow, C., & Klein, E. (Eds.), *The season of a man's life.* New York: Knopf, 1978.

Levitan, H. L. The etiologic significance of deafness in ulcerative colitis. *Psychiatry Medical,* 1973, *4*(4), 379–387.

Levitt, E., & Lubin, B. *Depression: Concepts, controversies, and some new facts.* New York: Springer, 1975.

Levy, D. Primary affect hunger. *American Journal of Psychiatry,* 1937, 643–652.

Levy, N., & Clark, J. Headaches in an angry diabetic patient. *Psychiatry Medical,* 1973, *4*(3), 323–331.

Lewinsohn, P. A behavioral approach to depression. In R. Friedman & M. Katz (Eds.), *The psychology of depression: Contemporary theory and research.* Washington, D. C.: Winston-Wiley, 1974.

Lewinsohn, P. A behavioral approach to depression. In M. Hersch, R. Eisler, & P. Miller (Eds.), *Progress in behavior modification.* New York: Academic Press, 1975.(a)

Lewinsohn, P. Engagement in pleasant activities and depression level. *Journal of Abnormal Psychology,* 1975, *84,* 729–731.(b)

Lewinsohn, P. Activity schedules in the treatment of depression. In J. Krumboltz & C. Thorsen (Eds.), *Counseling methods.* New York: Holt, Reinhart, and Winston, 1976.

Lewinsohn, P., Golding, M., Johansson, P., & Stewart, R. *Patterns of communications in depressed and nondepressed subjects.* Unpublished manuscript, University of Oregon, 1968.

Lewinsohn, P., & Graf, M. Pleasant activities and depression. *Journal of Consulting and Clinical Psychology,* 1973, *41,* 261–268.

Lewinsohn, P., & Libet, J. Pleasant events, activity schedules, and depression. *Journal of Abnormal Psychology,* 1972, *79,* 291–295.

Lewinsohn, P., & Shaffer, M. The use of home observations as an integral part of the treatment of depression: Preliminary report and case studies. *Journal of Consulting and Clinical Psychology,* 1971, *37,* 87–94.

Lewinsohn, P., Weinstein, M., & Alper, T. A behavioral approach to the group treatment of depressed persons: A methodological contribution. *Journal of Clinical Psychology,* 1970, *26,* 525–532.

Lewinsohn, P., Weinstein, M., & Shaw, D. Depression: A clinical research approach. In R. Rubin and C. Frank (Eds.), *Advances in behavior therapy, 1968.* New York: Academic Press, 1969.

Lewis, H. *Shame and guilt in neurosis.* New York: International Universities Press, 1971.

Lewis, M., & Lewis, D. A psychobiological view of depression in childhood. In A. P. French and I. P. Berlin (Eds.), *Depression in children and adolescents.* New York: Human Sciences Press, 1979.

Lewis, R., & James, N. Haloperidol and chlorpromazine: A double-blind crossover trial and clinical study in children and adolescents. *Australian New Zealand, Journal of Psychiatry,* 1973, *7*(1), 59–65.

Lewis, T. H. A culturally patterned depression in a mother after loss of a child. *Psychiatry,* 1975, *38*(1), 92–95.

Lidz, T. Commentary on a critical review of recent adoption, twin and family studies of schizophrenia: behavioral genetic perspectives. *Schizophrenia Bulletin,* 1976, *2,* 402–412.

Lidz, T., Lidz, R. W., & Rubenstein, R. An anaclitic syndrome in adolescent amphetamine addicts. *Psychoanalytic Study of the Child,* 1976, *31,* 317–348.

Lipkowitz, M. H. The child of two survivors: A report of an unsuccessful therapy. *Israel Annals of Psychiatry and Related Disciplines,* 1973, *11*(2), 141–155.

Loeb, L. R., Peal, S., Loeb, F. F. Jr., & Templeton, B. Screen memories in a pair of monozygotic twins discordant for involutional depression and psychophysiological disorders. *American Journal of Psychiatry,* 1973, *130*(2), 160–164.

Loevinger. *Ego development: Conceptions and theories.* San Francisco: Jossey-Bass, 1976.

Lokiec, F., Jacquot, C., Rapin, J. R., & Cohen, Y. Effects of amphetamine on brain biogenic amines in isolated and aggregated rats. *European Journal Pharmacology,* 1977, *44*(4), 391–395.

Lomont, J., Gilner, F., Spector, N., & Skinner, K. Group assertion training and group insight therapies. *Psychological Reports,* 1969, *25,* 463–470.

Lopez, I., Juan, J., & Michaelis, R. *Psychiatrie und Psychosomatik.* Basel; New York: Karger, 1976.

Lotter, V. Epidemiology of autistic conditions in young children. I. Prevalence. *Social Psychiatry,* 1966, *1,* 124–137.

Lubin, B. *Manual for the depression adjective check list.* San Diego: Educational and Industrial Testing Service, 1967.

Lubinsky, M. Behavioral consequences of congenital rubella. *Journal of Pediatrics,* 1979, *94*(4), 678.

L'utzenkirchen, J., & B'oning, J. Anorexic syndrome and depression. Considerations from a case history. *Schweiz Archives Neurological Neurochirgica Psychiatric,* 1976, 175–184.

Maccoby, E., & Jacklin, C. *The psychology of sex differences.* Stanford, Calif.: Stanford University Press, 1974.

MacKeith, R. The feelings and behaviour of parents of handicapped children. *Developmental Medical of Child Neurology,* 1973, *15*(4), 524–527.

Maher, B. *Principles of psychopathology.* New York: McGraw-Hill, 1966.

Mahler, M. On sadness and grief in infancy. *Psychoanalytic study of the child,* 1961, *16,* 332–351.

Mahler, M. Notes on the development of basic moods: The depressive affect in psychoanalysis. In R. Lowenstein (Ed.), *Psychoanalysis: A general psychology.* New York: International Universities Press, 1966, 152–168.

Mahler, M. *On human symbiosis and the vicissitudes of individuation.* Vol. 1: *Infantile psychosis.* New York: International Universities Press, 1968.

Mahler, M., Pine, F., & Bergman, A. *The psychological birth of the human infant.* New York: Basic Books, 1975.

Mahoney, M. The self management of covert behavior: A case study. *Behavior Therapy,* 1971, *2,* 575–578.

Maish, J. *The use of an individualized assertive training program in the treatment of depressed patients* (unpublished doctoral dissertation, Florida State University, 1972). *Dissertation Abstracts International,* 1972, *33,* 2816. (University microfilms No. 72-31, 413)

Malmquist, C. Depression in childhood and adolescence. Pts. 1 and 2. *New England Journal of Medicine,* 1971, *284,* 887–961.

Malmquist, C. The theoretical status of depressions in childhood. In E. J. Anthony and D. C. Gilpin (Eds.), *Three clinical faces of childhood.* New York: Spectrum Publications (Wiley), 1976, pp. 173–204.

Malmquist, C. Childhood depression: A clinical and behavioral perspective. In J. G. Schulterbrandt and A. Raskin. (Eds.), *Depression in childhood.* New York: Raven Press, 1977, pp. 33–59.

Marcus, L. *Studies of attention in children vulnerable to psychopathology.* Unpublished doctoral dissertation, The University of Minnesota, 1972.

Marriott, J. A. Family background and psychiatric disorders. Experience with admissions to the University Hospital of the West Indies. *Canadian Psychiatric Association Journal,* 1973, *18*(3), 209–214.

Masson, D., Fivaz, E., & Ciola, A. Experience in the joint hospitalization of mothers with their children at a psychiatric day center for adults. *Schweiz Archives Neurology Neurochirgica Psychiatria,* 1977, *120*(1), 83–100.

Mazet, P., & Sibertin-Blanc, D. Adolescent depression and early deprivation of maternal care. *Revue de Neuropsychiatrie Infantile et d'Hygiene Mentale de l'Enfance.* 1976, *24*(6), 309–318.

McAnarney, E. R. Suicidal behavior of children and youth. *Pediatric Clinics of North America,* 1975, *22*(3), 595–604.

McBride, A. B. The anger–depression guilt-go-round. *American Journal of Nursing,* 1973, *73*(6), 1045–1049.

McClellan, S., & Pugh, F. *Childhood development following maternal mental illness.* Paper presented at annual meeting, American Public Health Association, Miami, Florida, 1962.

McClelland, C., Staples, W., Weisberg, I., & Bergen, M. The practitioner's role in behavioral pediatrics. *Journal of Pediatrics,* 1973, *82*(2), 325–331.

McDermott, J., Jr. Parental divorce in early childhood. *American Journal of Psychiatry,* 1968, *124*(10), 1424–1432.

McGlashan, T., & Carpenter, W., Jr. Postpsychotic depression in schizophrenia. *Archives of General Psychiatry,* 1976, *33,* 235–239.

McIntire, M. S., & Angle, C. R. Psychological biopsy in self-poisoning of children and adolescents. *American Journal of Diseases of Childhood,* 1973, *46,* 386–397.

McKnew, D., Cytryn, L., Efron, A., Gershon, E., & Bunney, W. Offspring of patients with affective disorders. *British Journal of Psychiatry,* 1979, *134,* 148–152.

McKusick, V. A. *Heritable disorders of connective tissue* (4th Ed.). St. Louis: Mosby Company, 1972.

McKusick, V. *Mendelian inheritance in man* (5th Ed.). Baltimore: John Hopkins Press, 1978.

McLean, P. D., & Hakstian, A. R. Clinical depression: Comparative efficacy of outpatient treatments. *Journal of Consulting and Clinical Psychology,* 1979, *47,* 818–836.

McLean, P. D., Ogston, K., & Grauer, L. A behavioral approach to the treatment of depression. *Journal of Behavior Therapy and Experimental Psychiatry,* 1973, *4,* 323–330.

McNeil, T., & Kaij, L. Obstetric complications and physical size of offspring of schizophrenic, schizophrenic-like and control mothers. *British Journal of Psychiatry,* 1973, *123,* 341–348.

McNeil, T., & Kaij, L. Prenatal, perinatal, and post-partum factors in primary prevention of psychopathology in offspring. In G. Albee & J. Joffe (Eds.), *Primary prevention of psychopathology*. Hanover, N. H.: University Press of New England, 1977, pp. 92–116.

Mednick, S. A learning theory approach to research in schizophrenia. *Psychological Bulletin,* 1958, *55,* 316–327.

Mednick, S. A longitudinal study of children with high risk for schizophrenia. *Mental Hygiene,* 1966, *50,* 522–535.

Mednick, S. Breakdown in individuals at high risk for schizophrenia: Possible predispositional perimatal factors. *Mental Hygiene,* 1970, *54,* 50–63.

Mednick, B. Breakdown in high risk subjects: Familial and environmental factors. *Journal of Abnormal Psychology,* 1973, *82,* 469–475.

Mednick, S. Berkson's fallacy and high risk research. In L. Wynne, R. Cromwell & S. Matthysee (Eds.), *The nature of schizophrenia*. New York: Wiley, 1978, pp. 442–452.

Mednick, S., Maura, E., Schulsinger, F., & Mednick, B. Perinatal conditions and infant development in children with schizophrenic parents. *Social Biology,* 1973, *20,* 111.

Mednick, S., & Schaeffer, J. Mothers' retrospective reports in childrearing research. *American Journal of Orthopsychiatry,* 1963, *33,* 457–461.

Mednick, S., & Schulsinger, F. Some premorbid characteristics related to breakdown in children with schizophrenic mothers. In D. Rosenthal & S. Kety (Eds.), *The transmission of schizophrenia*. New York: Pergamon Press, 1968, pp. 267–292.

Mednick, S., & Schulsinger, F. Factors related to breakdown in children at high risk for schizophrenia. In M. Roff and D. Ricks (Eds.), *Life history research in psychopathology*. Minneapolis: The University of Minnesota Press, 1970, pp. 51–93.

Mednick, S., Schulsinger, F., Teasdale, T., Schulsinger, H., Venables, P., & Rock, D. Schizophrenia in high risk children: Sex differences in predisposing factors. In G. Serban (Ed.), *Cognitive defects in the development of mental illness*. New York: Brunner/Mazel, 1978, pp. 169–197.

Meehl, P. Schizotaxia, schizotypy and schizophrenia. *American Psychologist,* 1962, *17,* 827–838.

Meissner, W. Notes on identification: The concept of identification. *Psychoanalytic Quarterly,* 1972, *41,* 224–260.

Mendels, J. (Ed.), *Sinequan (doxepin HCl) IN; Symposium on sinequan (doxepin HCl) : A monograph of recent clinical studies*. Amsterdam: Excerpta Medica (distributed in the United States by American Elsevier, New York), 1975.(a)

Mendels, J. (Ed.), American Association for the Advancement of Science. *The psychobiology of depression*. New York: Spectrum Publications, 1975.(b)

Merrill, G. How husbands manage when wives are hospitalized for schizophrenia: An exploratory study. *Social Psychiatry,* 1969, *4,* 26–39.

Meyersburg, H. A., Ablon, S. L., & Kotin, J. A reverberating psychic mechanism in the depressive processes. *Psychiatry,* 1974, *37*(4), 372–386.

Middlemore, M., *The nursing couple*. London: Hamish-Hamilton Medical Books, 1941.

Miller, A. (with Cohler, B.). Identification and ego-development. *Bulletin of the Chicago Society for Adolescent Psychiatry,* 1971, *1,* 1–9.

Miller, D. Motivation and affect. In P. Mussen (Ed.), *Handbook of research methods in child development.* New York: Wiley, 1960, p. 688.

Minkowski, A., & Amiel-Tison, C. Obstetrical risk in the genesis of vulnerability. Bled Conference on Genetic–Constitutional and Early Childhood Factors in Risk (1972). In E. J. Anthony & C. Koupernik (Eds.), *The child in his family: Children at psychiatric risk.* New York: Wiley, 1974, pp. 139–147.

Mitchell, R. National association for mental health, London. *Depression.* Harmondsworth, England; Baltimore: Penquin Books (in association with MIND), 1975.

Mohrland, J., & Craigmill, A. Locomotor activity of isolated and aggregated mice after lethal doses of morphine sulfate. *Proceeding Western Pharmacology Society,* 1977, *20,* 381–383.

Montgrain, N. Depression: general psychopathology and psychogenesis. *Union Medical Canada,* 1973, *102*(11), 2279–2282.

Moon, L., & Palton, R. The alcoholic psychotic in New York State Mental Hospitals, 1951–1960. *Quarterly Journal of Studies in Alcohol,* 1963, *24,* 664–681.

Morrison, H. Children of depressed parents. Syllabus and proceedings. *American Psychiatric Association,* Atlanta, 1978.

Morrow, W., & Robbins, A. Family relations and social recovery of psychotic mothers. *Journal of Health and Human Behavior,* 1964, *5,* 14–24.

Morse, S. Perfecting the parents: a family romance resistance. *American Journal of Psychotherapy,* 1973, *17*(3), 410–420.

Morton, N., & Chung, C. S. *Genetic epidemiology.* New York: Academic Press, 1978.

Mumbauer, C., & Miller, J. Socioeconomic background and cognitive functioning in preschool children. *Child Development,* 1970, *41,* 361–470.

Murphree, O., Angel, C., DeLuca, D., & Newton, J. Longitudinal studies of genetically nervous dogs. *Biological Psychiatry,* 1977, *12*(4), 573–576.

Murphy, H. Long-term foster care and its influence on adjustment to adult life. In E. Anthony and C. Koupernik (Eds.), *The child in his family: Children at psychiatric risk.* New York: Wiley, 1974, pp. 425–446.

Nace, E. P., Mayers, A. L., O'Brien, C. P., et al. Depression in veterans two years after Viet Nam. *American Journal of Psychiatry,* 1977, *134*(2), 167–170.

Nagera, H. *Early childhood disturbances the infantile neurosis and the adulthood disturbances: Problems of a developmental psychoanalytic psychology.* New York: International Universities Press, Inc., 1966.

Neale, J., & Cromwell, R. Attention and schizophrenia. In B. Maher (Ed.), *Progress in experimental personality research.* New York: Academic Press, 1970, pp. 37–66.

Neale, J., & Weintraub, S. Children vulnerable to psychopathology: The Stony-Brook high risk project, *Journal of Abnormal Child Psychology,* 1975, *3,* 95–113.

Nelson, R., & Craighead, W. E. Selective recall of positive and negative feedback, self-control behaviors, and depression. *Journal of Abnormal Psychology,* 1977, *86,* 379–388.

Neugarten, B. L. Time, age and the life cycle. *The American Journal of Psychiatry,* 1979, *136,* 887–893.

Neugarten, B. L., & Guttman, D. L. Age–sex roles and personality in middle age: A TAT study. In B. L. Neugarten (Ed.), *Middle age and aging.* Chicago: University of Chicago Press, 1968.

Ney, P. G. Four types of hyperkinesis. *Canadian Psychiatric Association Journal,* 1974, *19*(6), 543–550.

Nichols, C. R. Some psychologic aspects of operations leading to infertility. *Southern Medical Journal,* 1973, *66*(4), 439–441.

Niederland, W. G. Scarred: A contribution to the study of facial disfigurement. *Psychoanalysis,* 1975, *44*(3), 450–459.

Noshpitz, J. Certain cultural and familial factors contributing to adolescent alienation. *Journal of the American Academy of Child Psychiatry,* 1970, *9*(2), 216–223.

Oberdalhoff, H. E. Matricide in a schizophrenic psychosis: Case report. *Confinia Psychiatrica,* 1974, *17*(2), 122–131.

Offer, D. *The psychological world of the teenager.* New York: Basic Books, 1969.

Opitz, J. M. Epistemological aspects of congenital anomalies and malformations in man. *Proceedings of the Fifth International Congress of Human Genetics,* 1977. Amsterdam: Excerpta Medica, 1977, pp. 155–166.

Opitz, J., & Herrmann, J. Terminal, diagnostic, nosological, and anatomical developmental aspects of developmental defect in man. *Advances in Human Genetics,* 1979, *9,* 71–132.

Opitz, J., Kaveggia, E., Durkin-Stamm, M., & Pendleton, E. Diagnostic/genetic studies in severe mental retardation. *Birth defects: Original article series,* 1978, *14*(6B), 1–38.

Ornitz, E., & Ritvo, E. The syndrome of autism: A critical review. *American Journal of Psychiatry,* 1976, *136,* 328–337.

Orvaschel, H., Weissman, M., Padian, N., & Lowe, T. Assessing psychopathology in children of psychiatrically disturbed parents. *Journal of the American Academy of Child Psychiatry,* 1981, *20,* 112–122.

Orzack, M., & Kornetsky, C. Environmental and familial predictors of attention behavior in chronic schizophrenics. *Journal of Psychiatric Research,* 1971, *9,* 21–29.

Overall, J. E., Henry, B. W., & Woodward, A. Dependence of marital problems on parental family history. *Journal of Abnormal Psychology,* 1974, *83*(4), 446–450.

Padfield, M. The comparative effects of two counseling approaches on the intensity of depression among rural women of low socio-economic status. *Journal of Counseling Psychology,* 1976, *23,* 209–214.

Paisse, J. M. A case of psychological muteness in a young child with cerebromotor disability. *Annales Medico-Psychologiques,* 1972, *2*(2), 227–239.

Paluszny, M., & McNabb, M. Therapy of a 6-year old who committed fratricide. *Journal of American Academy of Child Psychiatry,* 1975, *14*(2), 319–336.

Paluszny, M., Selzer, M. L., Vinokur, A., & Lewandowski, L. Twin relationships and depression. *American Journal of Psychiatry,* 1977, *134*(9), 988–990.

Parke, R. Fathering—its major role. *Psychology Today,* 1977, *11,* 108–113.

Parker, G. B. *The bonds of depression*. London: Angus & Robertson, 1978.

Parsons, T., & Bales, F. *Family, socialization and interaction*. New York: The Free Press, 1955.

Paschalis, A. P., & Kimmel, H. D. The high school student as change agent. Behavior modification of chronic depression. *American Journal of Community Psychology,* 1974, *2*(4), 351–356.

Patterson, W. E., Taulbee, E. S., Golsom, J., Horner, J., & Wright, H. W. Preliminary report: Comparison of two forms of milieu therapy in the treatment of depression. Unpublished manuscript, Veterans Administration Hospital, Tuscaloosa, Alabama, 1968.

Pavenstedt, E. *The drifters: Children of disorganized lower-class families*. Boston: Little, Brown, 1967.

Paykel, F. Classification of depressed patients: A cluster analysis derived grouping. *British Journal of Psychiatry,* 1971, *118,* 275–288.

Pedersen, F. Father participation in infancy. *American Journal of Orthopsychiatry,* 1969, *39,* 466–472.

Penot, B. On infantile depressions. *Psychiatric Enfant,* 1974, *16*(2), 301–380.

Perris, C., & Espvall, M. Depressive-type psychic reactions caused by success. *Psychiatric Clinical, Basel,* 1973, *38,* 169–179.

Person, E., & Ovesey, L. The transsexual syndrome in males. I. Primary transsexualism. *American Journal of Psychotherapy,* 1974, *28*(1), 4–20.

Peto, A. On affect control. *Psychoanalytic Study of the Child,* 1967, *22,* 36–51.

Pfeiffer, E., Verwolrdt, A., & Davis, G. Sexual behavior in middle life. *American Journal of Psychiatry,* 1972, *12,* 1262–1267.

Piaget, J. The construction of reality in the child (1937). (S. Milgram & A. Parsons trans.). New York: Basic Books, 1954.

Piaget, J. Piaget's theory. In P. H. Mussen (Ed.), *Carmichael's manual of child psychology*. New York: Wiley, 1970.

Piaget, J., & Inhelder, B. *Mental imagery in the child: A study of the development of imaginal representation*. New York: Basic Books, 1971.

Pichot, P., & Agathon, M. *Les Voies nouvelles de la d'epression*. Paris; New York: Masson, 1978.

Pick, A., Frankel, D., & Hess, V. Childrens' attention: The development of selectivity. In E. Hethertington (Ed.), *Reveiw of child development research* (Vol. 5). Chicago: The University of Chicago Press, 1975, pp. 325–384.

Pihl, R. O., Hickcox, P., & Costa, L. The discrimination of marijuana intoxication. *Journal of Clinical Psychology,* 1977, *33*(3), 908–911.

Pine, F. On the pathology of the separation–individuation process as manifested in later clinical work: An attempt at delineation. *International Journal of Psychoanalysis,* 1979, *60,* 225–242.

Pineo, P. C. Disenchantment in later years of marriage. In B. L. Neugarten (Ed.), *Middle age and aging*. Chicago: University of Chicago Press, 1968.

Pirojnikoff, L. A., & Tandy, S. Presentation: American Psychological Association, Annual Meeting, Toronto, 1978.

Plante, G., Cote, H., & Pilic, I. Study on a group of inhibited children from a deprived urban area. *Canadian Psychiatric Association Journal,* 1973, *18*(4), 321–325.

Pope, H. G., & Lipinski, J. F. Diagnosis of schizophrenia and manic–depressive illness. *Archives of General Psychiatry,* 1978, *35,* 811–828.

Pozanski, E. O., & Zrull, J. Childhood depression: Clinical characteristics of overtly depressed children. *Archives of General Psychiatry,* 1970, *23,* 8–15.

Pozanski, E. O., & Zrull, J. Childhood depression: Clinical characteristics of overtly depressed children. *Archives of General Psychiatry,* 1971, *1,* 1–9.

Pozanski, E. O., Krahenbuhl, V., & Zrull, J. P. Childhood depression. A longitudinal perspective. *Journal American Academy of Child Psychiatry,* 1976, *15*(3), 491–501.

Praag, H. *Depression and schizophrenia: A contribution on their chemical pathologies.* New York: S. P. Books Division of Spectrum Publications, 1977.

Procci, W. R. Schizoaffective psychosis: Fact or fiction. *Archives of General Psychiatry,* 1976, *33,* 1167–1178.

Provence, S. Some relationships between activity and vulnerability in the early years. From the Bled Conference on Genetic–Constitutional and Early Childhood Factors in Risk (1972). In E. J. Anthony & C. Koupernik (Eds.), *The child in his family: Children at psychiatric* risk. New York: Wiley, 1974, pp. 157–166.

Provence, S., & Ritvo, S. Effects of deprivation on institutionalized infants: Disturbances in development of relationship to inanimate objects. *Psychoanalytic Study of Child,* 1961, *16,* 189–205.

Raigins, N., Schachter, J., Elmer, E., Preisman, R., Bowes, A., Harway, Y. Infants and children at risk for schizophrenia. *Journal of the American Academy of Child Psychiatry,* 1975, 150–157.

Ramsay, R. A case study in bereavement therapy. In H. S. Eyensch (Ed.), *Case studies in behavior therapy.* London: Routledge & Kegan Paul, 1976.

Rapaport, D. On the psychoanalytic theory of thinking. *International Journal of Psychoanalysis,* 1950, *31,* 1–10.

Rapaport, D. On the psychoanalytic theory of affects (1953). In M. Gill (Ed.), *The collected papers of David Rapaport.* New York: Basic Books, 1967, pp. 476–512.

Raskin, A. Depression in children: Fact or fallacy? In J. Schulterbrandt & A. Raskin (Eds.), *Depression in Childhood: Diagnosis, Treatment and Conceptual Models.* New York: Raven Press, 1977, pp. 141–146.

Rau, J. H., & Kaye, N. Joint hospitalization of mother and child: Evaluation in vivo. *Bulletin Menninger Clinic,* 1977, *41*(4), 385–394.

Rehm, L. A self control model of depression. *Behavior Therapy,* 1977, *8,* 787–804.

Rehm, L., Fuchs, C., Roth, D., Komblith, S., & Romano, J. A comparison of self-control and assertion skills treatments of depression. *Behavior Therapy,* 1979, *10,* 429–442.

Rehm, L., & Kornblith, S. Behavior therapy for depression: A review of recent developments. In M. Hersen, R. Eisler, and P. Miller (Eds.), *Progress in behavior modification.* New York: Academic Press, 1979.

Rehm, L., Kornblith, S., O'Hara, M., Lamparski, J., Romano, J., & Volkin, R. *An evaluation of major elements in a self control therapy program for depression.* Paper presented at the meeting of the Association for the Advancement of Behavior Therapy, Chicago, November 1978.

Reinhold, M. A psychiatrist's view of problems in adolescence. *Proceedings Royal Society Medicine,* 1973, *66*(9), 847–850.

Reisby, N. Psychoses in children of schizophrenic mothers. *Acta Psychiatrics Scandinavica,* 1967, *43,* 8–20.

Reisinger, J. The treatment of anxiety-depression via positive reinforcement and response cost. *Journal of Applied Behavioral Analysis,* 1972, *5,* 125–130.

Remschmidt, H., Strunk, P., Methner, C. H., & Tegeler, E. Children of endogenically depressive parents: An investigation in the frequency of behavior disturbances and of personality structure. *Fortschritte Der Neurologie, Psychiatrie Und Ihrer Grenzgebiete,* 1973, *41*(6), 326–340.

Rice, E., Ekdahl, M., & Miller, L. *Children of mentally ill parents.* New York: Behavioral Publications, 1971.

Richman, N. The effects of housing on pre-school children and their mothers. *Developmental Medicine Child Neurology,* 1974, *16*(1), 53–58.

Richman, N. Depression in mothers of pre-school children. *Journal Child Psychology Psychiatry,* 1976, *17*(1), 75–78.

Rie, H. Depression in childhood: A survey of some pertinent contributions. *Journal of the American Academy of Child Psychiatry,* 1966, *5,* 653–685.

Rizzuto, A. M. Object relations and the formation of the image of God. *British Journal Medical Psychology,* 1974, *47*(1), 83–99.

Robbins, L. C. The accuracy of parental recall of aspects of child development of childrearing practices. *Journal of Abnormal and Social Psychology,* 1963, *66,* 261–270.

Robbins, L. *Deviant children grown up.* Baltimore: Williams & Wilkins, 1966.

Robertson, J. Mothering as an influence on early development: A study of well baby clinic records. *Psychoanalytic Study of the Child,* 1962, *17,* 245–264.

Robinson, J., & Lewinsohn, P. Behavior modification of speech characteristics in a chronically depressed man. *Behavior Therapy,* 1973, *4,* 150–152.(a)

Robinson, J., & Lewinsohn, P. Experimental analysis of a technique based on the Premack Principle changing verbal behavior of depressed individuals. *Psychological Reports,* 1973, *32,* 199–210.(b)

Rochman, N. S. *Journal of Social Medicine,* 1978, *71,* 489–493.

Rochlin, G. Loss and restitution. *Psychoanalytic Study of the Child,* 1953, *8,* 288–309.

Rodnick, E., & Goldstein, M. Premorbid adjustment and the recovery of the mothering function in acute schizophrenic women. *Journal of Abnormal Psychology,* 1974, *83,* 623–628.

Rolf, J. The social and academic competence of children vulnerable to schizophrenia and other behavior pathologies. *Journal of Abnormal Psychology,* 1972, *80,* 225–243.

Rolf, J. Peer status and the directionality of symptomatic behavior: Prime social competence predictors of outcome for vulnerable children. *American Journal of Orthopsychiatry,* 1976, *46,* 74–88.

Rolf, J., & Garmezy, N. The school performance of children vulnerable to behavior pathology. In D. Ricks, A. Thomas, & M. Roff (Eds.), *Life history research in psychopathology.* Minneapolis: The University of Minnesota Press, 1974, 87–107.

Rolf, J., & Hasazi, J. Identification of preschool children at risk and some guidelines for primary intervention. In G. Albee and J. Joffe (Eds.), *Primary prevention of psychopathology*. Hanover, N. H.: University Press of New England, 1977, pp. 121–152.

Romano, J., & Geertama, R. Parent assessment in research on the vulnerability of children and families to mental disorder. *American Journal of Psychiatry,* 1978, *135,* 812–815.

Rosenbaum, J. Organizational career mobility promotion chances in a corporation during periods of growth and contraction. *American Journal of Sociology,* 1979, *18*(1), 21–48.

Rosenblum, L. A., & Kaufman, I. C. Variations in infant development and response to maternal loss in monkeys. *American Journal of Orthopsychiatry,* 1968, *38*(3), 418–426.

Rosenfeld, A. A., Nadelson, C. C., Krieger, M., & Backman, J. H. Incest and sexual abuse of children. *Journal American Academy Child Psychiatry,* 1977, *16*(2), 327–339.

Rosenthal, D. The offspring of schizophrenic couples. *Journal of Psychiatric Research,* 1966, *4,* 169–188.

Rosenthal, D. *Genetics of Psychopathology*. New York: McGraw-Hill, 1970.

Rosenthal, D. Issues in high-risk studies of schizophrenia. In D. Ricks, A. Thomas, & M. Roff (Eds.), *Life history research in psychopathology* (Vol. 3). Minneapolis: University of Minnesota Press, 1974, pp. 25–41.

Rothenberg, M. B. Opportunities for psychological prophylaxis in the neonatal period. A checklist for the practicing pediatrician. *Clinical Pediatrics* (Philadelphia), 1976, *15*(1), 53–56.

Rowe, D. *The experience of depression*. Chichester (U.K.); Wiley, 1978.

Rubin, R. T., & Kendler, K. S. Psychoneuroendocrinology: Fundamental concepts and correlates in depression. In G. Usdin (Ed.), *Depression: Clinical, biological and psychological perspectives*. New York: Brunner/Mazel, 1977, pp. 122–138.

Rush, A. J., Beck, A. T., Kovacs, M., & Hollon, S. Comparative efficacy of cognitive therapy and pharmacotherapy in the treatment of depressed outpatients. *Cognitive Research and Therapy,* 1977, *1,* 17–38.

Rush, A. J., Hollon, S., Beck, A. T., & Kovacs, M. Depression: Must pharmacotherapy fail for cognitive therapy to succeed? *Cognitive Research and Therapy,* 1978, *2,* 199–206.

Rush, A. J., Khatami, M., & Beck, A. T. Cognitive and behavior therapy in chronic depression. *Behavior Therapy,* 1975, *6,* 398–404.

Rutschmann, J., Cornblatt, B., & Erlenmeyer-Kimling, N. Sustained attention in children at risk for schizophrenia. *Archives of General Psychiatry,* 1977, *34,* 571–575.

Rutter, M. *Children of Sick Parents*. London: Oxford University Press, 1966. (Maudsley Monograph No. 16).

Rutter, M. Parent–child separation: Psychological effects on the children. *Journal of Child Psychology and Psychiatry,* 1971, *12,* 233–260.

Rutter, M. *Maternal deprivation reassessed*. Baltimore: Penguin Books, 1972.

Rutter, M. Epidemiological strategies and psychiatric concepts in research on the vulnerable child. Bled Conference on Genetic–Constitutional and Early

Childhood Factors in Risk (1972). In E. J. Anthony & C. Koupernik (Eds.), *The child in his family: Children at psychiatric risk*. New York: Wiley, 1974, pp. 167–179.

Rutter, M., Lebovici, S., Eisenberg, L., Ineznevsky, A. V., Sadova, R., Brooke, E., & Lin, T. A triaxial classification of mental disorders in childhood: An international study. *Journal of Child Psychology and Psychiatry,* 1969, *10,* 41–61.

Rutter, M., Yule, B., Quinton, D., et al. Attainment and adjustment in two geographical areas: III—Some factors accounting for area differences. *British Journal of Psychiatry,* 1975, *126,* 520–533.

Sameroff, A. The mother's construction of the child. In M. Zax, A. Sameroff, & H. Babigian (Eds.), *American Journal of Orthopsychiatry,* 1977, *47,* 218–230.

Sameroff, A. Infant risk factors in developmental disability. In E. J. Anthony (Ed.), *The child in his family* (Vol. 4), *Vulnerable children*. New York: Wiley-Interscience, 1978, pp. 173–184.

Sameroff, A., & Zax, M. Neonatal characteristics of offspring of schizophrenic and neurotically-depressed mothers. *Journal of Nervous and Mental Disease,* 1973, *157,* 191.(a)

Sameroff, A., & Zax, M. Schizotoxia revisited: Model issues in the etiology of schizophrenia. *American Journal of Orthopsychiatry,* 1973, *43,* 744–754.(b)

Sameroff, A., & Zax, M. In search of schizophrenia: Young offspring of schizophrenic women. In L. Wynne, R. Cromwell, & S. Matthysee (Eds.), *The nature of schizophrenia: New approaches to research and treatment*. New York: Wiley, 1978, pp. 430–441.

Sanchez, V., Lewinsohn, P., & Larson, D. Assertion training: Effectiveness in the treatment of depression. *Journal of Clinical Psychology,* 1980, *36,* 526–529.

Sander, L. Issues in early mother–child interaction. *Journal of the American Academy of Child Psychiatry,* 1962, *2,* 141–166.

Sander, L. Adaptive relationships in early mother–child interaction. *Journal of the American Academy of Child Psychiatry,* 1964, *3,* 221–263.

Sander, L. The longitudinal course of early mother–child interaction: Cross-case comparison in a sample of mother–child pairs. In B. Foss (Ed.), *Determinants of infant behavior.* London: Metheun, 1969, pp. 189–228.

Sander, L. Infant and caretaking environment: Investigation and conceptualization of adaptive behavior in a system of increasing complexity. In E. J. Anthony (Ed.), *Explorations in child psychiatry.* New York: Plenum Press, 1975, pp. 129–166.

Sandler, J. The role of affects in psychoanalytic theory. In *Physiology, Emotion and Psychosomatic Illness*. Amsterdam: Elsevier, 1972.

Sandler, J., & Joffee, W. Notes on childhood depression. *International Journal of Psychoanalysis,* 1965, *46,* 88–96.

Scallon, R., & Herron, W. Field articulation of enuretic boys and their mothers. *Perceptual Motor Skills,* 1969, *28,* 407–413.

Schachtel, E. The development of focal attention and the emergency of reality. *Psychiatry,* 1954, *17,* 309–324.

Schachtel, E. On attention, selective inattention, and experience: An inquiry into attention as an attitude. In E. Wittenberg (Ed.), *Interpersonal explorations in psychoanalysis,* New Directions in Theory and Practice. New York: Basic Books, 1973.

Schachter, M. A study of depressions and depressive episodes in children and adolescents. *Acta Paedopsychiatrica,* 1971, *38*(7–8), 191–201.

Schain, R. J., & Yannet, H. Infantile autism. *Journal of Pediatrics,* 1960, *57,* 560–567.

Schechtman, J., Gilpin, D., & Worland, J. Symptomatic depression as seen in the clinic. In E. Anthony & D. Gilpin (Eds.), *Three clinical faces of childhood.* New York: Spectrum (Wiley), 1976, pp. 205–228.

Scher, J. M. The collapsing perimeter. A commentary on life, death, and death-in-life. *American Journal of Psychotherapy,* 1976, *30*(4), 641–657.

Schildkraut, J. Catecholamine hypothesis of affective disorders. *American Journal of Psychiatry,* 1965, *122,* 509–522.

Schlessinger, N., & Robbins, F. Assessment and follow-up in psychoanalysis. *Journal of American Psychoanalytical Association,* 1974, *22*(3), 542–567.

Schlitz, D. *The Gambler.* Nashville: Writer's Night Music, 1978.

Schmale, A. A genetic view of affects: With special reference to the genesis of helplessness and hopelessness. *Psychoanalytic Study of the Child,* 1964, *19,* 287–310.

Schmale, A., & Engel, G. The role of conservation–withdrawal in depressive reactions. In E. J. Anthony and T. Benedek (Eds.), *Depression in human existence.* Boston: Little, Brown, 1975, pp. 185–198.

Schmickley, V. G. *The effects of cognitive behavior modification upon depressed outpatients.* Unpublished doctoral dissertation, Michigan State University, 1976.

Schrut, A., & Michels, T. Suicidal divorced and discarded women. *Journal of the American Academy of Psychoanalysis,* 1974, *2*(4), 329–347.

Schulterbrandt, J. G., & Raskin, A. *Depression in childhood: Diagnosis, treatment, and conceptual models.* New York: Raven Press, 1977.

Schur, M. Affects and cognition. *International Journal of Psychoanalysis,* 1969, *50,* 647–653.

Seitz, F. C. A behavior modification approach to depression: A case study. *Psychology,* 1971, *8.* 58–63.

Seligman, M. Depression and learned helplessness. In R. Friedman and M. Katz (Ed.), *The psychology of depression: Contemporary theory and research.* Washington, D. C.: V. Winston, 1974, 83–126.

Seligman, M. *Helplessness: On depression, development and death.* San Francisco: Freeman, 1975.

Shafer, R. The clinical analysis of affects. *Journal of American Psychoanalytic Association,* 1964, *12,* 175–299.

Shakow, D. Segmental set: A theory of the formal psychological deficit in schizophrenia. *Archives of General Psychiatry,* 1962, *6,* 1–17.

Shakow, D. Psychological deficit in schizophrenia. *Behavioral Science,* 1963, *8,* 275–305.

Shakow, D. Some thoughts about schizophrenia research in the context of high risk studies (1973). In D. Shakow (Ed.), *Schizophrenia: Selected papers. Psychological Issues Monograph,* 1977, *38,* 316–334.

Shakow, D. The nature of deterioration in schizophrenic conditions (1946). In D. Shakow (Ed.), *Schizophrenia: Selected papers. Psychological Issues Monograph,* 1977, *38,* 4–86.

Shanok, S. S., & Lewis, D. O. Juvenile court versus child guidance referral: Psychosocial and parental factors. *American Journal of Psychiatry,* 1977, *134*(10), 1130–1133.

Shapiro, M., Neufeld, I., & Post, F. Note: Experimental study of depressive illness. *Psychological Reports,* 1962, *10,* 590.

Shapiro, V., Fraiberg, S., & Adeslon, E. Infant–parent psychotherapy on behalf of a child in a critical nutritional state. *Psychoanalytic Study of the Child,* 1976, *31,* 461–491.

Shaw, B. Comparison of cognitive therapy and behavior therapy in the treatment of depression. *Journal of Consulting and Clinical Psychology,* 1977, *45,* 543–558.

Shaw, P. A study of social problems in a group of young women treated with brief psychotherapy. *British Journal of Medical Psychology,* 1977, *50*(2), 155–161.

Shenken, L. Proceedings: A child is being beaten. *Aust. NZ Journal Psychiatry,* 1973, *7*(4), 243–248.

Shipley, C. R., & Fazio, A. Pilot study of a treatment for psychological depression. *Journal of Abnormal Psychology,* 1973, 82, 372–376.

Shmagin, B. G., & Pearlmutter, D. R. The pursuit of unhappiness; The secondary gains of depression. *Perspective Psychiatric Care,* 1977, *15*(2), 63–65.

Sieg, K. W. The nursing home: Occupational therapy services in an institution. *American Journal of Occupational Therapy,* 1977, *31*(8), 516–524.

Sigal, J. J. Enduring disturbances in behavior following acute illness in early childhood. In E. J. Anthony & C. Koupernik (Eds.), *The child in his family: Children of psychiatric risk.* New York: Wiley, 1974, pp. 415–424.

Sigal, J. J., Silver, D., Rakoff, V., & Ellin, B. Some second-generation effects of survival of the Nazi persecution. *American Journal of Orthopsychiatry,* 1973, *43,* 320–327.

Silver, M. J., St. Clair, C. H., & Siegel, J. M. Parental satisfaction at follow-up of child outpatients from an urban mental health center. *Journal of Community Psychology,* 1975, *3*(1), 36–39.

Silverman, C. *The Epidemiology of Depression.* Baltimore: John Hopkins Press, 1968.

Silverman, J. The problem of attention. *Psychological Bulletin,* 1964, *71,* 352–379.

Slaughter, W. C., & Cordes, C. K. Covert maternal deprivation and pathological sucking behavior. *American Journal of Psychiatry,* 1977, *134*(10), 1152–1153.

Smith, D. W. *Recognizable Patterns of Human Malformation* (2nd ed.). Philadelphia: Saunders, 1976.

Smoller, B., & Lewis, A. B., Jr. A psychological theory of child abuse. *Psychiatric Quarterly,* 1977, *49*(1), 38–44.

Sobel, D. Children of schizophrenic patients: Preliminary observations of early development. *American Journal of Psychiatry,* 1961, *118,* 512–517.(a)

Sobel, D. Infant mortality and malformations in children of schizophrenic women, preliminary data and suggested research. *Psychiatric Quarterly,* 1961, *35,* 60–65.(b)

Solnit, A., & Stark, M. Mourning and the birth of a defective child. *Psychoanalytic Study of the Child,* 1961, *16,* 523–537.

Soreff, S. The last child to school: A period of transition and decision for the mother. *Primary Care,* 1977, *4*(2), 355–365.

Sperber, M. A. Symbiotic psychosis and the need for fame. *Psychoanalytical Review,* 1975, *61*(4), 517–534.

Sperling, M. Equivalents of depression in children. *Journal of Hillside Hospital,* 1959, *8,* 138.

Spielberger, C., Gorsuch, R., & Lushene, R. *Manual for the State Trait Anxiety Inventory.* Palo Alto, California: Consulting Psychological Press, 1970.

Spitz, R. Hospitalism. *Psychoanalytic Study of the Child,* 1945, *1,* 53–74.

Spitz, R. A. Anaclitic depression. An inquiry into the genesis of psychiatric conditions in early childhood, II. *Psychoanalytic Study of the Child,* 1946, *2,* 312–342.

Spitzer, R. L. & Endicott, J. *Schedule for affective disorders and schizophrenia (2nd Ed.).* New York: Biometrics Research, New York State Psychiatric Institute, 1975.

Spitzer, R. L., Endicott, J., & Robins, E. *Research diagnostic criteria (RDC) for a selected group of functional disorders (3rd Ed.).* New York: Biometrics Research, New York State Psychiatric Institute, 1978.

Stainbrook, E. J. Depression: The psychosocial context. In G. Usdin (Ed.), *Depression: Clinical, biological and psychological perspectives.* New York: Brunner/Mazel, 1977, pp. 28–51.

Steele, C. I. Obese adolescent girls: some diagnostic and treatment considerations. *Adolescence,* 1974, *9*(33), 81–96.

Steiner, B. W. The crisis of middle age, *Canadian Medical Association Journal,* 1973, *109,* 1017–1018.

Steirlin, H. *Separating parents and adolescents.* New York: Quadrangle Press, 1974.

Stern, S. L., Rush, A. J., & Mendels, J. Toward a rational pharmacotherapy of depression. *American Journal of Psychiatry,* 1980, *137,* 545–552.

Stevenson, J. S. *Issues and crises during midalescence.* New York: Appleton Century Crofts, 1977.

Stewart, S., & Johansen, R. A family systems approach to home dialysis. *Psychotherapy Psychosomatics,* 1977, *27*(2), 86–92.

Stolorow, R. D. A note on devouring and being devoured. *American Journal of Psychoanalysis,* 1975, *35*(3), 285.

Stone, H. The birth of a child with Down's syndrome. A medico-social study of thirty-one children and their families. *Scott Medical Journal,* 1973, *18*(6), 182–187.

Strauss, J. S., Bartko, J. J., & Carpenter, W. T. The use of clustering techniques for the classification of psychiatric patients. *British Journal of Psychiatry,* 1973, *122,* 531–540.

Strauss, J. S., & Carpenter, W. T. The prediction of outcome in schizophrenia. Characteristics of outcome, *Archives of General Psychiatry,* 1972, *27,* 739–746.

Strauss, J. S., Kokes, R. F., Ritzler, B. A., Harder, & Van Ord. Patterns of disorder in first admission psychiatric patients. *Journal of Nervous and Mental Disease,* 1978, *166,* 611–623.

Studt, H. H., & Arnds, H. G., Psychological factors in bronchial asthma: II. *Zeitschrift Fur Psychosomatische Medizin Und Psychoanalyse,* 1968, *14*(4), 230–242.

Sullivan, H. S. *The interpersonal theory of psychiatry.* New York: Norton, 1953.

Suomi, S. J. Repetitive peer separation of young monkeys: Effects of vertical chamber confinement during separations. *Journal of Abnormal Psychology,* 1973, *81*(1), 1–10.

Swets, J., & Kristofferson, A. Attention. In P. Mussen and M. Rosenszeig (Eds.), *Annual review of Psychology,* 1970, 21–38.

Sylvester, E. Developmental truisms and their fate in child-rearing: Clinical observations. In M. Senn (Ed.), *Problems of infancy and childhood.* New York: Josiah Macy Foundation, 1953.

Syurek, S. *Clinical studies in child psychosis: Twenty-five years with collaborative treatment and research.* S. A. Syurek & I. N. Berlin (Eds.). New York: Bruner, Meizel, 1973.

Tasch, R. The role of the father in the family. *Journal of Experimental Education,* 1952, *20,* 319–361.

Taulbee, E. S., & Wright, H. W. A psychosocial–behavioral model for therapeutic intervention. In C. C. Spielberger (Ed.), *Current topics in clinical and community psychology.* New York: Academic Press, 1971, pp. 76–93.(a)

Taulbee, E. S., and Wright, H. W. Attitude therapy: A behavior modification program in a psychiatric hospital. In H. C. Rickard (Ed.), *Behavioral interventions in human problems.* New York: MacMillan, 1971, pp. 38–64.(b)

Taylor, C. J. A grief experience in juvenile diabetes. *Journal of Psychiatric Nursing,* 1977, *15*(1), 26–29.

Taylor, F. G. & Marshall, W. L. Experimental analysis of a cognitive–behavioral therapy for depression *Cognitive Therapy and Research,* 1977, *1,* 59–72.

Taylor, R. W. Depression and recovery at 9 weeks of age. *Journal of the American Academy of Child Psychiatry,* 1973, *12*(3), 506–510.

Thoa, N. B., Tizabi, Y., & Jacobowitz, D. M. The effect of isolation on catecholamine concentration and turnover in discrete areas of the rat brain. *Brain Research,* 1977, *131*(2), 259–269.

Thomas, A., Chess, S., Birch, H., & Hertzig, M. A longitudinal study of primary reaction patterns in children. *Comprehensive Psychiatry,* 1960, *1,* 103–112.

Thurnher, M. Midlife marriage: Sex differences in evaluation and perspectives. *International Journal of Aging and Human Development,* 1976, *7,* 129–135.

Tietz, W., McSherry, L., & Britt, B. Family sequelae after a child death due to cancer. *American Journal of Psychotherapy,* 1977, *31*(3), 417–425.

Tinbergen, N., & Tinbergen, E. A. Early childhood autism—A hypothesis. In *The animal in its world,* (Vol. 2). Cambridge: Harvard University Press, 1972, pp. 175–199.

Todd, F. J. Coverant control of self-evaluation responses in the treatment of depression: A new use for an old principle. *Behavior Therapy,* 1972, *3,* 91–94.

Tolpin, M. Self-objects and oedipal objects: A crucial developmental distinction. *Psychoanalytic Study of the Child,* 1978, *33,* 167–184.

Tolpin, M., & Kohut, H. The disorders of the self: The psychopathology of the first years of life. In S. Greenspan & G. Pollock (Eds.), *The course of life: Psychoanalytic contributions toward understanding personality development.* (Vol. 1). *Infancy and early childhood.* Washington, D.C.: U.S. Government Printing Office, 1980, 425–442.

Toolan, J. Depression in children and adolescents. *American Journal of Orthopsychiatry,* 1962, *32,* 404.

Tooley, K. M. The remembrance of things past: On the collection and recollection of ingredients useful in the treatment of disorders resulting from unhappiness, rootlessness and the fear of things to come. *American Journal of Orthopsychiatry* 1978, *48*(1), 174–182.

Trasler, D. G., & Fraser, F. C. Time position relationship, with particular reference to cleft lip and cleft palate. In J. G. Wilson & F. C. Fraser (Eds.), *Handbook of teratology* (Vol. 2). New York: Plenum Press, 1977, pp. 271–293.

Treffert, D. A. Epidemiology of infantile autism. *Archives of General Psychiatry,* 1970, *22,* 431–438.

Tsuang, M. T., and Wilson, R. F. Mortality in patients with schizophrenia, mania, depression and surgical conditions: A comparison with general population mortality. *British Journal of Psychiatry,* 1977, *130,* 162–166.

Tucker, L. S., Jr. A comparison of the value preferences of emotionally disturbed adolescents and their parents with normal adolescents and their parents. *Adolescence,* 1976, *11*(44), 549–567.

Tustin, F. Autistic processes. *Journal of Child Psychotherapy,* 1969, *2*(3), 23–42.

Turner, R., Ward, M., & Turner, D. Behavioral treatment for depression: An evaluation of therapeutic components. *Journal of Clinical Psychology,* 1979, *35,* 166–175.

Usdin, G. *Depression: Clinical, biological and psychological perspectives.* New York: Brunner/Mazel, 1977.

Valenstein, A. Affects, emotional reliving and insight in the psychoanalytic process. *International Journal of Psychoanalysis,* 1962, *43,* 315–324.

Valzelli, L., Bernasconi, S., & Cusumano, G. Annual and daily changes in brain serotonin content in differentially housed mice. *Neuropsychobiology,* 1977, *3*(1), 35–41.

Vanggaard, T. *Atypical endogenous depression: Diagnostic criteria.* Copenhagen: Munksgaard, 1976, p. 56.

Venables, P. Input dysfunction in schizophrenia. In B. Maher (Ed.), *Progress in experimental personality/research* (Vol. 1). New York: Academic Press, 1964, pp. 86–103.

Venzmer, G. Symptoms of senility. *Schwest Review,* 1977, *15*(8), 9–11.

Videbech, T. A study of genetic factors, childhood bereavement, and premorbid personality traits in patients with anancastic endogenous depression. *Acta Psychiatrica Scandanavia,* 1975, *52*(3), 178–222.

Viederman, M. Adaptive and maladaptive regression in hemodialysis. *Psychiatry,* 1974, *37*(1), 68–77.

Vilsvik, S. O. Use of psychopharmaceuticals in childhood. *Tidsskr nor laegeforen,* 1977, *97*(2), 76–78.

Vogel, F., & Motulsky, A. G. *Human genetics: Problems and approaches.* New York: Springer-Verlag, 1979.

von Bertalanffy, L. *General system theory.* New York: George Braziller, 1968.

Wadsworth, A., & Barker, B. A comparison of two treatments for depression: The antidepressive program vs. traditional therapy. *Journal of Clinical Psychology,* 1976, *32,* 445–449.

Walker, C. W. Persistence of mourning in the foster child as related to the poster mother's level of maturity. *Smith College Studies in Social Work,* 1971, *41*(3), 173–2461.

Wanderer, Z. W. Existential depression treated by desensitization of phobias: Strategy and transcript. *Journal of Behavioral Therapy and Experimental Psychiatry,* 1972, *3,* 111–116.

Wang, P. L., & Smyers, P. L. Psychological status after stroke as measured by the Hand Test. *Journal Clinical Psychology,* 1977, *33*(3), 879–882.

Waring, M., & Ricks, D. Family patterns of children who become adult schizophrenia. *Journal of Nervous and Mental Disease,* 1965, *140,* 351–364.

Warnes, H., & Fitzpatrick, C. Oral contraceptives and depression. *Psychosomatics,* 1979, *20,* 187–194.

Wasserman, S. The middle age separation crisis and ego supportive casework treatment. *Clinical Social Work Journal,* 1973, *1,* 38–47.

Waters, B. H. Risk to bipolar affective psychosis. In B. Shopsin (Ed.), *Manic Illness.* New York: Raven Press, 1979.

Watt, N. F. Longitudinal changes in the social behavior of children hospitalized for schizophrenia as adults. *Journal of Nervous and Mental Disease,* 1972, *155,* 41–54.

Watt, N. F., Stolorow, R. D., Lubensky, A. W. & McClelland, D. C. School adjustment and behavior of children hospitalized for schizophrenia as adults. *American Journal of Orthopsychiatry,* 1970, *40,* 637–657.

Wechsler, D. *Manual for the Wechsler intelligence scale for children.* New York: The Psychological Corporation, 1949.

Weintraub, S., Liebert, D., & Neal, J. Teacher ratings of children vulnerable to psychopathology. In E. J. Anthony (Ed.), *The child and his family* (Vol. 4), *Vulnerable children.* New York: Wiley-Interscience, 1978, pp. 335–346.

Weintraub, S., Neale, J., & Liebert, D. Teacher ratings of children vulnerable to psychopathology. *American Journal of Orthopsychiatry,* 1975, 45, 838–845.

Weintraub, S., Prinz, R., & Neale, J. Peer evaluations of the competence of children vulnerable to psychopathology. *Journal of Abnormal Child Psychology,* 1978, *6,* 461–473.

Weiss, A. L. The importance of the human environment for depressive reactions in psycho-organically disturbed children. *Acta Paedopsychiatrica* (Basel), 1973, *40*(1), 17–37.

Weissberg, M. P., & Dubovsky, S. L. Assessment of psychiatric emergencies in medical practice. *Primary Care,* 1977, *4*(4), 651–660.

Weissman, M. M. The psychological treatment of depression: Research evidence for the efficacy of psychotherapy alone, in comparison with, and in combination with pharmacotherapy. *Archives of General Psychiatry,* 1979, *36,* 1261–1269.

Weissman, M. M., & Klerman, G. Sex differences and the epidemiology of depression. *Archives of General Psychiatry,* 1977, *34,* 98–111.

Weissman, M. M., Orvaschel, H., & Padian, N. Children's symptom and social functioning self-report scales: Comparison of mothers' and childrens' reports. *Journal of Nervous and Mental Disease,* 1980, *168,* 736–740.

Weissman, M., & Paykel, E. S. The depressed woman as mother. *Social Psychiatry,* 1972, *7,* 98–108.

Weissman, M. M., & Paykel, E. S. *The depressed woman: A study of social relationships.* Chicago: University of Chicago Press, 1974.

Weissman, M., Paykel, E. S., & Klerman, G. The depressed woman as mother. *Social Psychiatry,* 1972, *7,* 98–108.

Weissman, M., Pincus, C., Radding, N., Lawrence, R., & Siegel, R. The educated housewife: Mild depression and the search for work. *American Journal of Orthopsychiatry,* 1973, *43,* 565–573.

Weissman, M., & Siegel, R. The depressed woman and her rebellious adolescent. *Social Casework,* 1972, *18,* 563–570.

Wells, C. E. Pseudomentia. *American Journal of Psychiatry,* 1979, *136,* 895–900.

Welner, Z. Childhood depression: An overview. *Journal of Nervous and Mental Disease,* 1978, *166,* 588–593.

Welner, Z., Welner, A., McCrary, M., & Leonard, M. Psychopathology in children of inpatients with depression: A controlled study. *Journal of Nervous and Mental Disease,* 1977, *164,* 408–413.

Wenar, C. The reliability of mothers' histories. *Child Development,* 1961, *32,* 491–500.

Wessler, R., & Iven, D. Social characteristics of patients readmitted to a community mental health center. *Community Mental Health,* 1970, *6,* 69–74.

Western Psychological Services, *Manual for the Shipley Institute of Living Scale.* Beverly Hills, California: Western Psychological Services, 1963.

White, B. (Ed.), *Experience and environment: Major influence on the development of the young child* (Vol. 2). Englewood Cliffs, N. J.: Prentice-Hall, 1978.

White, B., & J. Watts (Ed.), *Experience and environment: Major influences in the development of the young child* (Vol. 1). Englewood Cliffs, N. J.: Prentice-Hall, 1973.

White, R. Motivation reconsidered: The concept of competence. *Psychological Review,* 1959, *66,* 297–333.

White, R. Ego and reality in psychoanalytic theory. *Psychological Issues,* 1963, 11.

White, R. B., Davis, H. K., & Cantrell, W. A. Psychodynamics of depression: Implications for treatment. In G. Usdin (Ed.), *Depression: Clinical, biological and psychological perspectives.* New York: Brunner/Mazel, 1977, pp. 308–338.

Wieck, H. H. *Kopfschmerz, larvierte depression. Diagnostik und therapie in der praxis.* Stuttgart, New York: Schattauer, 1975.

Williams, F. S. Parenting the adolescent. *Pediatric Annual,* 1977, *6*(10), 647–652.

Wing, J. K., Cooper, J. E., & Sartorius, N. *The measurement and classification of psychiatric symptoms*. London: Cambridge University Press, 1974.

Winnicott, D. W. The depressive position in normal emotional development (1954). In D. W. Winnicott (Ed.), *Collected papers*. New York: Basic Books, 1958, pp. 262–277.

Winnicott, D. W. Anxiety associated with insecurity. (1952) In *Collected Papers*. London: Tavistock Publications, 1958.(b)

Winnicott, D. W. Reparation in respect of mother's organized defense against depression. (1948). In *Collected Papers: Through Pediatrics to Psycho-analysis*. London: Tavistock Publications, 1958.(a)

Winnicott, D. W. The effect of psychotic parents on the emotional development of the child. In D. W. Winnicott (Ed.), *The family and individual development*. London: Tavistock, 1965.

Winnicott, D. W. Primary maternal preoccupation. (1956). In *Collected papers: Through Pediatrics to psycho-analysis*. London: Tavistock Publications, 1958. *Playing and Reality,* London: Tavistock Publications, 1971.

Winnicott, D. Hate in the countertransference. *Through pediatrics to psycho-analysis*. London: Hogart Press, 1975.

Winokur, G. The genetics of manic-depressive illness. In R. R. Fieve (Ed.), *Depression in the 1970's: Modern theories and research*. The Hague, The Netherlands: Excerpta Medica, 1971.

Winokur, G., Clayton, P. J., & Reich, T. *Manic depressive disease*. St. Louis: Mosby, 1969.

Winokur, G., Morrison, J., Clancy, J., & Crowe, R. The Iowa 500: Familial and clinical findings favor two kinds of depressive illness. *Comprehensive Psychiatry,* 1973, *14*(2), 99–106.

Witkin, H. Individual differences in ease of perception of embedded figures. *Journal Personal,* 1950, *19,* 1–15.

Witkin, H. Psychological differentiation and forms of pathology. *Journal of Abnormal Psychology,* 1965, *70,* 317–336.

Witkin, H. A cognitive style approach to cross-cultural research. *International Journal of Psychology,* 1967, *2,* 233–250.

Witkin, H., Dyk, R., Faterson, H., & George, J. *Psychological differentiation*. New York: Wiley, 1962.

Witkin, H. A., & Goodenough, D. R. Field dependence and interpersonal behavior. *Psychology Bulletin,* 1977, *84*(4), 661–689.

Witkin, H., Oltman, P., Raskin, E., & Karp, S. *A manual for the embedded figures test*. Palo Alto, Claifornia: Consulting Psychologist Press, 1971.

Wright, S. *Evolution and the genetics of populations*. Chicago: The University of Chicago Press, 1968.

Yalom, I., Lunde, D., Moos, R., & Hamburg, D. Post-partum "blues" syndrome: A description and related variables. *Archives of General Psychiatry,* 1968, *18,* 16–27.

Yarrow, M., Campbell, J., & Burton, R. *Childrearing: An inquiry into research and methods*. San Francisco: Jossey-Bass, 1968.

Yarrow, M., Campbell, J., & Burton, R. Recollections of childhood: A study of the retrospective method. *Monographs of the Society for Research in Child Development,* 1970, *35,* 1–83.

Young, L. D., Suomi, S. S., Harlow, H. F., & McKinney, W. T., Jr. Early stress and later response to separation in rhesus monkeys. *American Journal of Psychiatry,* 1973, *130*(4), 400–405.

Yu, P., Prentky, R., Baldwin, A., Greenwald, Munson, Baldwin, Fisher. *Child competence as assessed by professionals, teachers, peers and parents.* Paper presented at the Risk Research Consortium Plenary Conference, San Juan, Puerto Rico, 1980.

Zeiss, A., Lewinsohn, D., & Muñoz, R. Nonspecific improvement effects in depression using interpersonal skills training, pleasant activities schedules, or cognitive therapy. *Journal of Consulting and Clinical Psychology,* 1979, *47,* 427–439.

Zetzel, E. Symposium on depressive illness. *International Journal of Psychoanalysis,* 1961, *43,* 467.

Zetzel, E. On the incapacity to bear depression. In E. Zetzel (Ed.), *The capacity for emotional growth.* New York: International Universities Press, 1965, pp. 80–114.

Zigler, E. A measure in search of a theory? *Contemporary Psychology,* 1963, *8,* 133–315.

Zubin, J., & Spring, B. Vulnerability—a new view of schizophrenia. *Journal of Abnormal Psychology,* 1977, *86,* 103–126.

Zuckerman, M., & Lubin, B. *Manual of the multiple affective adjective checklist.* San Diego: Educational and Industrial Service, 1965.

Index

a
b
3 c
4 d
5 e
6 f
7 g
8 h
9 i
8 0 j